Access to

ADVANCED LEVEL MATHS

D Butcher
S Megeney

Series editors
Ted Lister and Janet Renshaw

Stanley Thornes (Publishers) Ltd

Contents

Acknowledgements

The authors would like to thank Andrew Martin of Thorne Grammar School, Doncaster, who tried out much of the material with his pupils.

© D Butcher and S Megeney

The right of D Butcher and S Megeney to be identified as authors of this work has been asserted by them in accordance with the Copyright, Designs and Patents Act 1988.

First published in 1997 by Stanley Thornes (Publishers) Ltd
Ellengborough House
Wellington Street
Cheltenham
Gloucestershire GL50 1YW

97 98 99 00 01 / 10 9 8 7 6 5 4 3 2 1

A catalogue record for this book is available from the British Library

ISBN 0-7487-2999-2

Typeset by Mathematical Composition Setters Ltd, Salisbury
Printed and bound at Redwood Books, Trowbridge, Wiltshire

Introduction

This book is designed to help you get ready for a post-16 course in maths: Advanced Level, Advanced Supplementary Level, Scottish Higher, etc. The precise course you will be following doesn't matter because this book stresses the principles of maths which are the same for any course. You could use it before you begin your advanced course or during the first part of that course. You will also find it useful if you are aiming for the higher level GCSE papers. You can also refer to it during your advanced course. *Access to Advanced Level: Maths* has been designed so that you can work through it on your own and the answers to the exercises are at the end of the book. However, cheating won't help your understanding!

How to use this book

Teaching yourself how to do something needs confidence, and often that is the one thing that you don't have. We suggest that you work through each section slowly and don't move on to the next section until you have correctly answered the exercises. If you are getting most of them right, you are doing well. What if you aren't? One resource is a standard maths textbook. One of the skills you will have to develop for advanced study is independent learning. There are a variety of approaches to explain concepts and ours may not always be the best for you. At advanced level (and beyond), referring to textbooks and reading on your own initiative is going to give you a valuable skill and that essential ingredient confidence in your ability to learn by yourself.

Good luck and enjoy your maths!

Doris Butcher
Sarah Megeney

* There is a glossary of important terms on p. 83 for you to refer to.

Chapter 1

From arithmetic to algebra

Numbers

Numbers are the first part of mathematics that people discover and use. The rules that apply to them are very important and continue to be used throughout all the branches of mathematics. The numbers that you first learn are called **natural numbers** and they start 1, 2, 3, 4, 5, 6, …. Later we have **integers**, which look very similar to the natural numbers but can be positive or negative and include 0, i.e. … −4, −3, −2, −1, 0, +1, +2, +3, +4, ….

 **Task**

1 Here are some other sets of numbers. Write down three or more terms of each of the following sequences:

   a prime numbers
   b odd numbers
   c perfect square numbers
   d numbers between 1 and 2
   e powers of 10

2 Write down any other set of numbers that you know, and describe them.

Check the answers at the back of the book before you move on. Don't worry if you have not yet heard of some of the sets of numbers in the answers but try to remember the names for when you meet them later.

Rules

The rules for ordinary arithmetic must also be obeyed in algebra. For example, the order in which we add two numbers doesn't matter in arithmetic.

So, in arithmetic, $7 + 5 = 12$ and $5 + 7 = 12$.

In algebra this gives $a + b = b + a$.

The same is true of multiplication.

In arithmetic, $12 \times 4 = 4 \times 12 = 48$.

In algebra this gives $a \times b = b \times a$, which is usually written $ab = ba$.

The multiplication sign is usually left out in algebra. So, for example,

$6a = 6 \times a$, $pq = p \times q$, and $3(m + n) = 3 \times (m + n) = 3m + 3n$

This rule, where order does not matter, is called the **commutative rule** and it is true for addition and multiplication of all types of numbers.

Later, you will see that the commutative rule is *not* true for multiplication of matrices.

Subtraction and division do not obey the commutative rule.

For example:

$6 - 4 = 2$, but $4 - 6 = -2$ and $12 \div 2 = 6$ but $2 \div 12 = \frac{1}{6}$

Hence, in algebra, $m - n \neq n - m$,

and $p \div q \neq q \div p$, i.e. $\dfrac{p}{q} \neq \dfrac{q}{p}$

Task

3 Decide which of the following expressions are always equal:

    a $5pq, 5qp$ d rst, str, trs

    b $\dfrac{7}{x}, \dfrac{x}{7}$ e $p - q, q - p$

    c $2p + 3q, 3p + 2q$ f $\dfrac{3m}{n}, \dfrac{6m}{2n}$

If any are not equal, try to find particular values for which they would be.

There are two other important rules governing the processes used in ordinary arithmetic, which are then followed in algebra. They are both very simply stated using algebra.

The associative law
The **associative law** deals with the order in which we carry out operations on a set of numbers written down in a given sequence. The associative law holds if changing the order in which we carry out the operations makes no difference to the answer.

Example

If we are multiplying the numbers 5, 6 and 3,

$5 \times (6 \times 3) = 5 \times 18 = 90$

or $(5 \times 6) \times 3 = 30 \times 3 = 90$

and so $5 \times (6 \times 3) = (5 \times 6) \times 3$

In algebra, the associative law is written $a \times (b \times c) = (a \times b) \times c$.

The distributive law
The **distributive law** deals with what to do when you have a mixture of operations, i.e. addition and/or subtraction together with multiplication and/or division.

$7 \times (4 + 9) = 7 \times 13 = 91$

but $7 \times 4 + 7 \times 9 = 28 + 63 = 91$

and so $7 \times (4 + 9) = 7 \times 4 + 7 \times 9$
In algebra, the distributive law is written $p \times (s + t) = p \times s + p \times t$

or, $p(s + t) = ps + pt$.

The distributive law is very important when you are using equations that include brackets.

Task

4 Check the associative law using:

   a $a = 4$, $b = 3$, and $c = 9$

   b $a = -6$, $b = -2$, and $c = 8$

5 Check the distributive law using:

   a $p = 5$, $s = 7$, and $t = 2$

   b $p = -2$, $s = 9$, and $t = -10$

6 Check whether the associative law is true for subtraction, division, and addition.

Some necessary basics

If negative numbers cause problems for you, or any of the basic notation is unfamiliar, then work through this section. Do not use a calculator! Otherwise move to the section *Some methods of solving equations*.

A number written without a sign is taken to be a positive number but negative numbers must have their sign there all the time.

The number line goes to infinity in both directions:

$$\dots -7, -6, -5, -4, -3, -2, -1, 0, +1, +2, +3, +4, +5, +6, +7, \dots$$

When you add, move to the right. When you subtract, move to the left.

Task

7 What is the numerical difference between 7 and -7?

Make sure that you can use the number line to show that

$$7 + 2 = 9$$

$$-7 + 2 = -5$$

$$-6 - 7 = -13$$

$$7 - 9 = -2$$

Remember the sign combinations when you remove brackets.

Example

A $6 + (-2) = 6 - 2 = 4$

B $-3 - (+5) = -3 - 5 = -8$

C $7 - (-2) = 7 + 2 = 9$

D $-2 + (+5) = -2 + 5 = 3$

Task

8 Calculate:

   a $-3 + 7$ d $-3 - (-2)$

   b $-7 + (-3)$ e $6 + (-3) - 7 + (-2)$

   c $6 + (-2)$

Multiplication and division

Fig. 1.1 has the same diagram for both operations, × and ÷, and shows that if a represents any number,

$$+a \times +a = +a^2$$

$$+a \times -a = -a^2$$

$$-a \times +a = -a^2$$

$$-a \times -a = +a^2$$

Replacing the × by ÷ gives the rules for division.

×	+	−		÷	+	−
+	+	−		+	+	−
−	−	+		−	−	+

1.1

Task

> 9 Calculate:
>
>   a $7 \times (-3)$
>
>   b $(-2) \times (-8)$
>
>   c $(-6) \div 3$
>
>   d $16 \div (-2)$
>
>   e $(-6 + 3) \times (-5 - 2) \div (-3 + 1)$
>
> Now check that you get the same answers using your calculator.

The wise owl said as he flew through the bus – 'A minus times a minus must always be a plus'.

Now that we know how numbers behave, we can start to solve equations where we have unknown numbers.

Task

> 10 Try these equations, always checking your solutions:
>
>   a $5p + 8 = 33$ f $\dfrac{g}{4} + 3 = 5$
>
>   b $4q - 2 = 10$ g $\dfrac{m+3}{4} = 5$
>
>   c $5m + 2 = -8$ h $5 - 2x = 7$
>
>   d $2t - 11 = -15$ i $\dfrac{y}{2} + \dfrac{2y}{5} = 9$
>
>   e $6g + 8 = -22$

Some methods of solving equations

There are many types of equations. The first type is called a **simple** equation, which seems a sensible name for one such as $3x + 7 = 10$, but is not quite so obvious for $3(2y + 5) - 2(y - 4) = 31$, which is also a simple equation. All that *simple* means is that there is only one unknown, and it does not appear as a root or power or in a denominator.

The following examples are to remind you about notation:

A $7y$ means $7 \times y$

B $\dfrac{p}{3}$ means $p \div 3$

C $4(m + 7) = 4 \times m + 4 \times 7 = 4m + 28$

D $-2(3y + 8) = -6y - 16$

E $-5(2m - 7) = -10m + 35$

We need to keep the balance of an equation by dealing with both sides in the same way. You may have met a rule that said, 'change the side and change the sign', which often works but has limitations. Doing the same to both sides is safer.

A   Solve the equation (which means find the value of y for which the equation is true) $3(2y + 5) - 2(y - 4) = 31$.

Multiplying out the brackets (noticing the change of sign),

$6y + 15 - 2y + 8 = 31$

Collecting like terms,

$4y + 23 = 31$

Subtracting 23 from both sides,

$4y = 31 - 23$

$4y = 8$

Dividing both sides by 4,

$y = 2$

It is always a good idea to check whether your solution (answer) is correct by finding the value of each side of the original equation with your value replacing the unknown.

When $y = 2$,

LHS $= 3 \times 9 - 2 \times (-2)$

$= 27 - (-4)$

$= 27 + 4 = 31 =$ RHS

So $y = 2$ is the solution.

B   Solve $8 - 2(3 + m) + 5(4m - 1) = 6$.

Multiplying out the brackets (noting the change of sign when removing the first bracket, but not the second),

$8 - 6 - 2m + 20m - 5 = 6$

Collecting like terms,

$$2 + 18m - 5 = 6$$

$$18m - 3 = 6$$

Adding 3 to both sides,

$$18m = 9$$

Dividing both sides by 18,

$$m = \tfrac{1}{2}$$

Now check the solution in the original equation.

When $m = \tfrac{1}{2}$,

$$\text{LHS} = 8 - (2 \times 3.5) + (5 \times 1)$$

$$= 8 - 7 + 5 = 6 = \text{RHS}$$

So $m = \tfrac{1}{2}$ is the solution.

Task

11 Solve the following equations and remember

   i to multiply *all* the terms inside the bracket by the number in front of the bracket and

   ii that when the bracket is removed a '+' in front of a bracket gives no sign change, while a '−' in front of a bracket changes the signs inside the bracket.

   a $5(3x + 2) - 4(2x - 1) = 7$ d $2(1 - y) + 4(3y - 2) = 4$

   b $3(2m + 4) + 2(m + 5) = 38$ e $2(3t - 6) - 5(4 + t) = 5$

   c $3(5p - 1) - 4(p + 1) = 15$

You may have used a calculator to help with some of these but try not to use it for random selection of a possible solution!

Calculators in examinations

Buy a calculator of a type that you have already worked with successfully and remember where you have put the handbook. Check that the examination you are taking allows that type of calculator. You will probably find that the memory has to be cleared before the examination and handbooks will not be allowed so try to get to know your calculator well. Do not expect a calculator to find solutions for you on a random basis. Most questions require working to be shown.

Equations with the unknown on both sides

In the next equations we continue to use the inverses of +, −, × and ÷, which are, in order, −, +, ÷ and ×.

The sides of an equation are equal, hence its name.

Example

Solve $5x + 7 = 16 - (3 - x)$.

Removing the bracket (noting the change of sign),

$$5x + 7 = 16 - 3 + x$$

Collecting like terms,

$$5x + 7 = 13 + x$$

Subtracting x from both sides (this will remove the x on the right-hand side),

$$5x - x + 7 = 13 + x - x$$

Collecting like terms,

$$4x + 7 = 13$$

Subtracting 7 from both sides,

$$4x = 6$$

Dividing both sides by 4,

$$x = 1.5$$

Now check that the solution $x = 1.5$ satisfies the original equation.

$$\text{LHS} = 5 \times 1.5 + 7 = 7.5 + 7 = 14.5$$

$$\text{RHS} = 16 - (3 - 1.5) = 16 - 1.5 = 14.5$$

So LHS = RHS when $x = 1.5$, which is the solution.

As stated before, the rule 'change the side and change the sign' has limitations. The method above *always* works if you know the inverses and also helps to show why the other rule usually works.

Example

Solve $4(y + 3) + 6y = 5(4y - 6) - 3(y + 7)$.

Multiplying out the brackets (noting the change of sign),

$$4y + 12 + 6y = 20y - 30 - 3y - 21$$

Collecting like terms,

$$10y + 12 = 17y - 51$$

Subtracting 12 from both sides,

$$10y = 17y - 51 - 12$$

$$10y = 17y - 63$$

Subtracting $17y$ from both sides,

$$10y - 17y = -63$$

$$-7y = -63$$

Dividing both sides by -7 (remembering that a minus divided by a minus is a plus),

$$y = 9$$

Now check that the solution $y = 9$ satisfies the original equation.

$$\text{LHS} = 4(9 + 3) + 6 \times 9 = 4 \times 12 + 54 = 48 + 54 = 102$$

$$\text{RHS} = 5(36 - 6) - 3(9 + 7) = 5 \times 30 - 3 \times 16 = 150 - 48 = 102$$

So LHS = RHS when $y = 9$.

Identities

Not all apparent equations can be solved. Look closely at $5x + 7 = 9 - (2 - 5x)$. The right-hand side of this becomes $9 - 2 + 5x = 7 + 5x$, which is the same as the left-hand side, $5x + 7$ and so x can take any value. An equation like this is called an **identity**.

12 Solve the following equations, or identify the identities:

a $5y + 7 = 3y + 8$

b $13m - 6 = 3m + 14$

c $3p - 8 = p - 4$

d $12q + 4 = 3q - 23$

e $16 + h = 20 - h$

f $24 + 2(r + 4) = 32 - r + 3r$

g $5(2a + 5) - 4(a - 3) = 7 + 2(a - 1)$

h $12 + 3(2w - 5) = 3(2w - 1)$

i $4(y - 3) - 2(6 - y) = 0$

j $4x - 3(x + 4) = 2(5 - 4x) + 5$

When x is used as an unknown in an equation it helps if you write it as x, and not like a multiplication sign, ×.

SUMMARY

You should now be able to

- Identify types of sets of numbers
- Know the rules for addition, subtraction, multiplication and division of numbers
- Multiply out brackets
- Simplify and solve simple equations
- Recognise an identity

Chapter 2

Other useful equations

Simultaneous equations

Simultaneous equations involve any number of unknowns. If you are asked to solve the equation $p + q = 7$, there are infinitely many solutions, i.e. $p = 2$, $q = 5$ is a solution; as is $p = 0.5$, $q = 6.5$; and $p = -10$, $q = 17$, and so on.

But if we are also told that $2p + q = 9$, we know that the first set of results, $p = 2$ and $q = 5$, is the set needed, because only this set of solutions satisfies both equations.

In order to solve simultaneous equations, the equations must be essentially different. In the example above, if the second equation had been $2p + 2q = 14$, it would have given the same information as the first equation, and so would not have helped.

To solve for two unknowns, we must have two independent equations.

Methods of solution

You may have met at least two methods of solving simultaneous equations. Remember that all aim to finish up with a simple equation in one unknown.

The first method has two alternatives, depending on the signs involved.

Method 1
By subtraction

Example

We can use this method to solve the two equations above

$$p + q = 7 \tag{1}$$

$$2p + q = 9 \tag{2}$$

We can eliminate q by subtracting (1) from (2). Remember, 'Same sign – Subtract'.

$$p + 0 = 2$$

$$p = 2$$

Substituting for p in (1),

$$2 + q = 7$$

Subtracting 2 from both sides,

$$q = 5$$

So the solution is $p = 2$, $q = 5$, which is easily checked.

By addition

Let us use this method to solve

$$m - 2n = 1 \tag{1}$$

$$4m + 2n = 34 \tag{2}$$

We can eliminate n by adding (1) and (2). Remember, 'Different sign – aDD'.

$$5m = 35$$

$$m = 7$$

Substituting for m in (2),

$$28 + 2n = 34$$

Subtracting 28 from both sides,

$$2n = 34 - 28$$

$$2n = 6$$

Dividing both sides by 2,

$$n = 3$$

So the solution is $m = 7$, $n = 3$.

Check this in (1), LHS $= 7 - 6 = 1 =$ RHS

A   The addition method

$$5g + 3h = 2 \tag{1}$$

$$7g - 2h = 40 \tag{2}$$

Make the h terms have the same coefficient (number) in front of them.

Multiplying (1) by 2,

$$10g + 6h = 4 \tag{3}$$

and multiplying (2) by 3,

$$21g - 6h = 120 \tag{4}$$

Remembering the rule 'Different sign – aDD', add (3) and (4)

$$31g + 0 = 124$$

Dividing both sides by 31,

$$g = 4$$

Substituting for g in (1),

$$20 + 3h = 2$$

Subtracting 20 from both sides,

$$3h = 2 - 20$$

$$3h = -18$$

Dividing both sides by 3,

$$h = -6$$

So the required solution is $g = 4$, $h = -6$.

Check by substituting for g and h in (2).

LHS $= 7g - 2h = 28 - (-12) = 28 + 12 = 40 =$ RHS

B The subtraction method

$$5a - b = 15 \qquad\qquad\qquad\qquad (1)$$

$$3a - b = 11 \qquad\qquad\qquad\qquad (2)$$

Remember 'Same sign – Subtract',

$$5a - 3a - b - (-b) = 15 - 11$$

$$2a - b + b = 4$$

$$2a = 4$$

Dividing both sides by 2,

$$a = 2$$

Substituting this value of a in (1),

$$10 - b = 15$$

Subtracting 10 from both sides,

$$-b = 15 - 10$$

$$-b = 5$$

Finally, multiplying both sides by -1,

$$b = -5$$

So the solution is $a = 2$, $b = -5$.

You will have seen that when you have made the coefficients the same for one of the unknowns, you can look at the sign in front of the unknown in both equations and remember 'Same sign – Subtract' and 'Different sign – aDD'.

Method 2
This solves simultaneous equations by **substitution** from one equation into the other. It is most useful when one equation is much simpler than the other.

 **Example**

Solve the simultaneous equations

$$y = 5x + 4 \qquad\qquad\qquad\qquad (1)$$

$$4y + 3(2x - 1) = 39 \qquad\qquad\qquad (2)$$

Substituting from (1) into (2),

$$4(5x + 4) + 3(2x - 1) = 39$$

$$20x + 16 + 6x - 3 = 39$$

$$26x + 13 = 39$$

Subtracting 13 from both sides,

$$26x = 26$$

Dividing both sides by 26,

$$x = 1$$

Now substituting for x in (1),

$$y = 5 + 4 = 9$$

Check that the solution $x = 1$, $y = 9$ is correct by substituting for x and y in (2),

$$\text{LHS} = 36 + 3 \times (2 - 1) = 36 + 3 \times 1 = 36 + 3 = 39 = \text{RHS}$$

So the solution is $x = 1$, $y = 9$.

Task

1 Solve the following simultaneous equations. (Try using both the addition/subtraction method and the substitution method for f. You should get the same solution both times.)

a $5x + 7y = 27$ f $c - d = 8$
   $3x + 7y = 19$ $2c - 3d = 19$

b $2a + 3b = 24$ g $x = 5y + 7$
   $7a - 3b = 3$ $2y + 3x = 4$

c $p + 5q = 17$ h $g = 5 - h$
   $3p + q = 9$ $3g + 2h = 1$

d $2s + 9t = 1$ i $a + b = 10$
   $3s - 2t = 17$ $20a - 5(b + 6) + 40 = 10$

e $5m + 3n = 60$
   $2m - 9n = 24$

j Two numbers add up to 54. Half of one of them added to a quarter of the other one makes 31. Use this information to write down two equations and solve them to find the two numbers.

In theory, three unknowns can be found if you have three equations, four unknowns need four equations, and, in general, n unknowns need n independent equations for solutions to be found. Calculation by the methods above gets very complicated and computer programs used to solve a set of equations use other methods. The method of solution for three equations will be dealt with at the end of this chapter.

Simultaneous equations can also be solved graphically: see Chapter 3.

We now look at equations with one unknown but more than one possible solution.

Quadratic equations

If we are told that the square of a number is 16, then there are two possible solutions, 4 and -4.

Similarly, if, for example, $(y - 2)^2 = 16$,

then $y - 2 = 4$ or -4

so $y = 6$ or -2.

By multiplying out the brackets, we could have written $(y - 2)^2 - 16$ as $y^2 - 4y + 4 = 16$.

Then, taking 16 from both sides,

$$y^2 - 4y + 4 - 16 = 0$$

$$y^2 - 4y - 12 = 0$$

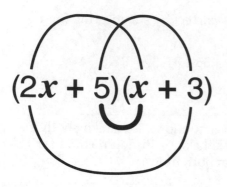

$(2x + 5)(x + 3)$

The algebraic expression – it can wink or sleep too.

Factorising,

$$(y - 6)(y + 2) = 0$$

If two or more numbers multiply together to make zero then one of them must be zero.

So $y - 6 = 0$ or $y + 2 = 0$

and $y = 6$ or $y = -2$, as before.

This sort of equation is a called a **quadratic equation**.

If you are not sure how to factorise then the next section may help, but if you still find it difficult then the quadratic equation formula can be used.

Multiplying out brackets

Each term in the first bracket is multiplied by each term in the second. So, for example,

$$(2p - 3q)(p + q) = 2p \times p - 3q \times p + 2p \times q - 3q \times q$$
$$= 2p^2 - 3pq + 2pq - 3q^2$$
$$= 2p^2 - pq - 3q^2$$

To get back to the factors:

1 Draw the brackets: $2p^2 - pq - 3q^2 = ($ $)($ $)$
2 Write down the possibilities that will give $2p^2$ and $-3q^2$ (ignoring the pq term for now):

$(2p - 3q)(p + q)$, $(2p + 3q)(p - q)$, $(2p - q)(p + 3q)$, and $(2p + q)(p - 3q)$

3 Work out the middle term for each of these possibilities:

$-3pq + 2pq = -pq$, $3pq - 2pq = +pq$, $-qp + 6pq = +5pq$, and $pq - 6pq = -5pq$

Only the first of these gives the required middle term, so

$$2p^2 - pq - 3q^2 = (2p - 3q)(p + q)$$

Example

A Factorise $x^2 - 5x + 6$.

Looking at only the first and last term we have the following possibilities

$(x - 2)(x - 3)$, $(x + 2)(x + 3)$, $(x + 6)(x + 1)$, and $(x - 6)(x - 1)$

Checking the middle terms for each of these possibilities we get

$-5x$, $+5x$, $+7x$, and $-7x$

The first is correct, so

$$x^2 - 5x + 6 = (x - 2)(x - 3)$$

B Factorise $9y^2 - 16z^2$.

Notice that there is no middle term. There seem to be many possibilities here so it is worth remembering the format called *the difference of two squares*. The square of 3 is 9, and the square of 4 is 16. Check that the middle term disappears if we take the set of brackets:

$(3y - 4z)(3y + 4z)$
$= 9y^2 - 12zy + 12yz - 16z^2$
$= 9y^2 - 16z^2$

Task

2 Factorise:

   a $x^2 + 5x + 6$ d $y^2 - 2y - 15$

   b $x^2 + 16x + 63$ e $m^2 + 3m - 18$

   c $x^2 - 7x + 10$

Solving a quadratic equation by factorising

We have seen that quadratic equations can be factorised and we know that if two terms multiplied together equal 0 then one of the terms must be 0. This means that we can solve quadratic equations by factorising.

Example

Solve $2x^2 + x - 10 = 0$.

Factorising, we have

$$2x^2 + x - 10 = (2x + 5)(x - 2) = 0$$

Either $2x + 5 = 0$ or $x - 2 = 0$

So $2x = -5$ or $x = 2$

The solution is $x = -2.5$ or $x = 2$.

The solutions of a quadratic equation are often called its **roots**.

Check your roots

In an equation $ax^2 + bx + c = 0$, the sum of the roots $= -\dfrac{b}{a}$.

We can use this to check that our solution is correct.

In the example above, the sum of the roots (the solutions for x) is $-2.5 + 2 = -0.5$

Now, $-\dfrac{b}{a} = -\dfrac{1}{2} = -0.5$

Proof of this, and a caution regarding its use, are given after the answers to Task 3.

Task

3 Find the roots (solutions) for:

   a $x^2 + 4x + 3 = 0$ f $3q^2 + 7q + 4 = 0$

   b $x^2 + 7x + 10 = 0$ g $6m^2 - 13m + 6 = 0$

   c $x^2 - 7x + 12 = 0$ h $8h^2 - 2h - 21 = 0$

   d $y^2 - 7y - 30 = 0$ i $25p^2 - 1 = 0$

   e $p^2 - 12p + 32 = 0$ j $9x^2 - 49 = 0$

Check that the sum of the roots is always equal to the fraction, $-\dfrac{\text{coefficient of } x}{\text{coefficient of } x^2}$, where x represents the unknown of each equation. Try to see why this is the case. There is an explanation in the answers.

A formula for solving quadratic equations

We have seen that a general quadratic equation is written

$$ax^2 + bx + c = 0$$

where a is the coefficient of x^2, b is the coefficient of x and c is the constant term (independent of x).

In the equation $3x^2 - 5x - 7 = 0$, we have $a = 3$, $b = -5$ and $c = -7$.

The formula for solving the equation is

$$x = \frac{-b \pm \sqrt{b^2 - 4ac}}{2a}$$

For this formula to apply, the original quadratic equation must be in the form LHS = 0. This formula can then be used for all quadratic equations.

If the square root involved is that of a perfect square, then the equation would have factorised easily. When the square roots are of other numbers, the answers have to be approximated or they would go on to infinity. Before using the formula to solve a quadratic equation, we will find out how to deal with the approximation of these numbers.

Approximating numbers

These are two main ways of approximating numbers.

Approximating to a given number of decimal places
Count, from the decimal point, the figures to the right of it until the number of figures you have counted is the the number of decimal places required. Call this your 'cut-off' point. Look at the next figure. If it is less than 5, simply remove all the figures after the cut-off point. If it is greater than 5 add 1 to the figure in front of the cut-off point and remove all the figures after it. If the next figure is 5, add 1 to the figure before the cut-off point and remove all the figures after it as before. The following example should make this clear.

Example

Approximate 7.562595

a to 2 decimal places

b to 4 decimal places

c to 5 decimal places

d to the nearest whole number

a Count 2 figures after the decimal point. The cut-off point is after the figure 6. The next figure is 2, which is less than 5, so 7.562595 = 7.56 to 2 decimal places.

b Count 4 figures after the decimal point. The cut-off point is after the figure 5. The next figure is 9, which is greater than 5, so add 1 to the figure before the cut-off point before removing the remaining figures. Then 7.562595 = 7.5626 to 4 decimal places.

c Count 5 figures after the decimal point. The cut-off point is after the figure 9. The next figure is 5, so add 1 to the figure before the cut-off point before removing the remaining figures. Then 7.562595 = 7.56260 to 5 decimal places.

d The cut-off point *is* the decimal point. The next figure is 5, so add 1 to the figure before the cut-off point before removing the remaining figures. Then 7.562595 = 8 to the nearest whole number.

Approximating to a given number of significant figures
Here we start counting from the beginning (left) of the number, and not from the decimal point, but must still show the place values. We round up using the same reasoning as before.

For example, 5736.258 to 3 significant figures is 5740. We put in the 0 to show the place value.

5736.258 to 1 significant figure is 6000

5736.258 to 6 significant figures is 5736.26

4 Write down the following:

  a $\frac{12}{13}$ to 4 decimal places

  b $\frac{5}{7}$ to 3 significant figures

  c $\frac{2}{11}$ to 5 significant figures

  d $\frac{4}{17}$ to 7 decimal places

  e $\frac{9}{23}$ to 1 decimal place

  f $\sqrt{23}$ to 3 significant figures

  g $\sqrt{127}$ to 4 decimal places

  h $\sqrt{5.82}$ to 4 significant figures

  i $\sqrt{83.61}$ to 2 significant figures

  j $7.6 + \sqrt{8.3}$ to 3 significant figures

Standard form
You will often meet numbers written in **standard form** where the number is written as the product of a number between 1 and 10 and a power of 10.

For example, 17364 can be written in standard form as 1.7364×10^4, which is 1.74×10^4 to 3 significant figures.

Similarly, 0.0058129 can be written in standard form as $5.8129 \times 10^{-3} = 5.813 \times 10^{-3}$ to 4 significant figures.

Powers and this way of writing numbers are further explained in Chapter 5.

Using the formula to solve a quadratic equation

The following examples show how we can use the formula to solve a quadratic equation. Use care when dealing with answers to a number of significant figures or decimal places. Do not approximate too early in your calculation and do not think that your calculator display is exact: it can only be correct to the number of figures it can display.

Example

A Solve $2x^2 + x - 10 = 0$.

In this case, $a = 2$, $b = 1$, and $c = -10$.

Using the formula, $x = \dfrac{-1 \pm \sqrt{1 - 4 \times 2 \times (-10)}}{2 \times 2}$

$x = \dfrac{-1 \pm \sqrt{1 - (-80)}}{4}$

$x = \dfrac{-1 \pm \sqrt{81}}{4}$

$x = \dfrac{-1 + 9}{4}$ or $\dfrac{-1 - 9}{4}$

$x = \dfrac{8}{4}$ or $\dfrac{-10}{4}$

so $x = 2$ or $x = -2.5$, which is the answer that we obtained when we worked it out by factorising.

B Solve $x^2 + 6x - 10 = 0$, giving solutions correct to 3 significant figures.

In this case, $a = 1$, $b = 6$, and $c = -10$.

Using the formula, $x = \dfrac{-6 \pm \sqrt{6^2 - 4 \times 1 \times (-10)}}{2 \times 1}$

$x = \dfrac{-6 \pm \sqrt{36 - (-40)}}{2}$

$x = \dfrac{-6 + \sqrt{76}}{2}$ or $\dfrac{-6 - \sqrt{76}}{2}$

$x = \dfrac{-6 + 8.717797887}{2}$ or $\dfrac{-6 - 8.717797887}{2}$

$x = \dfrac{2.71779788}{2}$ or $\dfrac{-14.717797887}{2}$

$x = 1.358898943$ or -7.358888943

$x = 1.36$ or -7.36, correct to 3 significant figures.

This would have been 1.359 or -7.359 to 3 decimal places.

Check this solution by noting that the sum of the roots is $1.36 + (-7.36) = -6$.

In the original equation, $-\dfrac{\text{coefficient of } x}{\text{coefficient of } x^2} = -\dfrac{6}{1} = -6$

i.e. the sum of the roots (solutions) for $ax^2 + bx + c = 0$ is $-\dfrac{b}{a}$.

C Solve $3x^2 - 5x = 10$, giving solutions correct to 3 decimal places.

We must first put the equation in the required form $f(x) = 0$, to give $3x^2 - 5x - 10 = 0$.

Then $a = 3$, $b = -5$, and $c = -10$.

Using the formula, $x = \dfrac{5 \pm \sqrt{(-5)^2 - 4 \times 3 \times (-10)}}{2 \times 3}$

$x = \dfrac{5 \pm \sqrt{25 - (-120)}}{6}$

$x = \dfrac{5 \pm \sqrt{25 + 120}}{6}$

$x = \dfrac{5 \pm \sqrt{145}}{6}$

$x = \dfrac{5 \pm 12.04159458}{6}$

correct to the number of figures given by the calculator used.

$x = \dfrac{17.04159458}{6}$ or $-\dfrac{7.04159458}{6}$

$x = 2.840265763$ or -1.173599097

$x = 2.840$ or -1.174, correct to 3 decimal places.

Check that these solutions are correct by noting that their sum is

$2.840265763 - 1.173599097 = 1.666666666 = 1.667$ to 3 decimal places

and $-\dfrac{b}{a} = -\left(\dfrac{-5}{3}\right) = 1.667$

 **Task**

5 Solve the following quadratic equations using the formula and giving solutions correct to 3 decimal places:

a $x^2 + 5x + 3 = 0$ e $a^2 + 13a + 2 = 0$

b $2v^2 + 8v + 1 = 0$ f $5p^2 + 9p + 1 = 0$

c $y^2 + 2y - 5 = 0$ g $x^2 - x - 1 = 0$

d $4m^2 + 3m - 5 = 0$ h $4t^2 - 3t - 5 = 0$

i $5(\sin \theta)^2 + 12(\sin \theta) \times 7 = 0$

j $(\tan \theta)^2 - 2 \tan \theta - 6 = 0$

Hint for i and j: let $\sin \theta = x$ and let $\tan \theta = y$.

Remember the quick check for your solutions, sum of roots
(solutions) $= -\dfrac{\text{coefficient of } x}{\text{coefficient of } x^2}$, where coefficient means 'the
number multiplying the quantity concerned'. Did you use this check? If not, look in the answers.

θ is the Greek letter 'theta'

Tasks 5i and j used trigonometric functions in an unusual way. These functions will be dealt with in Chapter 7, both in their use in triangles and as functions in their own right.

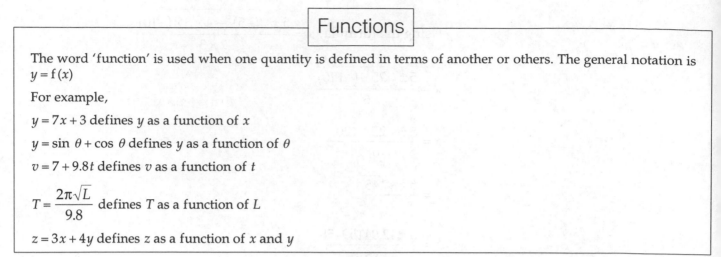

Functions

The word 'function' is used when one quantity is defined in terms of another or others. The general notation is $y = f(x)$

For example,

$y = 7x + 3$ defines y as a function of x

$y = \sin\theta + \cos\theta$ defines y as a function of θ

$v = 7 + 9.8t$ defines v as a function of t

$T = \dfrac{2\pi\sqrt{L}}{9.8}$ defines T as a function of L

$z = 3x + 4y$ defines z as a function of x and y

Quadratic equations often occur when solving problems, but sometimes only one of the solutions obtained is required. Always look carefully at the question being asked.

Example

A positive number is squared and multiplied by 5. The two answers are added, making 24. What was the number?

We will call the number p.

From the question we know that $p^2 + 5p = 24$

We can rearrange this so $p^2 + 5p - 24 = 0$

Factorising, we have $(p - 3)(p + 8) = 0$

So $p - 3 = 0$ or $p + 8 = 0$

Then $p = 3$ or $p = -8$.

We could also have used the formula to get the same result. Reading the original question, we know that we need the positive number, so the number is 3.

Task

6   Use quadratic equations to solve the following problems.
    (Remember that the product of numbers is given by multiplying them together.)

    a   I think of a number between 1 and 10 and square it. I also multiply the original number by 5 and add the two answers together to get 14. What was the original number?

    b   The product of two numbers that differ by 11 is 180. What is the value of the larger number?

    c   A girl is 6 years older than her brother. The product of their ages is 187. How old is the brother?

    d   Three angles together make a straight line. One of them is 120° and the product of the other two is 611°. Find the larger of the two unknown angles.

    e   Two sides of a rectangular field differ in length by 9 m. The area of the field is 220 m². Find the length of the shorter side.

    f   The sides of a right-angled triangle are known to be x cm, $(x - 7)$ cm and $(x + 2)$ cm. Use Pythagoras' Theorem to find the length of the hypotenuse (longest side) of the triangle.

More complicated cases

A simple equation can be paired with a quadratic to be solved simultaneously.

We can, in theory, solve simultaneous equations for any number, n, of unknowns if we have n independent equations.

Equations that contain powers greater than 2 do not have formulae to solve them and often need approximation methods.

A later chapter will deal with those in which the unknown is a *power*. These are called **exponential equations**. An example of an exponential equation is $7^x = 4$.

Simultaneous equations where one equation is simple and the other is a quadratic

Example

$$x + 2y = 5 \qquad (1)$$
$$x^2 + 3xy + 5y^2 = 27 \qquad (2)$$

We will use the **substitution** method.

From (1), $x = 5 - 2y$

Substituting for x in (2),

$$(5 - 2y)^2 + 3y(5 - 2y) + 5y^2 = 27$$

Expanding brackets we get

$$25 - 20y + 4y^2 + 15y - 6y^2 + 5y^2 = 27$$

Collecting terms,

$$3y^2 - 5y + 25 = 27$$

Subtracting 27 from both sides,

$$3y^2 - 5y - 2 = 0$$
$$(3y + 1)(y - 2) = 0$$
$$3y = -1 \text{ or } y = 2$$
$$y = -\tfrac{1}{3} \text{ or } y = 2$$

So now, substituting for y in (1), $x = 5\tfrac{2}{3}$ or $x = 1$.

Check that the solutions $x = 5\tfrac{2}{3}$, $y = -\tfrac{1}{3}$ and $x = 1$, $y = 2$ are correct by substituting them in (2).

$$\text{LHS} = \tfrac{289}{9} - \tfrac{17}{3} + \tfrac{5}{9} = \tfrac{243}{9} = 27 = \text{RHS}$$

$$\text{LHS} = 1 + 6 + 20 = 27 = \text{RHS}$$

Task

7 Solve the following pairs of equations where one is simple and the other is a quadratic equation.

a $y = x + 5$
   $x^2 - 5xy + y^2 = -47$

b $w = 3u + 4$
   $u^2 - 12uw + 3w^2 = 64$

c $m = 2n - 1$
   $m^2 - mn - n^2 = 1$

d $p = 6 - q$
   $p^2 + 2pq + 3q^2 = 38$

e $v = 5 + 3t$
   $t^2 + 2tv - v^2 = -73$

Simultaneous equations in three unknowns

Chapter 3 explains that simultaneous equations in two unknowns cannot be solved when the equations represent parallel lines. With three unknowns the situation has more possibilities. We only deal here with the ones that give a definite value of the three unknowns. (Geometrically the equations each represent a plane and the solution is, in these cases, their point of intersection.)

Find the values of x, y, and z that satisfy the three equations

$$x + y + z = 8 \tag{1}$$
$$2x - 3y - 5z = 5 \tag{2}$$
$$x - 10y - 6z = 9 \tag{3}$$

We know how to solve equations in two unknowns and so we need to eliminate one of these unknowns. First we decide which one to eliminate, then we deal with the two new equations that result.

Step 1 Eliminate z from (1) and (2).

We need to make the coefficients of z the same in (1) and (2).

Multiplying (1) by 5,

$$5x + 5y + 5z = 40$$

And we have (2),

$$2x - 3y - 5z = 5$$

Using 'Different sign – aDD',

$$7x + 2y = 45 \tag{4}$$

Step 2 Eliminate z from (1) and (3)

We need to make the coefficients of z the same in (1) and (3).

Multiplying (1) by 6,

$$6x + 6y + 6z = 48$$

And we have (3),

$$x - 10y - 6z = 9$$

Using 'Different sign – aDD',

$$7x - 4y = 57 \tag{5}$$

In both (4) and (5) we have $7x$, so straight away we can use 'Same sign – Subtract' to give

$$2y - (-4y) = 45 - 57$$
$$2y + 4y = -12$$
$$6y = -12$$
$$y = -2$$

Substituting this value for y into (1), (2) and (3) gives,

$$x - 2 + z = 8 \tag{6}$$
$$2x + 6 - 5z = 5 \tag{7}$$
$$x + 20 - 6z = 9 \tag{8}$$

Using (6) and (8) to eliminate x (remember 'Same sign – Subtract') gives:

$$-2 - 20 + z - (-6z) = 8 - 9$$

$$-22 + 7z = -1$$

$$7z = -1 + 22$$

$$7z = 21$$

$$z = 3$$

Now, substituting for z in (6) gives

$$x - 2 + 3 = 8$$

$$x = 7$$

The values we have obtained are $x = 7$, $y = -2$, and $z = 3$. Check these values in (7), as that equation was not used in the last stage.

$$\text{LHS} = 2x + 6 - 5z = 14 + 6 - 15 = 5 = \text{RHS}$$

Task

8 Find the unknown values in these equations.

a $3x + 2y - z = 14$
   $x - y + z = 6$
   $x + 3y - z = 4$

b $5p + q - 3r = -9$
   $2p + q + r = 9$
   $p - q + 2r = 15$

c $3f - g + 2h = 0$
   $2f + g - 8h = 1$
   $f - g + 2h = -1$

d $4u - 2v - w = -14$
   $2u + 6v + 4w = 13$
   $10u - 2v - 2w = -25$

e $2a + 3b - c = 11$
   $a - 5b = 10$
   $2b - 3c = 10$

f $5r + 2s - 6t = 0$
   $10r - 4s + 3t = 1$
   $3t = 1$

SUMMARY

You should now be able to

- Solve simultaneous equations

- Solve quadratic equations by factorising

- Write numbers to specified numbers of significant figures and decimal places

- Use formulae to solve quadratic equations

- Use quadratic equations to solve problems

Graphs and equations

Could you draw the graph of $y = 6x - 2$?

You will need graph paper to do this. If you are not sure, work through the next section.

How to draw a graph

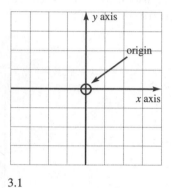

3.1

1 Draw the axes.
2 Label your axes, marking in the origin. Remember that the x-axis is horizontal, and the y-axis is vertical. The origin is the point $(0, 0)$, where the two axes cross.
3 Work out the coordinates of some of the points on the graph.

- Start by picking some simple values of x, such as $-1, 0, 1, 2$, etc.
- Put these values into the equation and work out the value of y.
- Plot the points on your graph.
- Join the points up using a smooth line.

 **Example**

A Draw the line $y = 6x - 2$.

Work out the values of y for several simple values of x to get some coordinates.

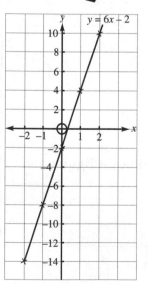

3.2

x	Substituting for x	y	Coordinates (x, y)
2	$6 \times 2 - 2 = 10$	10	$(2, 10)$
1	$6 \times 1 - 2 = 4$	4	$(1, 4)$
0	$6 \times 0 - 2 = -2$	-2	$(0, -2)$
-1	$6 \times -1 - 2 = -8$	-8	$(-1, -8)$
-2	$6 \times -2 - 2 = -14$	-14	$(-2, -14)$

You now have some points (coordinates) to plot on your line, and so should be able to draw the curve in Fig. 3.2.

Note that the line crosses the y-axis at the point $(0, -2)$.

The line in this example is a straight line. The equation for a straight line can always be manipulated into the same form, which we will see in a later section. Once you recognise from the equation that you have a straight line you only need to work out two points, although a third is a useful check.

B Draw the curve $y = 3x^2 + 4$.

x	Substituting for x	y	Coordinates (x, y)
2	$(3 \times 2 \times 2 + 4 = 16)$	16	$(2, 16)$
1	$(3 \times 1 \times 1 + 4 = 7)$	7	$(1, 7)$
0	$(3 \times 0 \times 0 + 4 = 4)$	4	$(0, 4)$
-1	$(3 \times -1 \times -1 + 4 = 7)$	7	$(-1, 7)$
-2	$(3 \times -2 \times -2 + 4 = 16)$	16	$(-2, 16)$

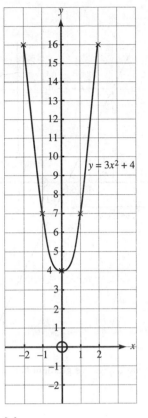

3.3

1 Draw the graphs of the following:

a $y = 7x - 4$

b $y = 0.5x$

c $y = 3x^2 + 2$

Gradients of straight line graphs

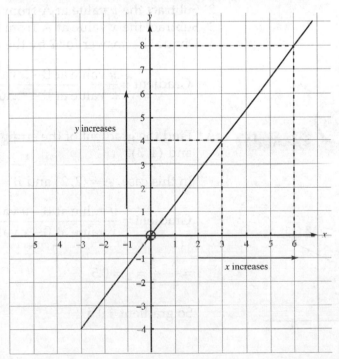

3.4 This line has a positive gradient because as the *x*-value increases so does the *y*-value.

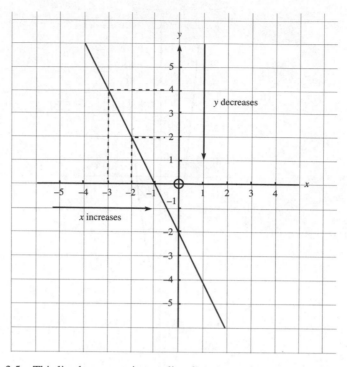

3.5   This line has a negative gradient because as the *x*-value increases the *y*-value decreases.

Gradients tell us how steep a line is and in which direction it is sloping. For example, a gradient of −2 tells us that:

- The line slopes down from top left to bottom right because the sign is negative.
- For every unit the line moves to the right it goes down two units.

Calculating gradients

1 Pick any two points on your straight line. We will call the point furthest to the left A and the point furthest to the right B.
2 Subtract the *y* value at A from the *y* value at B.
3 Subtract the *x* value at A from the *x* value at B.
4 Divide the answer for 2 by the answer for 3. This is the gradient.

$$\text{Gradient} = \frac{y \text{ value at B} - y \text{ value at A}}{x \text{ value at B} - x \text{ value at A}}$$

Example

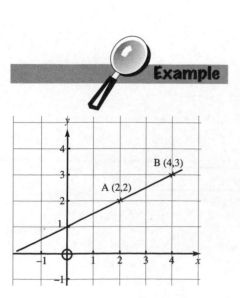

A   Find the gradient of the straight line passing through points $(2, 2)$ and $(4, 3)$.

In this case, A $= (2, 2)$ and B $= (4, 3)$

$$\text{Gradient} = \frac{y \text{ value at B} - y \text{ value at A}}{x \text{ value at B} - x \text{ value at A}}$$

$$= \frac{3-2}{4-2} = \frac{1}{2} = 0.5$$

So gradient $= 0.5$

3.6

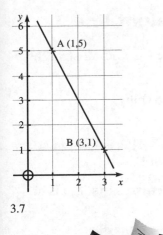

3.7

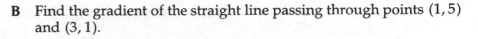

B Find the gradient of the straight line passing through points $(1, 5)$ and $(3, 1)$.

In this case, $A = (1, 5)$ and $B = (3, 1)$

$$\text{Gradient} = \frac{y \text{ value at } B - y \text{ value at } A}{x \text{ value at } B - x \text{ value at } A}$$

$$= \frac{1 - 5}{3 - 1} = -\frac{4}{2} = -2$$

So gradient $= -2$

Task

2 Work out the gradients of the lines in Fig. 3.8.

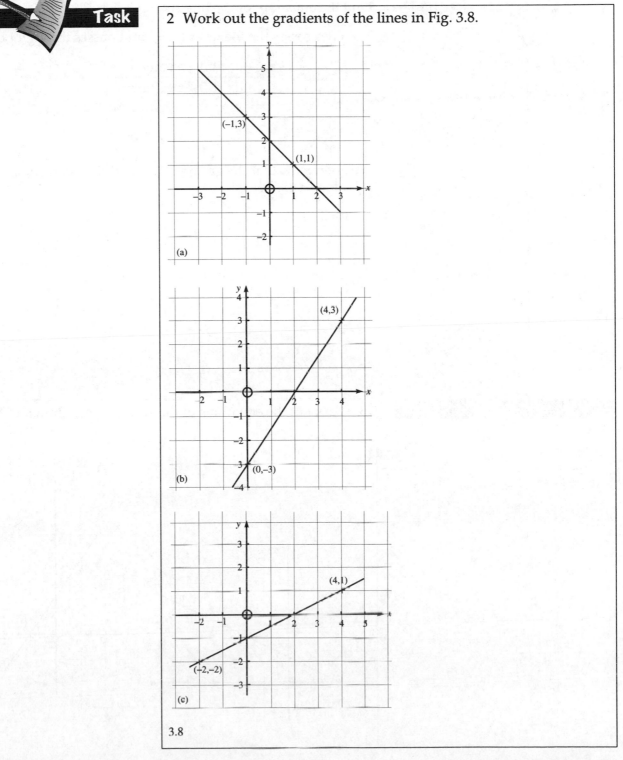

3.8

The general equation of a straight line

The general equation of a straight line is $y = mx + c$, and all straight line equations can be put into this form.

From the general equation, we can find out two things:

1 The gradient of the line.
2 The value of y when the line crosses the y-axis. This is known as the **y-intercept** (or more commonly as the intercept).

A straight line, $y = mx + c$, has gradient m and crosses the y-axis at the point $(0, c)$, i.e. the intercept is c.

Example

Find the equation for the line shown in Fig. 3.9.

The line crosses the y-axis at $(0, 3)$, and passes through point $(2, 7)$.

$$\text{Gradient} = \frac{y \text{ value at B} - y \text{ value at A}}{x \text{ value at B} - x \text{ value at A}}$$

$$= \frac{7 - 3}{2 - 0} = \frac{4}{2} = 2$$

We now know that the gradient is 2, and the intercept is 3, so the equation of the line is:

$$y = 2x + 3$$

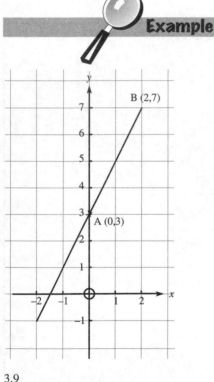

3.9

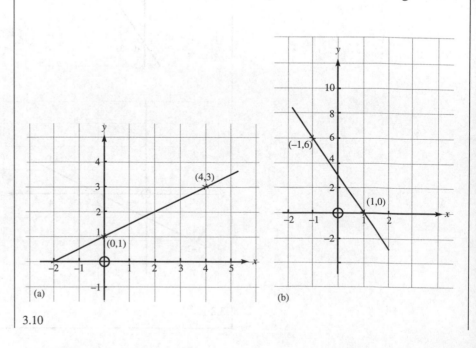
Task

3 Work out the equations of the straight lines shown in Fig. 3.10.

3.10

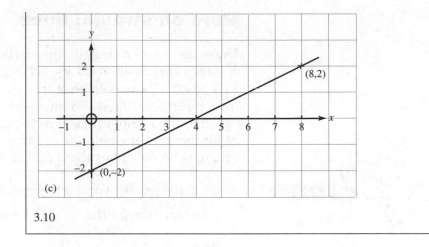

(c)

3.10

Parallel lines

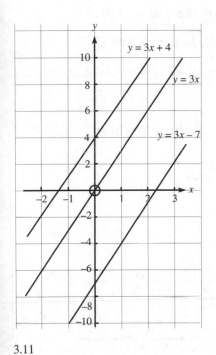

3.11

Parallel lines have the same gradient but cross the y-axis at different points. The lines $y = 3x - 7$, $y = 3x + 4$ and $y = 3x$ all have the same gradient, so they are parallel (see Fig. 3.11).

If the gradient of a line is zero, the equation of the line is $y = c$, where c is a constant. This line is horizontal (see Fig. 3.12a). If the gradient of the line is infinite then the equation of the line is $x = c$ where c is a constant. This line is vertical (see Fig. 3.12b).

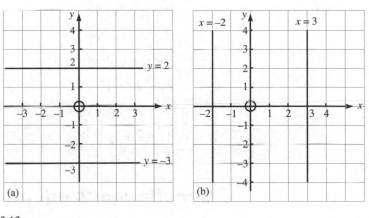

(a) (b)

3.12

 **Task**

4 Which of the following lines:

  a are parallel?
  b have zero gradient?
  c have infinite gradient?

  (1) $y = 4x + 3$
  (2) $y = -24$
  (3) $y = 4x - 5$
  (4) $y = 3x - 5$
  (5) $y = 6$
  (6) $x = 24$
  (7) $y = 2x + 3$
  (8) $y = 5 - 4x$
  (9) $x = -6$

More on straight lines

The equation for a straight line can be written in different forms, all of which are variations of $y = mx + c$. For example, $4y - 2x = 3$ or $\frac{2}{3}x + 3y + 2 = 0$ can both be rearranged to the form $y = mx + c$, and from this the gradient and intercept can be found as before. Once an equation for a straight line is in the form $y = mx + c$, it is easy to draw its line because the point $(0, c)$ can be obtained immediately from the equation, so only one other point is needed.

 **Example**

A Find the gradient and intercept of the line $4y - 2x = 3$.

The equation for the line can be rearranged to $4y = 2x + 3$

so $y = \dfrac{x}{2} + \dfrac{3}{4}$

This line has a gradient of $\frac{1}{2}$ and cuts the y-axis at $(0, \frac{3}{4})$.

B Find the gradient and intercept of the line $\frac{2}{3}x + 3y + 2 = 0$.

We rearrange the equation to $3y = -\frac{2}{3}x - 2$

so $y = -\frac{2}{9}x - \frac{2}{3}$

This line has a gradient of $-\frac{2}{9}$ and cuts the y-axis at $(0, -\frac{2}{3})$.

 **Task**

5 By rearranging the equations, work out

  i the gradient

  ii the y-intercept

    for the following lines.

  a $3y - 2x = 15$

  b $5x + 2 + 5y = 0$

  c $2x = 7 + 4y$

Simultaneous equations

Simultaneous equations can be solved using graphs. If you have two equations involving x and y you can find the numbers that make both equations true (the solutions), by drawing both lines on the same set of axes. You know that any points where the lines cross satisfy both equations.

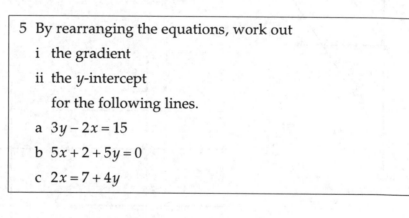 **Example**

Find x and y such that $y = 2x + 1$ and $y = 9 - 2x$.

Draw both lines on one set of axes, as in Fig. 3.13. The lines cross at $(2, 5)$, so the solution is $x = 2$, $y = 5$.

Check to make sure you have the correct answer by putting your solutions back into the original equations.

  $y = 2x + 1$, so for $x = 2$, $y = 2 \times 2 + 1 = 5$

  $y = 9 - 2x$, so for $x = 2$, $y = 9 - 2 \times 2 = 5$

If the two lines are parallel they don't intersect, and so have no common points. In that case there is no solution.

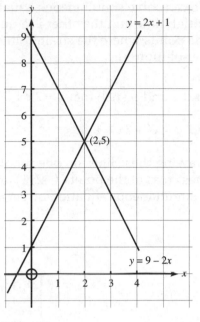

3.13

Task

6 Use graphs to solve (where possible) the following pairs of simultaneous equations:

a $y = 4x - 4$
   $y = 3x + 2$

c $y = x + 6$
   $y = 2x + 2$

b $y = 6 - x$
   $y = 3x + 2$

d $\frac{1}{2}y = x + \frac{3}{2}$
   $3y - 6x + 3 = 0$

Quadratic equations

Graphs of quadratic equations, with the general formula
$y = ax^2 + bx + c$ always have the general shapes shown in Fig. 3.14.
This shape is called a **parabola**.

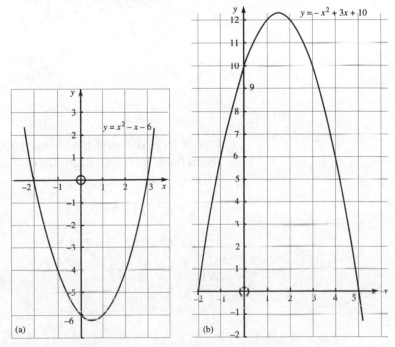

3.14 $y = +x^2$ has a minimum point; $y = -x^2$ has a maximum point.

We can solve simultaneous equations where one of the equations is a straight line and the other is a quadratic by drawing graphs as before. The points where the straight line intersects (or touches) a curve give the solution(s).

Find x and y such that $y = 2x + 5$ (1)

and $y = x^2 + 2x + 1$ (2)

Drawing these lines on one set of axes, we produce Fig. 3.15. The lines cross at the points $(-2, 1)$ and $(2, 9)$, so the solutions to this set of simultaneous equations are $x = -2$, $y = 1$ and $x = 2$, $y = 9$.

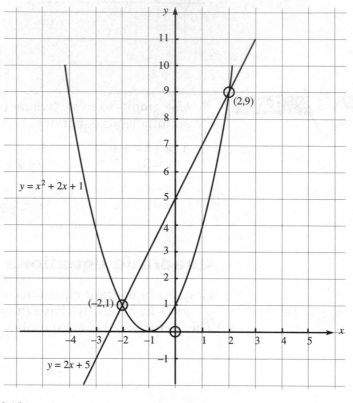

3.15

Check to make sure that these solutions are correct by substituting them back into the original equations:
When $x = 2$,

$$y = (2 \times 2) + 5 = 9 \qquad (1)$$

$$y = (2 \times 2) + (2 \times 2) + 1 = 9 \qquad (2)$$

When $x = -2$,

$$y = (-2 \times 2) + 5 = -4 + 5 = 1 \qquad (1)$$

$$y = (-2 \times -2) + (-2 \times 2) + 1 = 4 - 4 + 1 = 1 \qquad (2)$$

SUMMARY

You should now be able to

- Draw a graph from an equation in x and y
- Recognise the equation for a straight line as $y = mx + c$
- Find the equation of a straight line from its graph
- Find the gradient and the y-intercept, given the equation of a straight line
- Work out whether straight lines are parallel without drawing them
- Solve simultaneous equations using graphs

Chapter 4

Vectors

Sometimes it is not enough to know the size (magnitude) of something; we may need to know its direction too. We use vectors to describe quantities which require both magnitude and direction, such as velocity and acceleration.

Representing vectors

Vectors can be written in column form or can be represented pictorially. Written in column form, $\begin{pmatrix} x \\ y \end{pmatrix}$, the top number describes the change in the x direction and the bottom number describes the change in the y direction.

The direction is given by whether these numbers are positive or negative. Positive x means move right; negative x means move left. Positive y means move up; negative y means move down. The + sign is often omitted.

A $\begin{pmatrix} 3 \\ -2 \end{pmatrix}$

This vector means move three units to the right and two units down from a starting point, which may be anywhere. The arrow in Fig. 4.1 indicates the direction of the vector.

B $\begin{pmatrix} -1 \\ 5 \end{pmatrix}$

This means move one unit to the left and five units up. The arrow in Fig. 4.2 indicates the direction of the vector.

C Vectors may be drawn on the same diagram, as shown in Fig. 4.3. It doesn't matter where you start each vector.

a $\begin{pmatrix} 2 \\ -1 \end{pmatrix}$ b $\begin{pmatrix} -2 \\ -3 \end{pmatrix}$ c $\begin{pmatrix} -3 \\ 4 \end{pmatrix}$

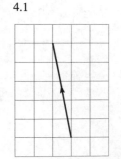

4.1

4.2

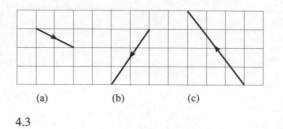

(a)   (b)   (c)

4.3

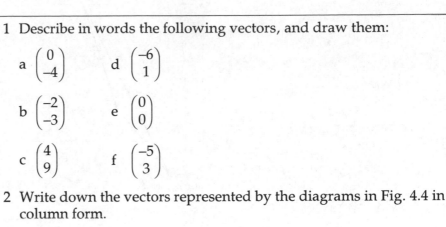

1 Describe in words the following vectors, and draw them:

a $\begin{pmatrix} 0 \\ -4 \end{pmatrix}$ d $\begin{pmatrix} -6 \\ 1 \end{pmatrix}$

b $\begin{pmatrix} -2 \\ -3 \end{pmatrix}$ e $\begin{pmatrix} 0 \\ 0 \end{pmatrix}$

c $\begin{pmatrix} 4 \\ 9 \end{pmatrix}$ f $\begin{pmatrix} -5 \\ 3 \end{pmatrix}$

2 Write down the vectors represented by the diagrams in Fig. 4.4 in column form.

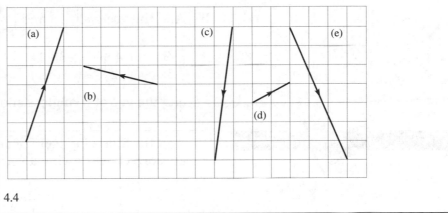

4.4

Addition and subtraction of vectors

We can add vectors together and subtract them from each other but we do not multiply them together or divide them by each other.

Adding vectors

When we add two vectors together we add together the two values that describe the movement in the x direction and then we add together the two values that describe the movement in the y direction.

$$\begin{pmatrix} a \\ b \end{pmatrix} + \begin{pmatrix} c \\ d \end{pmatrix} = \begin{pmatrix} a+c \\ b+d \end{pmatrix}$$

The final vector, the answer, is called the **resultant** vector because it is the end result. We can check to see if the resultant vector is correct by drawing a diagram called a **vector triangle**. The vectors you are adding form two sides of a triangle. Where one vector finishes the next one starts. The resultant vector forms the third side.

A Add the vectors $\begin{pmatrix} 3 \\ 4 \end{pmatrix}$ and $\begin{pmatrix} 2 \\ 6 \end{pmatrix}$, and draw the vector triangle.

We perform the addition as described above,

$$\begin{pmatrix} 3 \\ 4 \end{pmatrix} + \begin{pmatrix} 2 \\ 6 \end{pmatrix} = \begin{pmatrix} 3+2 \\ 4+6 \end{pmatrix} = \begin{pmatrix} 5 \\ 10 \end{pmatrix}$$

and the vector triangle is shown in Fig. 4.5.

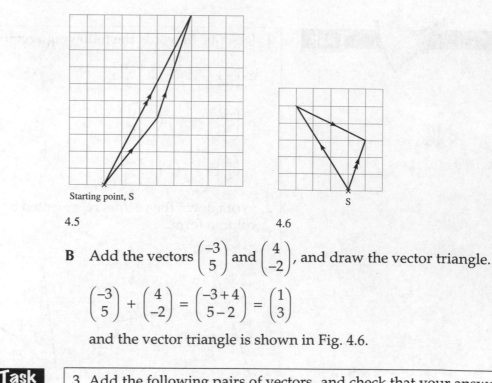

Starting point, S   S

4.5   4.6

B   Add the vectors $\begin{pmatrix} -3 \\ 5 \end{pmatrix}$ and $\begin{pmatrix} 4 \\ -2 \end{pmatrix}$, and draw the vector triangle.

$$\begin{pmatrix} -3 \\ 5 \end{pmatrix} + \begin{pmatrix} 4 \\ -2 \end{pmatrix} = \begin{pmatrix} -3+4 \\ 5-2 \end{pmatrix} = \begin{pmatrix} 1 \\ 3 \end{pmatrix}$$

and the vector triangle is shown in Fig. 4.6.

3   Add the following pairs of vectors, and check that your answers are correct by drawing a vector triangle for each one.

a $\begin{pmatrix} 6 \\ 3 \end{pmatrix}, \begin{pmatrix} 9 \\ 7 \end{pmatrix}$ c $\begin{pmatrix} -3 \\ -2 \end{pmatrix}, \begin{pmatrix} -6 \\ 8 \end{pmatrix}$

b $\begin{pmatrix} 9 \\ 11 \end{pmatrix}, \begin{pmatrix} -2 \\ 4 \end{pmatrix}$ d $\begin{pmatrix} 7 \\ -2 \end{pmatrix}, \begin{pmatrix} 6 \\ 5 \end{pmatrix}$

More than two vectors can be added at a time. All you need to do is add together *all* the values that describe movement in the x direction and add together *all* the values that describe movement in the y direction.

$$\begin{pmatrix} a \\ b \end{pmatrix} + \begin{pmatrix} c \\ d \end{pmatrix} + \begin{pmatrix} e \\ f \end{pmatrix} = \begin{pmatrix} a+c+e \\ b+d+f \end{pmatrix}$$

Example   Add the vectors $\begin{pmatrix} 3 \\ 4 \end{pmatrix}, \begin{pmatrix} -1 \\ 6 \end{pmatrix}, \begin{pmatrix} 7 \\ -5 \end{pmatrix}, \begin{pmatrix} -1 \\ -2 \end{pmatrix}$.

$$\begin{pmatrix} 3 \\ 4 \end{pmatrix} + \begin{pmatrix} -1 \\ 6 \end{pmatrix} + \begin{pmatrix} 7 \\ -5 \end{pmatrix} + \begin{pmatrix} -1 \\ -2 \end{pmatrix} = \begin{pmatrix} 3+(-1)+7+(-1) \\ 4+6+(-5)+(-2) \end{pmatrix} = \begin{pmatrix} 8 \\ 3 \end{pmatrix}$$

Even though there are more than two vectors being added you can still draw them to check your answer. The diagram is a vector polygon, and is shown in Fig. 4.7.

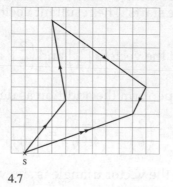

S

4.7

Task

4 Add the following sets of vectors, and draw the vector polygons to check your answers:

a $\begin{pmatrix} 3 \\ 2 \end{pmatrix}$, $\begin{pmatrix} -1 \\ -1 \end{pmatrix}$, $\begin{pmatrix} 4 \\ 5 \end{pmatrix}$

b $\begin{pmatrix} -1 \\ 3 \end{pmatrix}$, $\begin{pmatrix} 6 \\ -5 \end{pmatrix}$, $\begin{pmatrix} 4 \\ 3 \end{pmatrix}$, $\begin{pmatrix} -6 \\ 2 \end{pmatrix}$

c $\begin{pmatrix} 7 \\ 11 \end{pmatrix}$, $\begin{pmatrix} 8 \\ 7 \end{pmatrix}$, $\begin{pmatrix} -9 \\ -6 \end{pmatrix}$

d $\begin{pmatrix} -9 \\ 4 \end{pmatrix}$, $\begin{pmatrix} -3 \\ -7 \end{pmatrix}$, $\begin{pmatrix} 11 \\ 6 \end{pmatrix}$, $\begin{pmatrix} 0 \\ -9 \end{pmatrix}$

Subtracting vectors

When subtracting one vector from another we subtract the values of the second vector that describe movement in the x direction and movement in the y direction from the values in the same positions in the first vector. The order is the same as in normal arithmetic.

$$\begin{pmatrix} a \\ b \end{pmatrix} - \begin{pmatrix} c \\ d \end{pmatrix} = \begin{pmatrix} a-c \\ b-d \end{pmatrix}$$

Example

A Subtract $\begin{pmatrix} 5 \\ 2 \end{pmatrix}$ from $\begin{pmatrix} 9 \\ 6 \end{pmatrix}$.

$$\begin{pmatrix} 9 \\ 6 \end{pmatrix} - \begin{pmatrix} 5 \\ 2 \end{pmatrix} = \begin{pmatrix} 9-5 \\ 6-2 \end{pmatrix} = \begin{pmatrix} 4 \\ 4 \end{pmatrix}$$

The vector diagram is shown in Fig. 4.8.

B Subtract $\begin{pmatrix} -4 \\ 1 \end{pmatrix}$ from $\begin{pmatrix} 7 \\ -5 \end{pmatrix}$.

$$\begin{pmatrix} 7 \\ -5 \end{pmatrix} - \begin{pmatrix} -4 \\ 1 \end{pmatrix} = \begin{pmatrix} 7-(-4) \\ -5-1 \end{pmatrix} = \begin{pmatrix} 11 \\ -6 \end{pmatrix}$$

The vector diagram is shown in Fig. 4.9.

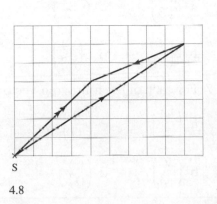

4.8

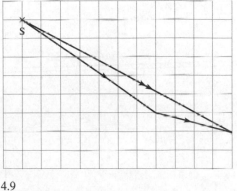

4.9

Task

5 Workout the following subtractions:

a $\begin{pmatrix} 9 \\ 6 \end{pmatrix} - \begin{pmatrix} 5 \\ 4 \end{pmatrix}$ c $\begin{pmatrix} 5 \\ 7 \end{pmatrix} - \begin{pmatrix} 3 \\ 2 \end{pmatrix}$

b $\begin{pmatrix} -3 \\ 2 \end{pmatrix} - \begin{pmatrix} 4 \\ 5 \end{pmatrix}$ d $\begin{pmatrix} -1 \\ -3 \end{pmatrix} - \begin{pmatrix} -2 \\ -4 \end{pmatrix}$

More than two vectors can be subtracted from each other, but it is best to perform the subtractions using one pair of vectors at a time to avoid getting confused. Once again, you can draw all the vectors being subtracted on one diagram to form a vector polygon.

Multiples of vectors

We can multiply a vector by a number (a constant, or **scalar**). For example if we are going to use a vector five times we wouldn't bother writing it down five times and adding the five vectors, we would simply write 5 in front of the vector. Multiplying by 5 is like walking five times as far in the same direction.

So for example,

$$\begin{pmatrix} 2 \\ 3 \end{pmatrix} + \begin{pmatrix} 2 \\ 3 \end{pmatrix} + \begin{pmatrix} 2 \\ 3 \end{pmatrix} + \begin{pmatrix} 2 \\ 3 \end{pmatrix} + \begin{pmatrix} 2 \\ 3 \end{pmatrix} = \begin{pmatrix} 10 \\ 15 \end{pmatrix}$$

is the same as

$$5\begin{pmatrix} 2 \\ 3 \end{pmatrix} = \begin{pmatrix} 5 \times 2 \\ 5 \times 3 \end{pmatrix} = \begin{pmatrix} 10 \\ 15 \end{pmatrix}$$

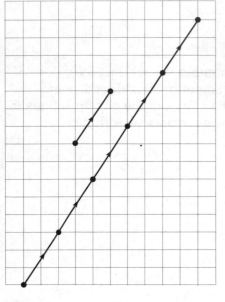

4.10

The resultant vector is the same. Notice also that $\begin{pmatrix} 2 \\ 3 \end{pmatrix}$ and $\begin{pmatrix} 10 \\ 15 \end{pmatrix}$ are parallel (see Fig. 4.10).

In general,

$$a\begin{pmatrix} b \\ c \end{pmatrix} = \begin{pmatrix} a \times b \\ a \times c \end{pmatrix} = \begin{pmatrix} ab \\ ac \end{pmatrix}$$

If vectors are multiples of each other then they are parallel.

Task

6 Write down the resultant vectors for the following:

a $4\begin{pmatrix} 4 \\ 5 \end{pmatrix}$ c $6\begin{pmatrix} -3 \\ 2 \end{pmatrix}$

b $3\begin{pmatrix} 6 \\ -1 \end{pmatrix}$ d $5\begin{pmatrix} -4 \\ -3 \end{pmatrix}$

7 For each of the following vectors write down three parallel vectors:

a $\begin{pmatrix} -4 \\ 5 \end{pmatrix}$ c $\begin{pmatrix} 9 \\ 11 \end{pmatrix}$

b $\begin{pmatrix} 7 \\ -3 \end{pmatrix}$ d $\begin{pmatrix} 6 \\ 0 \end{pmatrix}$

Translations

Vectors can be used to describe how something has moved or is going to move. For example we can use vectors to plot a course.

In the following example, $(3, 4)$ describes a fixed position in relation to a set of axes (i.e. a coordinate), and the vectors $\begin{pmatrix} 2 \\ -7 \end{pmatrix}$ and $\begin{pmatrix} -4 \\ 5 \end{pmatrix}$ denote movement.

Example

If a ship is at position $(3, 4)$ and moves $\begin{pmatrix} 2 \\ -7 \end{pmatrix}$ followed by $\begin{pmatrix} -4 \\ 5 \end{pmatrix}$, at what position does it end up?

Fig. 4.11 shows the movement of the ship. It ends up at $(1, 2)$.

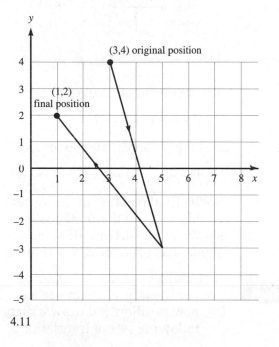

4.11

To check, determine where the x-coordinate moves to by adding all movements in the x direction to the original x-coordinate,

$$3 + 2 + (-4) = 1,$$

and determine where the y-coordinate moves to by adding all movements in the y direction to the original y-coordinate,

$$4 + (-7) + 5 = 2.$$

Hence the final position is $(1, 2)$.

Shape shifting

In the above example we used vectors to move a point, but we can also use them to move shapes.

Example

The vertex of a square is at the point $(3, 0)$. If the square is translated $\begin{pmatrix} 5 \\ 4 \end{pmatrix}$ followed by $\begin{pmatrix} -9 \\ -7 \end{pmatrix}$ where does the vertex move to?

The movement of the square is shown in Fig. 4.12.

Take care! $(3, 4)$ shows a *position* and $\begin{pmatrix} 3 \\ 4 \end{pmatrix}$ shows a *movement*.

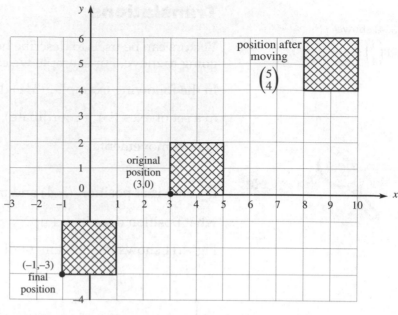

4.12

The x-coordinate moves to

$$3 + 5 + (-9) = -1,$$

and the y-coordinate moves to

$$0 + 4 + (-7) = -3.$$

So the final position of the vertex originally at $(3, 0)$ is $(-1, -3)$. You could work out the final positions for the other vertices of the square shown in Fig. 4.12 in the same way. If you do, you will notice that the square has been moved without changing its shape.

8 For the triangle with vertices $(0, 0)$, $(0, 2)$ and $(2, 2)$, calculate the new position and draw a diagram to show the effect of the following sets of translations:

a $\begin{pmatrix} 5 \\ 3 \end{pmatrix}, \begin{pmatrix} 4 \\ 2 \end{pmatrix}$ c $\begin{pmatrix} -2 \\ -5 \end{pmatrix}, \begin{pmatrix} 0 \\ 3 \end{pmatrix}$

b $\begin{pmatrix} -3 \\ 0 \end{pmatrix}, \begin{pmatrix} 5 \\ -4 \end{pmatrix}$ d $\begin{pmatrix} 1 \\ 4 \end{pmatrix}, \begin{pmatrix} 4 \\ 5 \end{pmatrix}, \begin{pmatrix} -6 \\ -11 \end{pmatrix}$

Writing vectors in terms of each other

We don't have to have specific vectors in mind to work with them. We can use letters to represent them in the same way as we use letters to represent numbers in algebra. Vectors can be denoted by underlining a letter, writing an arrow over the top, or by writing it in bold type. So $\underline{a}$, $\vec{a}$ and **a** are all vectors. We can also write two capital letters next to each other in bold or put an arrow over the top to represent a vector. This is most useful when we want to consider a vector that represents movement between points A and B, say. So, then **AB** or $\overrightarrow{AB}$ denote the vector which goes from A to B. The arrow shows the direction of the vector.

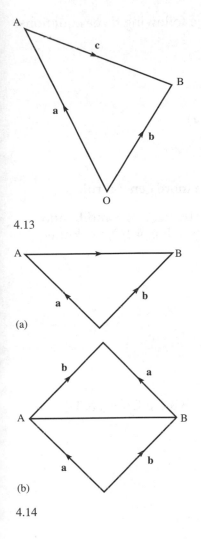

4.13

(a)

(b)

4.14

In this book we will use bold letters to represent vectors, but you will find it easier to write them with arrows over them, or lines underneath.

Two vectors can be used to describe a third. So we can write **a** + **c** = **b**, the vector diagram for which is shown in Fig. 4.13.

By starting at A (see Fig. 4.13) you can walk the 'wrong' way along **a** (i.e. walk in the direction −**a**) and then go the right way along **b**, finishing at B. This means that **c** = −**a** + **b**, which is the same as **c** = **b** − **a**, or **a** + **c** = **b**.

As in Fig. 4.13, **a** and **b** do not follow head to tail, but they can still be used to describe the vector **AB**. Some people find it easier to change the triangle diagram into a parallelogram diagram (Fig. 4.14b), where opposite sides represent equal vectors. Imagine that you want to drive from A to B but the path is blocked so you can't get there directly. Instead you must drive the 'wrong' way along **a** and then drive up **b** (Fig. 4.14a).

The opposite sides of the parallelogram are the same. To go from A to B you could also go along **b** and then backwards along **a**.

$$\mathbf{AB} = -\mathbf{a} + \mathbf{b} = \mathbf{b} - \mathbf{a}$$

So whichever way you go, **AB** = **b** − **a**.

Travelling along another vector

If there is a point C somewhere on the line joining points A and B, and the vectors to A and B from some other point O are **a** and **b**, then we can derive a useful relationship which helps us to find the vector from O to C, **c**.

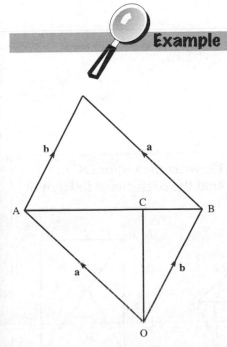

4.15

Consider Fig. 4.15. We know that the point C is a third of the way along the line BA. In other words,

$$\mathbf{BC} = \tfrac{1}{3}\mathbf{BA},$$

which is the same as

$$\mathbf{BC} = -\tfrac{1}{3}\mathbf{AB}.$$

Starting from point A, we have

$$\mathbf{AC} = \tfrac{2}{3}\mathbf{AB}.$$

We also know that **AB** = **b** − **a** (from our work in the section above).

To get from O to C you can go along **OB** and then along **BC**. But **OB** = **b** and

$$\mathbf{BC} = -\tfrac{1}{3}\mathbf{AB} = -\tfrac{1}{3}(\mathbf{b} - \mathbf{a})$$

So

$$\mathbf{OC} = \mathbf{OB} + \mathbf{BC} = \mathbf{b} - \tfrac{1}{3}(\mathbf{b} - \mathbf{a})$$

$$\mathbf{c} = \mathbf{b} - \tfrac{1}{3}\mathbf{b} + \tfrac{1}{3}\mathbf{a}$$

$$\mathbf{c} = \tfrac{2}{3}\mathbf{b} + \tfrac{1}{3}\mathbf{a}$$

Consider this result carefully. We have the following three equations:

1 $AC = \frac{2}{3}AB$

2 $CB = \frac{1}{3}AB$

3 $OC = \frac{2}{3}OB + \frac{1}{3}OA$, i.e. $(c = \frac{2}{3}b + \frac{1}{3}a)$

Notice that $\frac{2}{3} + \frac{1}{3} = 1$.

In fact, the result above is an example of a more general rule.

For points A and B, reached from point O by vectors **a** and **b**, and some point C on the line joining A and B (see Fig. 4.16), we know that

$AC = x\,AB$.

Then

$OC = x\mathbf{b} + y\mathbf{a}$,

where $x + y = 1$ (or $1 - x = y$)

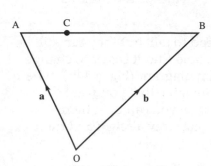

4.16

Example Write OC in terms of **a** and **b** when $AC = \frac{1}{4}AB$ (so $CB = \frac{3}{4}AB$).

The vector diagram is shown in Fig. 4.17.

We have $OA = a$, $OB = b$ and $AB = b - a$.

Also, $OC = OA + \frac{1}{4}AB$

So

$OC = OA + \frac{1}{4}AB = a + \frac{1}{4}(b - a)$

$= a + \frac{1}{4}b - \frac{1}{4}a$

$OC = \frac{3}{4}a + \frac{1}{4}b$

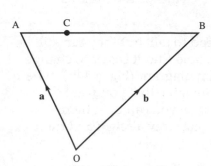

4.17

Task

9 For each vector diagram in Fig. 4.18, write the vector **OC** in terms of the vectors given. Check that the coefficients in front of the two vectors always add up to 1.

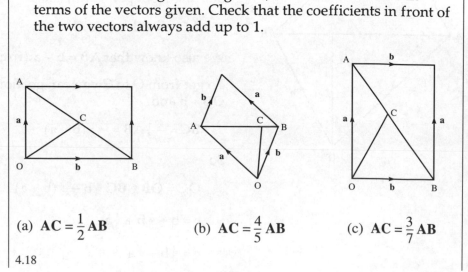

(a) $AC = \frac{1}{2}AB$ (b) $AC = \frac{4}{5}AB$ (c) $AC = \frac{3}{7}AB$

4.18

10 For each vector diagram in Fig. 4.19, write the vector **OC** in terms of the vectors given. Check that the coefficients in front of the two vectors always add up to 1.

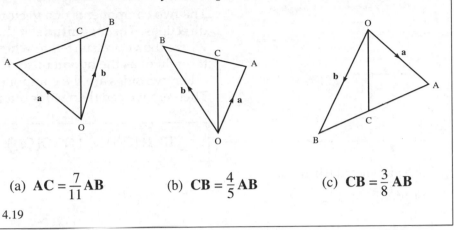

(a) $AC = \dfrac{7}{11} AB$ (b) $CB = \dfrac{4}{5} AB$ (c) $CB = \dfrac{3}{8} AB$

4.19

It doesn't matter where C lies on the line joining A and B for this rule to be true. In fact, C can also lie on a continuation of the line AB, as shown in the following example.

Example

For the vector diagram in Fig. 4.20, write OC in terms of **a** and **b**.

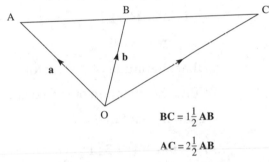

$$BC = 1\tfrac{1}{2} AB$$

$$AC = 2\tfrac{1}{2} AB$$

4.20

$$OC = OB + BC$$

We know that $OB = b$, and $BC = 1\tfrac{1}{2}(b - a)$, so

$$OC = b + 1\tfrac{1}{2}(b - a)$$

$$OC = b + 1\tfrac{1}{2}b - 1\tfrac{1}{2}a$$

$$OC = 2\tfrac{1}{2}b - 1\tfrac{1}{2}a$$

$$OC = \tfrac{5}{2}b - \tfrac{3}{2}a$$

Check: $\tfrac{5}{2} + \left(-\tfrac{3}{2}\right) = 1$.

Task

11 For points A and B, reached from point O by vectors **a** and **b**, and some point C on the line extending from AB, work out **OC** in terms of **a** and **b** given the following information:

a $AC = 1\tfrac{1}{4} AB$

b $AC = 2\tfrac{1}{3} AB$

c $AC = 3\tfrac{3}{5} AB$

Finding the magnitude and direction of vectors

The two components of a vector describe the changes in the x and y directions. The **magnitude** of the vector is the shortest distance from where the vector started to where it finished. The magnitude can be thought of as the hypotenuse of a right-angled triangle where the other two sides are the components of the vector. Using Pythagoras' Theorem we can then work out the length of this hypotenuse.

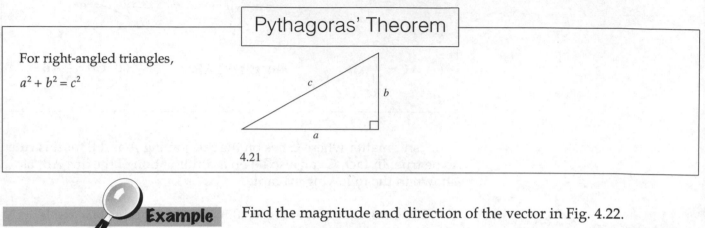

Pythagoras' Theorem

For right-angled triangles,

$a^2 + b^2 = c^2$

4.21

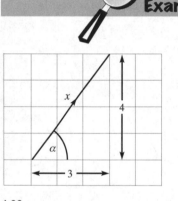

4.22

Example

Find the magnitude and direction of the vector in Fig. 4.22.

To find the magnitude of the vector, we use Pythagoras' Theorem

$$x^2 = 3^2 + 4^2 = 25$$

$$x = 5$$

so the magnitude of the vector is 5.

To find the direction of the vector we use trigonometry (see Chapter 7).

We know that $\tan \alpha = \frac{4}{3}$

So $\alpha = \tan^{-1}\left(\frac{4}{3}\right) = 53.1°$

We usually give direction as a **bearing** from North, measuring in a clockwise direction.

So the direction is $90° - 53.1° = 36.9°$ from North.

Bearings

One way of specifying the direction of a vector is to give its bearing. This is the angle it makes with some agreed direction, such as 'the horizontal' or 'the y-axis'. One common way of doing this is to measure the angle clockwise from North.

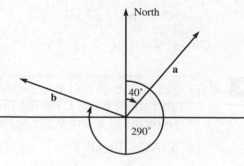

4.23

Vector **a** in Fig. 4.23 has a bearing of 40° and vector **b** has a bearing of 290°, both measured clockwise from North.

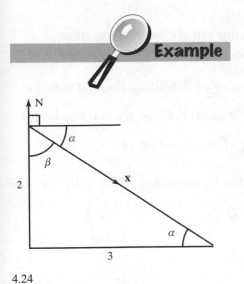

4.24

Example Work out the magnitude and direction of the vector **x**, $\begin{pmatrix} 3 \\ -2 \end{pmatrix}$.

First draw the diagram to represent the vector, as shown in Fig. 4.24.

Using Pythagoras' Theorem we know that $x^2 = 3^2 + (-2)^2 = 13$

and $\sqrt{13} = 3.6$

so the magnitude of **x** is 3.6.

The bearing from North is given by $90° + \alpha$, and we know that $\tan \alpha = \frac{2}{3}$.

So $\alpha = \tan^{-1} \frac{2}{3} = 33.7°$

So the bearing is 123.7° from North.

Task

> 12 Find the magnitude and direction of each of the following vectors:
>
> a $\begin{pmatrix} 3 \\ 2 \end{pmatrix}$ c $\begin{pmatrix} 4 \\ -3 \end{pmatrix}$
>
> b $\begin{pmatrix} -6 \\ -6 \end{pmatrix}$ d $\begin{pmatrix} 0 \\ 9 \end{pmatrix}$

Vectors and equations of straight lines

If we know the coordinates of two points on a straight line then the equation of the line can be written in vector form. The equation of a line in vector form has two parts. The first part is found by moving from the origin to one of the points on the line. Once on the line, you have to travel forwards or backwards in the same direction to reach any other point on the line, so the second part describes the direction of the line.

Example

A Find the equation of the straight line passing through the points (5, 6) and (10, 4).

We go through the following steps (see Fig. 4.25).

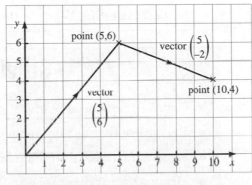

4.25

a To get from the origin to point (5, 6) we need to move along the vector $\begin{pmatrix} 5 \\ 6 \end{pmatrix}$.

b To get from point $(5, 6)$ to point $(10, 4)$, we need to move $10 - 5 = 5$ in the x direction, and $4 - 6 = -2$ in the y direction.

So we now know that the vector $\begin{pmatrix} 5 \\ -2 \end{pmatrix}$ lies along the line passing through $(5, 6)$ and $(10, 4)$, and once on the line we can reach any point along the line by moving in the direction of $\begin{pmatrix} 5 \\ -2 \end{pmatrix}$. So we would reach any point on the line by moving $\begin{pmatrix} 5 \\ 6 \end{pmatrix}$ from the origin, followed by some multiple of $\begin{pmatrix} 5 \\ -2 \end{pmatrix}$.

So the general equation for any point on the line is

$$\begin{pmatrix} x \\ y \end{pmatrix} = \begin{pmatrix} 5 \\ 6 \end{pmatrix} + a \begin{pmatrix} 5 \\ -2 \end{pmatrix},$$

where a is a constant.

B Find the equation of the straight line passing through the points $(4, 11)$ and $(-2, 19)$.

The situation is illustrated in Fig. 4.26.

To get from the origin $(0, 0)$ to the point $(4, 11)$ we need to move along the vector $\begin{pmatrix} 4 \\ 11 \end{pmatrix}$.

To get from the point $(4, 11)$ to $(-2, 19)$ we need to move $-2 - 4 = -6$ in the x direction, and $19 - 11 = 8$ in the y direction, i.e. along the vector $\begin{pmatrix} -6 \\ 8 \end{pmatrix}$.

So the equation of the line is

$$\begin{pmatrix} x \\ y \end{pmatrix} = \begin{pmatrix} 4 \\ 11 \end{pmatrix} + a \begin{pmatrix} -6 \\ 8 \end{pmatrix}$$

for some constant a.

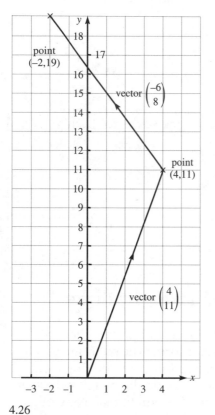

4.26

Task

13 Find the equations for the straight lines passing through the following points:

a $(1, 4)$ and $(5, 9)$ c $(1, 1)$ and $(5, 5)$

b $(22, 4)$ and $(6, 17)$ d $(21, 13)$ and $(3, 9)$

SUMMARY

You should now be able to

- Recognise that vectors have magnitude (size) and direction
- Represent a vector in diagram form
- Draw a vector diagram
- Add and subtract vectors
- Identify parallel vectors
- Represent the equation of a straight line in diagram form

Chapter 5

Indices and logarithms

Indices

When we multiply a number by itself, we say that we raise it to a power, the value of the power being the number of times that the number is multiplied by itself. The power is written as a superscript number, called the index. So, for example, 7^5 is 7 raised to the power 5 and the index, 5, indicates that 7 is multiplied by itself five times, i.e. $7^5 = 7 \times 7 \times 7 \times 7 \times 7$.

Most calculators have a button 'x^y' which will work out the value of these powers. For example, to work out 7^5 on your calculator, press the buttons 7, 'x^y', 5, and =, to give 16807.

Task

> 1 Use your calculator to help you to work out the values of:
>
> a 7^9 d $(0.5)^6$
>
> b 6^3 e 5^0
>
> c 19^4

The answer to e may surprise you, but try some other numbers to the power 0. Can you think why this value occurs?

Multiplication of terms with indices

Consider the following two results.

$$5^2 \times 5^4 = (5 \times 5) \times (5 \times 5 \times 5 \times 5) = 5^6 = 15625$$
$$5^{(2+4)} = 5^6 = 15625$$

Task

> 2 Work out the following using both of the methods above:
>
> a $7^3 \times 7^5$ d $10^3 \times 10^4$
>
> b $11^4 \times 11^2$ e $0.5^5 \times 0.5^3$
>
> c $9^2 \times 9^6$

This leads to the rule

$$y^a \times y^b = y^{a+b}$$

Using this rule,

$$3^2 \times 3^0 = 3^{2+0} = 3^2$$

But we also know that

$$3^2 \times 1 = 3^2$$

And so it seems that $3^0 = 1$.

It should be clear that, in general, for x and y not equal to 0,
$y^x \times y^0 = y^x$.

The general rules are:

$y^0 = 1$ for all values of y except 0

$0^x = 0$ for all values of x except 0

There is an exception to the rule that any number raised to the power 0 gives the answer 1. Can you think what it is? Since in general $0^x = 0$ and $y^0 = 1$, we have a problem when considering 0^0. In fact, 0^0 remains undefined. Try it on your calculator.

There is a similar problem for $\dfrac{x}{y}$. We know that, for some y not equal to 0, when $x = 0$, $\dfrac{x}{y} = 0$. But what happens when x is a number (not 0) and y gets very small? Then $\dfrac{x}{y}$ gets very big. As y gets smaller, $\dfrac{x}{y}$ gets bigger and bigger. We say that as y tends to 0, $\dfrac{x}{y}$ tends to infinity (undefined on your calculator). When x and y are both 0, $\dfrac{x}{y}$ is undefined.

These types of numbers are known as **indeterminate forms**.

Division of terms with indices

Consider the following examples:

$$5^6 \div 5^2 = 15625 \div 25 = 625 = 5^4$$

Notice that subtracting the indices gives $6 - 2 = 4$.

$$6^5 \div 6^3 = 7776 \div 216 = 36 = 6^2.$$

Notice that $5 - 3 = 2$.

> 3 Work out the following using both methods to see if you can formulate a rule.
>
> a $7^3 \div 7^2$ d $11^8 \div 11^3$
>
> b $10^6 \div 10^3$ e $0.5^4 \div 0.5^1$
>
> c $9^5 \div 9^3$

The rule that we can formulate is:

$$x^a \div x^b = x^{a-b}$$

Negative indices

Work out 2^{-1} on your calculator. You will find that $2^{-1} = 0.5 = \frac{1}{2}$.
Similarly, we get $5^{-1} = 0.2 = \frac{1}{5}$.

The general rule is:

$$x^{-1} = \frac{1}{x}$$

$$x^{-y} = \frac{1}{x^y}$$

Task

> 4 Write the following as exact fractions. Use your calculator to check your answers:
>
> a 4^{-1} d 8^{-1}
>
> b 10^{-2} e 6^{-3}
>
> c 2^{-3}

Fractions

We can also combine negative indices with fractions, but do take care as it is easy to go wrong.

$$\left(\tfrac{1}{4}\right)^{-1} = \frac{1}{\left(\tfrac{1}{4}\right)} = 1 \times 4 = 4$$

Task

> 5 Simplify:
>
> a $\left(\tfrac{1}{2}\right)^{-1}$ d $\left(\tfrac{1}{10}\right)^{-5}$
>
> b $\left(\tfrac{1}{4}\right)^{2}$ e $\left(\tfrac{1}{5}\right)^{3}$
>
> c $\left(\tfrac{1}{5}\right)^{-4}$ f $\left(\tfrac{1}{10}\right)^{7}$

Standard form

Your calculator will sometimes give answers in **standard form**. This is where a number is given as a multiple of a power of 10, i.e. $a \times 10^n$, where a is between 0 and 10 and n is a positive or negative integer.

Standard form is a convenient way of expressing large or small numbers, so you will often find it used in physics when measuring large distances, velocities, etc. and in chemistry when measuring small concentrations or large numbers, such as the mole. The a gives the numerical value between 1 and 10 to the number of significant figures required and the power of 10 governs the size of the number, making comparison of size easier.

Example

$7\,856\,000 = 7.86 \times 10^6$ to 3 significant figures

$0.006\,312\,4 = 6.3 \times 10^{-3}$ to 2 significant figures

Note that your calculator usually writes this in an abbreviated form, usually with the 10 missing, and with the index separated from the main number, e.g. the display may show 6.3 −3 or 6.3 $^{-3}$. This is *not* an acceptable shorthand to use in written work, but make sure you know how to use the EXP button (or its equivalent – usually EE) to input numbers in this form on your calculator.

Task

> 6 Write the following in standard form, correct to 3 significant figures:
>
> | a 5 672 000 000 | f 4^{-8} |
> |---|---|
> | b 76.89 | g 3^{-5} |
> | c 0.004 362 9 | h 5.2^6 |
> | d 2 989 | i 10^{-9} |
> | e 0.000 000 056 731 | j 9^{-7} |

Power of a power

Consider the following:

$$(5^2)^4 = 25^4 = 390625$$

$$5^{2 \times 4} = 5^8 = 390625$$

The general rule is:

$$(m^x)^y = m^{xy} = (m^y)^x$$

Task

> 7 Write each of the following as a power of a power in at least two ways:
>
> | a 6^{30} | d $y^{\frac{3}{4}}$ |
> |---|---|
> | b 5^8 | e p^{-12} |
> | c 10^{24} | |

Fractional indices

By definition, $\sqrt{y} \times \sqrt{y} = y$ but from the work above, we also know that $y^{\frac{1}{2}} \times y^{\frac{1}{2}} = y^1 = y$.

So it seems that $\sqrt{y} = y^{\frac{1}{2}}$.

Similarly $\sqrt[3]{m} \times \sqrt[3]{m} \times \sqrt[3]{m} = m$,

and $m^{\frac{1}{3}} \times m^{\frac{1}{3}} \times m^{\frac{1}{3}} = m$.

So $m^{\frac{1}{3}} = \sqrt[3]{m}$

In general,

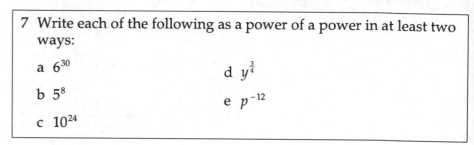

$$p^{\frac{a}{b}} = \sqrt[b]{p^a} = \left(\sqrt[b]{p}\right)^a$$

For example, $8^{\frac{2}{3}} = \sqrt[3]{8^2} = \sqrt[3]{64} = 4$

and $8^{\frac{2}{3}} = \left(\sqrt[3]{8}\right)^2 = 2^2 = 4$

It doesn't matter which method you use.

8 Try to do these without a calculator as it important for algebraic calculations that you really understand indices:

a $16^{\frac{3}{4}}$ d $4^{\frac{9}{2}}$

b $125^{\frac{2}{3}}$ e $\left(\frac{1}{25}\right)^{-\frac{1}{2}}$

c $1\,000\,000^{\frac{5}{6}}$

Logarithms

Before the advent of the pocket calculator, logarithms (logs) were an essential tool in calculation. We know that 100 can be written as 10^2. The logarithm of 100 (to the base 10) is 2. Similarly, 1000 can be written as 10^3. The logarithm of 1000 (to the base 10) is 3 and so on.

Any number can be written in the form 10 raised to a power.

For example, 2.0 is $10^{0.30103}$, so the logarithm of 2 (to the base 10) is 0.30103 and 50 is $10^{1.69897}$, so the logarithm of 50 (to the base 10) is 1.69897.

I think I've lost a 2 somewhere.

Remember the rules concerning indices in the previous sections. Using these:

- multiplication problems can be changed to addition problems
- division problems can be changed to subtraction problems
- powers can be changed to multiplication by a number
- roots can be changed to division by a number.

Logarithms are a way of converting numbers to indices, and we can use the special rules for indices to do complicated arithmetic. Indeed, this was once the only practical way to do complicated arithmetic quickly. For example, to multiply numbers, the logarithms of the numbers were looked up in tables and then added. The answer was then 'anti-logged' to change it back to a normal number.

Multiply 57.8 and 6.35.

$57.8 \times 6.35 = 10^{1.762} \times 10^{0.803}$

Using the laws on indices, $10^{1.762} \times 10^{0.803} = 10^{(1.762 + 0.803)} = 10^{2.565} = 367$.

So to perform this calculation using logarithms, we could calculate $\log_{10} 57.8$ (where $\log_{10}$ means take the log to base 10) and $\log_{10} 6.35$. This would give us 1.762 and 0.803, respectively. Adding these, $1.762 + 0.803 = 2.565$. Taking the 'anti-log' (the button marked 10^x on your calculator) of 2.565, the answer is 367, as before.

The logarithm is a useful function in its own right and helps with the solutions of exponential equations. These are equations in which the unknown is a power.

For example, $5^x = 785$ is an exponential equation.

Logarithms and calculators

Logarithms appear on calculators in two ways. Note that some calculators require the keys to be pressed in different orders, so be familiar with the calculator you use.

Some calculators use the 10^x button for INV log.

1 The **log** button. Numbers are given as powers of 10 – the base.

For example, to find the log of 1000, enter 1 000 and press 'log'. The answer should be 3, since $10^3 = 1000$. We have $\log_{10} 1000 = 3$.

If you know the logarithm of a number, and want to find that number, enter the logarithm and press the INV button followed by the log button. This has the effect of calculating 10^x, where x is the logarithm that you know. So we have INV log 3 = 1000.

2 The **ln** button gives a logarithm to a different base number called e (i.e. if $\ln x = y$, then $e^y = x$), which is chosen to fit in with other parts of mathematics. Look out for e in the calculus. A logarithm to base e is written $\log_e x$ or $\ln x$.

Task

9 Find the value of e on your calculator. (Remember that $x^1 = x$, so find out how to enter e^1.)

So we have seen that the logarithm of a number is the power to which the base must be raised to give the number. The usual bases are 10 and e.

$$10^{\log x} = x$$

$$e^{\ln y} = y$$

Task

10 In the following examples, only logarithms to base ten will be used so you will need the log and 10^x buttons on your calculator. To get used to how the buttons work, choose a number. Press the log button and then, keeping the display, press the 10^x button. Try this with four other numbers of different sizes. Note what happens when you find the inverse log. Watch out for other inverses and inverse processes. Now, without a calculator write down:

a log 1 000 000   d log 1

b log 10   e log $\frac{1}{1000}$

c log $\frac{1}{10}$

Since logarithms are associated with powers we have the following rules, which apply provided the same base is used throughout.

● To multiply two numbers, add their logs.

$\log a + \log b = \log (ab)$,

e.g. $\log 3 + \log 2 = \log 6$

● To divide two numbers, subtract their logs.

$\log a - \log b = \log \left(\dfrac{a}{b}\right)$,

e.g. $\log 12 - \log 4 = \log 3$

● To raise a number to a power, multiply the log of the number by the required power.

$\log c^d = d \log c$,

e.g. $2 \log 3 = \log 3^2 = \log 9$

- To find the *d*th root of a number, divide the log of the number by *d*.

$$\log \sqrt[d]{c} = \frac{\log c}{d},$$

e.g. $\log \sqrt[3]{8} = \frac{\log 8}{3}$

In each case use INV log to finish the calculation.

Using logarithms to solve exponential equations

An exponential equation is one where the unknown quantity is a power. These kinds of equations occur in growth and decay problems where, for instance, something is doubling every second or is halving every minute. Examples include cell growth and radioactive decay.

Example

Find x such that $5^x = 785$.

Take the logarithms of both sides

$\log 5^x = \log 785$

But $\log 5^x = x \log 5 = \log 785$

Substituting the logarithms for 5 and 785,

$0.698970004 x = 2.894869657$

$x = 2.894869657 \div 0.698970004$

$x = 4.141622159$

$x = 4.1416$ to 5 significant figures.

Check by substituting this value for x into the original equation.

$5^{4.141622159} = 785.0000005$, which is correct allowing for the rounding errors involved in using logarithms.

Task

> 11 Solve the following to 3 significant figures:
>
> a $1.7^y = 2\,000\,000$ d $16\left(\frac{1}{2}\right)^t = \frac{1}{32}$
>
> b $(0.8)^m = 0.028$
>
> e $60(1.05)^t = 75$
>
> c $5^q = 4$

The last of these questions could be used to solve the following problem. Try to see why.

Example

A £60 is invested at 5 per cent per annum until there is a total amount of £75. How long does this take if interest is also given on the interest? This is called **compound interest**.

Amount at the end of the first year = £60 + $\frac{5}{100}$ of £60

£60 × (1 + 0.05) = £60 × 1.05

Amount at the end of the second year = £60 × 1.05 + $\frac{5}{100}$ (£60 × 1.05)

(£60 × 1.05)(1 + $\frac{5}{100}$)

£60 × (1.05)^2

Similarly, at the end of t years there is £60 × (1.05)^t, and you should have t from Task 11e above.

B How long would it take for £220 invested at 6.5 per cent per annum (compound interest) to become £300?

Each year, $\frac{6.5}{100}$ of the amount at the beginning of the year is added to give $1 + \frac{6.5}{100} = 1.065$ times the previous year's money.

At the end of t years there is £220 × $(1.065)^t$

And so we need to solve $220(1.065)^t = 300$

$(1.065)^t = \frac{300}{220} = 1.36363636\ldots$

Taking the log of both sides, $\log(1.065)^t = \log 1.363636$

$t\log 1.065 = \log 1.363636$

$0.027349607t = 0.134698573$

$t = 0.134698573 \div 0.027349607$

$t = 4.925064298$

So at the end of 5 years there will be just over £300.

As before, it is better to work with the full calculator display for as long as possible and approximate at the end of the problem. Working must be shown in the problem but need not always include all of the display. Three or four figures will usually indicate the method.

Task

12 Use logarithms to solve the following problems:

a After how many years would £210 invested at 7 per cent per annum reach £600?

b A pile of 1 million sheets of paper is halved each day. After how many days will it contain just under 1000 sheets?

c Viewing figures for a new programme were found to be increasing by 4 per cent each week. After how many weeks would there be an increase of 25 per cent on the original?

d The risk of infection from a new flu virus is estimated to halve each week after the first case. After how many weeks has it reduced to 1 per cent of the original risk?

e Find a value, correct to 3 significant figures, for $\frac{s}{t}$ if $8^s = 7^t$.

Graphs of these functions

Figure 5.1 shows the shape of the graphs of a logarithmic function and of the exponential function. Notice that if the functions are an inverse pair one can be obtained from the other by reflection in the line $y = x$.

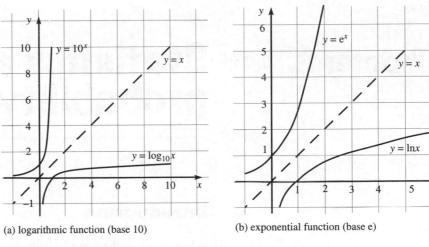

(a) logarithmic function (base 10)

(b) exponential function (base e)

5.1

SUMMARY

You should now be able to

- Understand index notation
- Multiply and divide numbers expressed in index notation
- Use numbers expressed in standard form
- Solve exponential equations using logarithms

Chapter 6

Statistics and probability

Introduction

What are the chances of winning the National Lottery? Most people who buy a ticket do not know the odds against them and would probably still buy the ticket if they did! At the end of this chapter you may be able to work out the odds.

Any probability must be based on what actually happens and not just on theory. It seems obvious that if you toss a coin you stand an equal chance of getting heads or tails. But if you threw the coin 10 times and got heads 8 times would that mean the coin was biased? Probably not, but if it happened 800 times in 1000 throws then you might well think that a bias was there. Probability theory tries to put such conclusions on a firmer mathematical basis. It has many important applications. For example, it helps anyone doing a national survey to know how large their survey must be if their conclusions are likely to be correct for the whole country. It is used in the prediction of election results and even to help to judge the popularity of television programmes.

Statistics

The following sets of figures all have something in common. Can you see what it is?

a 5, 4, 6, 2, 1, 7, 5, 5, 1, 4

b 17, −3, 4, 2, 3, −3, 10, 1, 8, 1

c 100, −30, 200, −75, 100, −150, 80, 20, −125, −80

In each case there are ten numbers and they add up to 40. The 'average' of each set – the total, 40, divided by the number of numbers, 10 – is 4.

This seems realistic in a, because most of the numbers are around 4, but many of the numbers in b are not close to this 'average' and those in c are even further from 4. To take account of these differences we have two other ways of defining an average and also a way of estimating how far the numbers range from that average.

Three ways of finding an average

1 The **mean** average is the sum of the numbers divided by how many numbers there are. (This was used above and is 4 for all three of the examples given).

2 The **median** is the middle number when the figures (elements) are written in size (ranking) order.

Example

Find the medians for each list of numbers above.

a   The numbers in rank order are 1, 1, 2, 4, 4, * 5, 5, 5, 6, 7.

   The median is 4.5, i.e. half way between the fifth and sixth numbers, 4 and 5.

b   The numbers in rank order are −3, −3, 1, 1, 2, * 3, 4, 8, 10, 17.

   The median is 2.5, i.e. half way between 2 and 3.

c   The numbers in rank order are −150, −125, −80, −75, −30, * 20, 80, 100, 100, 200.

   The median is −5, i.e. half way between −30 and 20.

3   The **mode** (modal average) is the number that occurs most often. In a it is 5, in b there is no mode since both −3 and 1 occur twice and in c it is 100.

Task

1   Find the mean, mode and median for the following sets of numbers:

   a   5, 7, 3, 1, 7, 2, 3

   b   −3, 8, −2, 6, 8, −1, 8, 4

   c   19, 25, 0, 25, 18, 25, 16, 10, 15

   d   6, −5, 2, −3, 15

   e   1.9, 3.2, 4.3, 5.7, 1.9

   f   108, 111, 114, 136, 145, 152, 200

Different averages are used for different tasks. For example, if you were making shoes for four-year-olds in one size only, you would need to decide the most suitable size. Using the mean and the median averages could produce shoes that fitted nobody, so the modal average would be the one to use here.

Task

2   Discuss which average is best for working out each of the following:

   a   The height of the pegs in the cloakroom for the reception class of an infant school.

   b   The average goals scored per match by a footballer in one season.

   c   The number of vehicles daily using the main road through a village, to decide if a by-pass is needed.

   d   The number of chairs to keep in a room if it used by groups of 18, 22, 13, 40, 27 and 19 people.

   e   The height and width of a doorway to a new house.

Standard deviation from the mean

We have seen that a mean average gives a limited amount of information and it may be more useful to know how far the elements are from the mean and how they are spread. The **standard deviation** from the mean is used to do this, as the following example will show.

Example

Find the standard deviation from the mean for the numbers 5, 4, 6, 2, 1, 7, 5, 5, 1, 4.

From a previous example we know that the mean for this set of numbers is 4. We first find the difference between the mean, m, and each number. We are not interested in whether this is positive or negative, so we will use squares to make everything positive. The mean of this set of squares is called the **variance from the mean**, and we use this to find the standard deviation.

Values (x)	$x - m$	$(x - m)^2$
5	1	1
4	0	0
6	2	4
2	-2	4
1	-3	9
7	3	9
5	1	1
5	1	1
1	-3	9
4	0	0
		38 $\div 10 = 3.8$

So the 'average' of the squares of the amounts that the values differ from their mean, also called their variance from the mean, is 3.8.

The standard deviation is the square root of the variance, and so the standard deviation from the mean is $\sqrt{3.8} = 1.95$ to 3 significant figures. The symbol s or σ is used for standard deviation.

The standard deviation gives us an indication of the spread of the values from the mean – the smaller the number, the smaller the spread.

Standard deviation

The formula for the standard deviation often includes the Greek letter capital sigma, Σ, which is used throughout mathematics to denote 'the sum of'.

The standard deviation of the set of n numbers x_1, x_2, x_3, ..., x_n from their mean, m, is given by:

$$\sqrt{\frac{\Sigma (x - m)^2}{n}}$$

The variance is the square of the standard deviation,

$$\frac{\Sigma (x - m)^2}{n}$$

Task

3 Find the mean and the standard deviation from the mean for the following sets of numbers:

a 7, 3, 5, 1, 2, 0

b −5, −1, 7, 3, 8, 7, 1, 8, 4, −2

c 0.5, 0.125, 1.6, 5, 0.6

d 302, 158, 66, 402

e −10, −4, −1, 0, 2, 7, 11, 15

Using your calculator for statistical functions

As always, use your calculator manual or find someone who knows how to use your particular calculator so that you are familiar with the way it works. The calculator will need to be in SD (statistical) mode. The following symbols will be used in theoretical statistics:

Σ (capital sigma) the numbers entered are to be added together

μ (mu) or $\bar{x}$ the mean of the numbers entered is to be found

σ (sigma) the standard deviation from the mean

σ^2 (sigma squared) the variance from the mean

The Greek alphabet is used throughout mathematics.

In the following example, check that you get the same answers on your calculator.

For the numbers 8, 5, 6, 10, and 16 find the sum, the mean, the standard deviation from the mean and the variance.

Sum $= 8 + 5 + 6 + 10 + 16 = 45$

Mean $= 45 \div 5 = 9$

$$s \text{ (or } \sigma) = \sqrt{\frac{(9-8)^2 + (9-5)^2 + (9-6)^2 + (9-10)^2 + (9-16)^2}{5}}$$

$$= \sqrt{\frac{1+16+9+1+49}{5}}$$

$$= \sqrt{\frac{76}{5}}$$

$$= 3.899 \text{ to 3 decimal places}$$

Variance $= \sigma^2 = 76 \div 5 = 15.2$

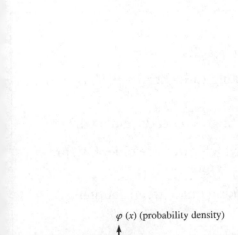

4 Use your calculator to work out the sum, the mean, the standard deviation and the variance from the mean for the following sets of numbers.

  a 7.5, 6.3, 1.5, 9.2, 6.1, 5.3

  b 900, 905, 967, 833, 895

  c 0.0712, 0.0865, 0.0324, 0.0194, 0.0557, 0.0444, 0.0123

  d 56, −36, 67, −23, 39, −89, 61, 78, 54, −91

  e 6×10^3, 4×10^5, 3.2×10^4, 5.8×10^2

Always try to judge whether your answer is reasonable, and if it isn't look for the error.

The normal distribution

Many natural occurrences happen in a way that follows a pattern where most things happen near to a mean. The characteristic curve is as shown in Fig. 6.1 and is called a **normal distribution**.

Once a distribution is known to be normal and the mean and standard deviation from it are known, there are tables designed to help with further calculations. Almost all the events happen within three standard deviations on either side of the mean. There are countless examples that fit this pattern including the time that similar

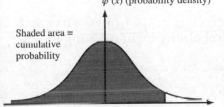

$\varphi(x)$ (probability density)

Shaded area = cumulative probability

x

6.1

seeds planted at the same time take to grow, times that people arrive to catch a train, and the height or weight of a population.

Probability

There are many occasions when people try to predict what is going to happen. Probability theory links with statistics and tries to put predictions on a firmer basis, such as when forecasting weather, results of football matches, results of elections, or the success of a new product.

Data (known facts) must be collected, but then theory can be used to decide how large a sample of the whole population can be taken to give a valid result.

The first basic mathematical definition of the probability that event A happens in N trials is:

$$p(A) = \frac{\text{number of possible times event } A \text{ can occur}}{N, \text{ the total number of possible outcomes}}$$

Example

A Find the probability of tossing a coin and getting a head, $p(H)$.

There are two possible outcomes, heads (H) or tails (T), and one way of obtaining a head, so

$p(H) = \frac{1}{2}$

B Find the probability of obtaining two heads when two coins are tossed, $p(H, H)$.

Write down all the possibilities. They are (H, H), (H, T), (T, H) and (T, T). So there are four equally likely possible outcomes and one way of obtaining two heads.

$p(H, H) = \frac{1}{4}$

Task

5 Three coins are tossed.

   a Write down the eight possible results.

   b What is the probability of getting three heads, $p(H, H, H)$, in these throws?

   c What is the probability of getting two heads and a tail?

6 A bag contains ten counters of which three are blue, four are green, two are yellow and one is white.

   a What is the probability of picking out a green counter in a random draw?

   b If you have already drawn a green counter from the bag and kept it out, what would the probability be of drawing another green counter?

You should have found in Task 5b that

$$p(H, H, H) = \tfrac{1}{8} = \tfrac{1}{2} \times \tfrac{1}{2} \times \tfrac{1}{2} = p(H) \times p(H) \times p(H)$$

This is an example of a useful rule:

If the events concerned are independent then the probabilities can be combined as follows

$$p(A \text{ and } B) = p(A) \times p(B)$$

This rule can be extended to any number of events *provided that they are independent*.

Example

What is the probability of getting four heads when tossing four coins?

The probability of heads for each coin is $\frac{1}{2}$, so the probability of throwing four heads is $\frac{1}{2} \times \frac{1}{2} \times \frac{1}{2} \times \frac{1}{2} = \frac{1}{16}$, which can be written $\left(\frac{1}{2}\right)^4$.

Task

7 Write down the probability of getting five tails when tossing five coins.

8 The probability that a school's soccer and netball teams win a match is $\frac{5}{6}$ and $\frac{3}{4}$, respectively, and these events are independent.

a What is the probability that both teams win?

b What is the probability that they both lose?

c What is the probability that one team loses and the other team wins?

d Find the sum of your answers to a, b and c and explain why you should expect this number.

Example

Fig. 6.2 shows all the outcomes when two normal dice are thrown.

A What is the probability of throwing a 6 with one die?

There are 6 possible outcomes, and only one of these is 6. So $p(6) = \frac{1}{6}$.

B What is the probability of throwing a double 6?

The number on one die does not affect the number on the other, so the events are independent. We can use the rule above to show that

$$p(6, 6) = \frac{1}{6} \times \frac{1}{6} = \frac{1}{36}.$$

You should be able to see that this is the right answer by looking at Fig. 6.2.

C What is the probability of throwing a total of 7 with two dice?

Using Fig. 6.2, find all the combinations that add up to 7. The possibilities are $(6, 1)$, $(1, 6)$, $(2, 5)$, $(5, 2)$, $(4, 3)$ and $(3, 4)$, i.e. the event could occur in six ways, and there are 36 possible outcomes. Using our original definition of probabilities, we can see that

$$p(\text{total } 7) = \frac{6}{36} = \frac{1}{6}.$$

Note also that

$$p(6, 1) + p(1, 6) + p(2, 5) + p(5, 2) + p(4, 3) + p(3, 4) = \frac{6}{36} = \frac{1}{6}$$
$$= p(\text{total } 7)$$

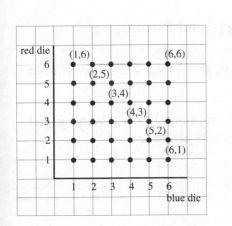

6.2

This is an example of the 'or' rule, which says

$$p(A \textbf{ or } B) = p(A) + p(B) - p(A \text{ and } B)$$

If A and B cannot happen at the same time (independent events), $p(A \text{ and } B) = 0$, and the rule becomes

$$p(A \text{ or } B) = p(A) + p(B)$$

Example

A bag contains six yellow balls, two white balls and three blue balls. What is the probability of drawing out a yellow ball or a white ball?

$p(Y) = \frac{6}{11}$ and $p(W) = \frac{2}{11}$, and the events are independent.

$$p(Y \text{ or } W) = p(Y) + p(W) = \frac{6}{11} + \frac{2}{11} = \frac{8}{11}$$

Task

9 Two dice are thrown.

   a What is the probability of throwing a total of 8?

   b What is the probability of throwing a total of 10 or more?

10 Three coins are tossed. What is the probability of getting a head and two tails in any order?

11 What is the probability of being born on a Wednesday?

12 What is the probability that five people all choose an even number if they have to choose from the list 6, 10, 15, 31, 39, 50?

Tree diagrams

A **tree diagram** can help to put probabilities together. The diagrams are constructed as follows:

- Each branch represents a different possibility.
- The probabilities at each set of branches always add up to one.
- We use the previous rule for independent events, extending it where necessary.

   i.e. $p(A \text{ and } B) = p(A) \times p(B)$, so $p(A \text{ and } B \text{ and } C) = p(A) \times p(B) \times p(C)$, etc.

The following example shows how we would use a tree diagram to solve Task 8.

Example

The probability that a school's soccer and netball teams win a match is $\frac{5}{6}$ and $\frac{3}{4}$, respectively, and these events are independent.

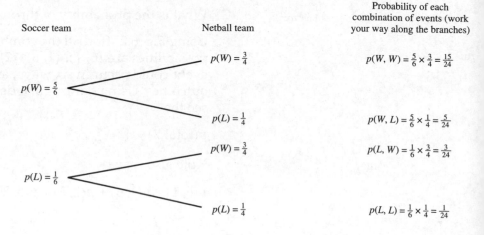

A What is the probability that both teams win?

B What is the probability that they both lose?

C What is the probability that one team loses and the other team wins?

We move along the branches to find the probabilities of various combinations of events.

A Moving along the top branch, $p(W, W) = \frac{5}{6} \times \frac{3}{4} = \frac{15}{24}$

B Moving along the bottom branch, $p(L, L) = \frac{1}{6} \times \frac{1}{4} = \frac{1}{24}$

C We can see that $p(W, L) = \frac{5}{6} \times \frac{1}{4} = \frac{5}{24}$ and that
$p(L, W) = \frac{1}{6} \times \frac{3}{4} = \frac{3}{24}$ by moving along the respective branches.

Now, $p(\text{one game won, one lost}) = p((L, W) \text{ or} (W, L))$
$= p(L, W) + p(W, L) = \frac{5}{24} + \frac{3}{24} = \frac{8}{24} = \frac{1}{3}$

Leaving the fractions unsimplified makes it easy to check that all the probabilities in the last column of the tree diagram add up to 1 as required.

Task

13 There are five green counters and three red counters in a bag. A counter is drawn and then replaced and a second one is drawn. Use a tree diagram to find the probabilities of each possible outcome, i.e. $p(G, G)$, $p(G, R)$, $p(R, G)$, and $p(R, R)$. What is the probability of drawing one of each colour?

14 Use a tree diagram to find the probability of drawing at least one Ace, King, Queen or Jack from a pack of cards if two draws are allowed and the card is replaced after the first draw.

15 You have two multiple choice questions, each with three choices.

  a Draw a tree diagram to show the possible events.

  b What is the probability of getting one question right and one wrong?

  c Now suppose that you have three questions, each with three choices. What is the probability of getting two correct and one wrong?

16 A group of children are asked to choose a game to play from tennis, Monopoly, clock golf and badminton. They must then choose either an orange drink or an ice cream. In each case choices are equally likely.

  a Use a tree diagram to work out the probability that a child chooses Monopoly followed by an ice cream.

  b Later results then show that the probabilities are in fact $\frac{1}{5}$ for tennis, $\frac{3}{10}$ for Monopoly, $\frac{3}{10}$ for clock golf and $\frac{1}{5}$ for badminton. For refreshment the probability is $\frac{3}{7}$ for the drink and $\frac{4}{7}$ for ice cream and this is independent of the first choice. Draw another tree diagram to show the possibilities and find:

   i the probability that tennis or golf are played and not followed by an ice cream

   ii that Monopoly or badminton are played, followed by the drink.

17 Three friends are choosing between going to see a film, going swimming and watching television. Each event is equally likely to be chosen and they choose independently.

  a What is the probability that they all choose to go swimming?

  b What is the probability that two of them want to go to a film and one wants to go swimming?

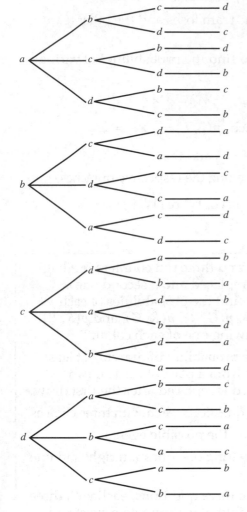

What about the National Lottery?

In the National Lottery, each player has to choose six different numbers from the set 1–49. What is the probability of matching these to the winning numbers?

There are 49 numbers, so the number of possible choices for the first number drawn is 49. The number of choices for the second number drawn is 48, and so on. So the total number of possible choices (total number of outcomes) is $49 \times 48 \times 47 \times 46 \times 45 \times 44$. The order the numbers are drawn in does not matter, so we need some way of dealing with that.

Arrangements or permutations

We can choose the six numbers in any order, so it might be useful to find out how many ways there are of arranging six numbers.

Consider the following:

For one number, there is one way: a

For two numbers, there are two ways: ab, ba

For three numbers, there are six ways: $abc, acb, bac, bca, cab, cba$

For four numbers, there are 24 ways: $abcd, abdc, acbd, acdb, adbc,$ $adcb, bcda, bcad, bdac, bdca, bacd, badc, cdab, cdba, cadb, cabd, cbda,$ $cbad, dabc, dacb, dbca, dbac, dcab, dcba$

We clearly need a formula for higher numbers!

We can think of arranging the four numbers to fit them into four spaces. We could choose any of the four for the first position, but there would only be three left for the second, two left for the third and just one for the last position. From the tree diagram, we see that we have a total of 24 different arrangements, given by $4 \times 3 \times 2 \times 1 = 24$.

For five numbers there are $5 \times 4 \times 3 \times 2 \times 1 = 120$ arrangements. And so for six numbers there are $6 \times 5 \times 4 \times 3 \times 2 \times 1 = 720$.

These kinds of numbers are called **factorials** and can be found on a calculator marked with the symbol '!', and written, for example, $6! = 720$.

18 Find the value of:

a 10!

b 20!

c 32!

19 Find the number of arrangements of the numbers:

a 1, 4, 3, and 5

b 1, 3, 3, and 5

c 1, 3, 3, and 3

20 Try to formulate a rule for when a number occurs more than once.

The probability of winning the Lottery Jackpot

We know that the number of possible ways of choosing six numbers from 49 possibilities is $49 \times 48 \times 47 \times 46 \times 45 \times 44$. The order the numbers are drawn in doesn't matter, and the number of orders for six numbers is 6!

p(choosing the correct six numbers)

$$= \frac{\text{number of times event can occur}}{\text{total number of possible outcomes}}$$

$$= \frac{6!}{49 \times 48 \times 47 \times 46 \times 45 \times 44}$$

$$= 7.1 \times 10^{-8}$$

$$= 0.000\,000\,071, \text{ which is very small, about 1 in 14 million.}$$

Task

21 Bob remembers that his friend's phone number contains the digits 5, 3, 3, 3, 3, and 2 but has forgotten the correct order. How many calls might he have to make before he gets through to his friend?

22 How many ways are there of arranging the letters of MATHEMATICS in a line with the 'M's at the beginning and the 'S' at the end?

23 What is the probability of picking out the letters of YOU WIN in any order from the 26 letters of the alphabet distributed face down on a table?

24 Find the probability of being able to make a two-digit number greater than 20 by choosing two of the digits 0, 1, 2, and 3, placed face down on table.

25 From the set of numbers 9, 16, 18, 21, 29, 30, 32, 42, 48, 50, 54, 60, 66, 71, and 96, find the probability of choosing:

a an even number

b an odd number

c a number divisible by 3

d an even number which is also divisible by 3.

SUMMARY

You should now be able to

- Understand mean, median and mode
- Calculate the mean and the standard deviation from the mean
- Use the statistical functions on your own calculator
- Recognise the shape of a normal distribution
- Know the notation for writing the probability of an outcome
- Know that $p(A \text{ and } B) = p(A) \times p(B)$, if events A and B are independent
- Use tree diagrams to see all the possibilities

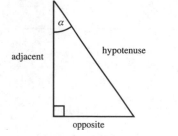

(a)

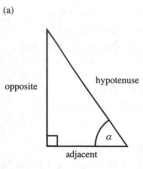

(b)

Chapter 7 ▶ **Trigonometry**

Right-angled triangles

The sides of a right-angled triangle are named in relation to one of the angles.

The hypotenuse is the longest side. The adjacent is the side next to the angle and the opposite is the side opposite the angle.

The ratios of the lengths of the sides to one another also have names:

$$\sin \alpha = \frac{\text{opposite}}{\text{hypotenuse}}$$

$$\cos \alpha = \frac{\text{adjacent}}{\text{hypotenuse}}$$

$$\tan \alpha = \frac{\text{opposite}}{\text{adjacent}}$$

For similar triangles these ratios have the same value.

7.1

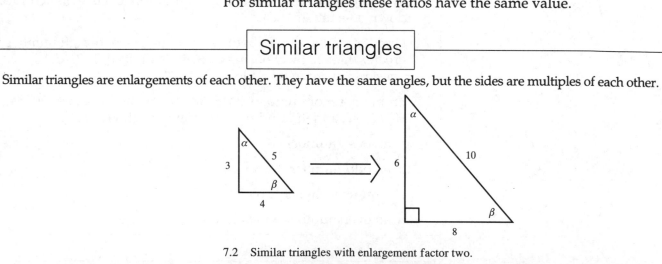

Similar triangles

Similar triangles are enlargements of each other. They have the same angles, but the sides are multiples of each other.

7.2   Similar triangles with enlargement factor two.

Some officers have curly auburn hair till old age.

If you find it difficult to remember how to work out the sine, cosine and tangent of an angle, you may find that making up a sentence that uses letters to represent the words helps. One example is

S	Some
O	Officers
H	Have
C	Curly
A	Auburn
H	Hair
T	Till
O	Old
A	Age

i.e. $S = \dfrac{O}{H}$; $C = \dfrac{A}{H}$; $T = \dfrac{O}{A}$

sin is the abbreviation
for sine,
cos is the abbreviation
for cosine,
tan is the abbreviation
for tangent.

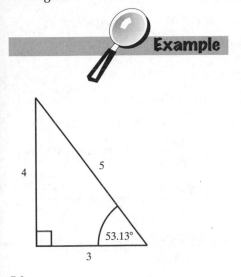

7.3

Using sine

To find the sine of an angle, we know that we must divide the opposite by the hypotenuse

i.e. $\sin \alpha = \dfrac{\text{opposite}}{\text{hypotenuse}}$

Example

Find the sine of the angle 53.13°, shown in Fig. 7.3.

From Fig. 7.3 we see that opposite = 4 and hypotenuse = 5, so

$\sin 53.13° = \frac{4}{5} = 0.8$

Notice that the units of the sides are not given in this chapter. The answers are not affected by the units as long as the units used throughout an example are all the same, i.e., all in centimetres, metres, inches or feet. This is because trigonometric relationships are all ratios so the units are cancelled out.

Using cosine

To find the cosine of an angle, we know that we must divide the adjacent by the hypotenuse

i.e. $\cos \alpha = \dfrac{\text{adjacent}}{\text{hypotenuse}}$

Example

Find the cosine of the angle 53.13° in Fig. 7.3.

From Fig. 7.3 we can see that adjacent = 3 and hypotenuse = 5, so

$\cos 53.13° = \frac{3}{5} = 0.6$

Using tangent

To find the tangent of an angle, we know that we must divide the opposite by the adjacent

i.e. $\tan \alpha = \dfrac{\text{opposite}}{\text{adjacent}}$

Example

Find the tangent of the angle 53.13° in Fig. 7.3.

From Fig. 7.3 we can see that opposite = 4 and adjacent = 3, so

$\tan 53.13° = \frac{4}{3} = 1.33$ to 2 decimal places

Task

1 Find, to 3 decimal places, the sines of the angles given in Fig. 7.4.

2 Find, to 4 decimal places, the cosines of the angles given in Fig. 7.4.

3 Find, to 4 decimal places, the tangents of the angles given in Fig. 7.4.

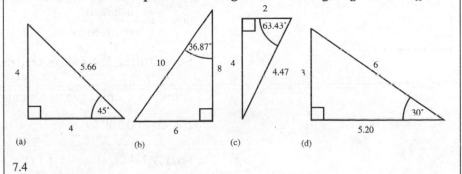

7.4

Check your answers by using the sin, cos and tan buttons on your calculator.

Using trigonometry to find missing lengths

We can rearrange the sine, cosine and tangent equations to find missing lengths of right-angled triangles.

Because we know that $\sin \alpha = \dfrac{\text{opposite}}{\text{hypotenuse}}$, $\cos \alpha = \dfrac{\text{adjacent}}{\text{hypotenuse}}$ and

$\tan \alpha = \dfrac{\text{opposite}}{\text{adjacent}}$,

we also have

$$\text{hypotenuse} \times \sin \alpha = \text{opposite} \qquad \dfrac{\text{opposite}}{\sin \alpha} = \text{hypotenuse}$$

$$\text{hypotenuse} \times \cos \alpha = \text{adjacent} \qquad \dfrac{\text{adjacent}}{\cos \alpha} = \text{hypotenuse}$$

$$\text{adjacent} \times \tan \alpha = \text{opposite} \qquad \dfrac{\text{opposite}}{\tan \alpha} = \text{adjacent}$$

It is usually easiest to rearrange your equation after you have substituted all the values that you know into it.

 Example

A Find the length a in Fig. 7.5.

We are given hypotenuse $= 8$ and a is the *opposite* side to the angle $30°$. We therefore use

$$\sin \alpha = \dfrac{\text{opposite}}{\text{hypotenuse}}$$

Substituting the values that we know,

$\sin 30° = \dfrac{a}{8}$, and we use a calculator (or sine tables) to find that

$\sin 30° = 0.5$

So $0.5 = \dfrac{a}{8}$

$a = 8 \times 0.5 = 4$

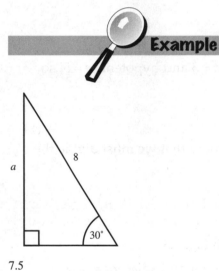

7.5

B Find the length b in Fig. 7.6.

We are given hypotenuse $= 6$ and b is the *adjacent* side to the angle $45°$. We therefore use:

$$\cos \alpha = \dfrac{\text{adjacent}}{\text{hypotenuse}}$$

Substituting the values that we know,

$\cos 45° = \dfrac{b}{6}$, and we use a calculator (or cosine tables) to find that

$\cos 45° = 0.707$

So $0.707 = \dfrac{b}{6}$

$b = 0.707 \times 6 = 4.242$

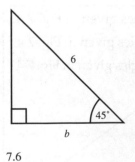

7.6

Task

4 Find the length of side *a* in each of the triangles in Fig. 7.7.

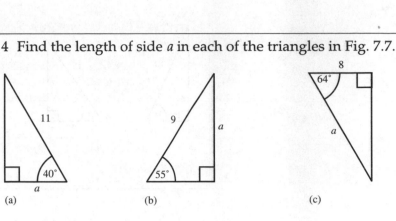

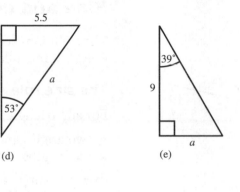

(a) (b) (c)

(d) (e)

7.7

Using trigonometry to find missing angles

We can use the inverse functions of sine, cosine and tangent to work out missing angles using the lengths of two sides of a right-angled triangle.

Example

Find angle α in Fig. 7.8.

The equation we use depends on the sides that we know in relation to the angle. In this case we know the opposite and the hypotenuse so we use

$$\sin \alpha = \frac{\text{opposite}}{\text{hypotenuse}},$$

and we have opposite = 5 and hypotenuse = 9.

$$\sin \alpha = \tfrac{5}{9} = 0.556$$

$$\alpha = \sin^{-1} 0.556 = 33.7°$$

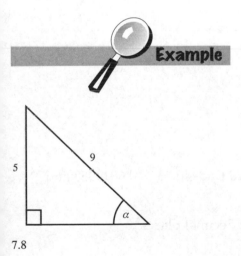

7.8

The expression $\sin^{-1} x$ means 'the angle whose sine is x', and not sine raised to the power of −1. It is the inverse sine function. There are similar inverse functions, $\cos^{-1}$ and $\tan^{-1}$, for cosines and tangents. On your calculator, you would use the inverse function (or shift button), to find the angle, given the ratio that is the sine, cosine or tangent. For example, if the tangent of an angle is n, key in 'n INV tan' to find the angle.

Task

5 Using sine, cosine and tangent and their inverses − 'inverse' or 'shift' button on your calculator − work out the angle α in the triangles in Fig. 7.9.

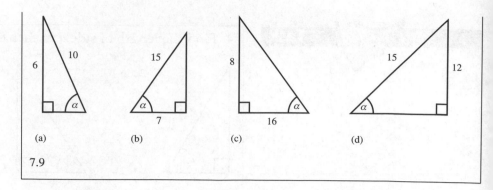

7.9

Sine and cosine rules

The equations we have seen so far have been for right-angled triangles only, but the following rules can be used for any type of triangle.

The sine rule

For any triangle, if you know:

- two angles and the length of one side, or
- the lengths of two sides and a non-included angle,

then you can use the **sine rule** to find the missing side or angle. Note that you should watch out for the ambiguous case, which is summarised below.

For a triangle with angles A, B, C as shown in Fig. 7.10, and opposite side lengths a, b, and c, the sine rule is:

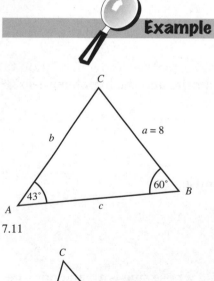

7.10

$$\frac{a}{\sin A} = \frac{b}{\sin B} = \frac{c}{\sin C}$$

 Example

A Find b in the triangle in Fig. 7.11.

We know that $a = 8$, $A = 43°$ and $B = 60°$.

$$\frac{a}{\sin A} = \frac{b}{\sin B}$$

So $b = a\dfrac{\sin B}{\sin A}$

Use a calculator (or sine table) to find $\sin 43° = 0.6819983$ and $\sin 60° = 0.866024$

So $b = 8 \times \dfrac{0.866024}{0.681998} = 10.16$ to 2 decimal places.

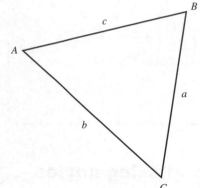

7.11

B Find angle A in the triangle in Fig. 7.12.

We know that $a = 15$, $b = 20$, and $B = 65°$.

Use a calculator (or sine table) to find $\sin 65° = 0.906308$

$$\frac{15}{\sin A} = \frac{20}{0.906308} = 22.075$$

$$\frac{\sin A}{15} = \frac{1}{22.0675}$$

$$\sin A = \frac{15}{22.0675} = 0.6795$$

$$A = \sin^{-1} 0.6795 = 42.8°$$

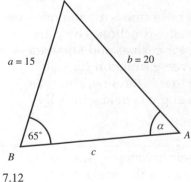

7.12

Task

6 Find side x for each part of Fig. 7.13.

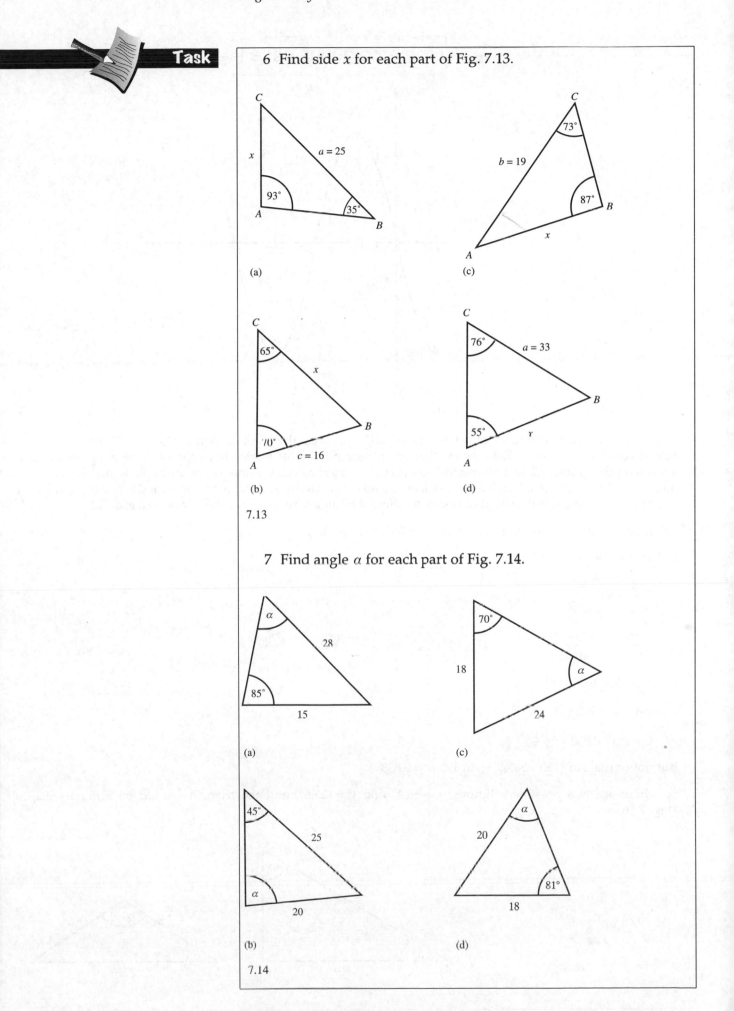

(a)

(c)

(b)

(d)

7.13

7 Find angle α for each part of Fig. 7.14.

(a)

(c)

(b)

(d)

7.14

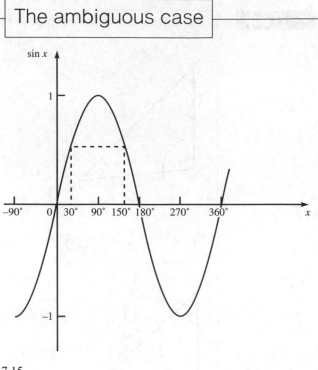

7.15

If we plot the sine of an angle against the angle itself, we obtain the graph shown in Fig. 7.15. Notice that it repeats every 360°. This means that an infinite number of angles have the same sine. An example is shown on the graph. When you use the function $\sin^{-1}$, your calculator only gives the angle lying between $-90°$ and $+90°$. This can sometimes be a problem, because the 'two sides and a non-included angle' that we have when we use the sine rule, could define two different triangles. Watch out for it. Here is an example.

Triangle ABC has $c = 10$ cm, $a = 6$ cm and $A = 30°$. Find angle C.

Using the sine rule,

$$\frac{a}{\sin A} = \frac{b}{\sin B}$$

$$\frac{6}{\sin 30°} = \frac{10}{\sin C}$$

$6 \sin C = 10 \sin 30°$

$\sin C = \frac{5}{6} = 0.833$

$C = \sin^{-1} 0.833 = 56.4°$

But notice that $\sin (180 - 56.4)° = \sin 123.6° = 0.833$

So, there are two possible solutions, $C = 56.4°$ and $C = 123.6°$, and the triangles would be different shapes (Fig. 7.16).

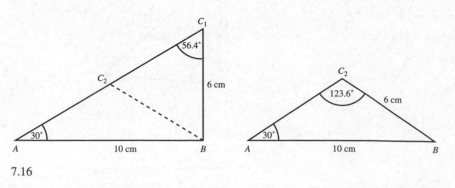

7.16

There is no problem with the cosine rule, as the cosine of an 'obtuse' angle (greater than 90°) is negative.

The cosine rule

For any triangle, if you know

- the lengths of all three sides, or
- the lengths of two sides and the angle they enclose,

then you can use the **cosine rule** to find the missing angles or side.

For a triangle with angles A, B, C and opposite side lengths a, b, and c as before, the cosine rule is:

$$a^2 = b^2 + c^2 - 2bc \cos A$$

$$b^2 = a^2 + c^2 - 2ac \cos B$$

$$c^2 = b^2 + a^2 - 2ab \cos C$$

We can rearrange these equations to find a missing angle, as follows.

$$\cos A = \frac{b^2 + c^2 - a^2}{2bc}$$

$$\text{So } A = \cos^{-1}\left(\frac{b^2 + c^2 - a^2}{2bc}\right)$$

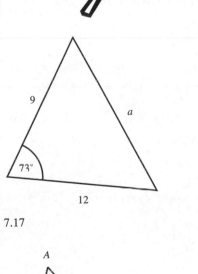

Example

A Find side a in Fig. 7.17.

We know that $b = 9$, $c = 12$ and $A = 73°$ and $\cos A = \cos 73° = 0.29237$

Using the cosine rule,

$$a^2 = b^2 + c^2 - 2bc \cos A = 81 + 144 - 2 \times 9 \times 12 \times 0.29237$$

$$= 81 + 144 - 63.15192 = 161.84808$$

$a = 12.72$ to 2 decimal places.

Remember to work out the $2bc \cos A$ *before* subtracting it.

B Find angle A in Fig. 7.18.

We know that $a = 7$, $b = 5$ and $c = 6$

The cosine rule is $a^2 = b^2 + c^2 - 2bc \cos A$

$$\text{So } \cos A = \frac{b^2 + c^2 - a^2}{2bc}$$

$$A = \cos^{-1}\left(\frac{b^2 + c^2 - a^2}{2bc}\right)$$

$$A = \cos^{-1}\left(\frac{25 + 36 - 49}{60}\right) = \cos^{-1} 0.2$$

$A = 78.46°$ to 2 decimal places.

Figure at left showing triangle ABC with sides a, b, c, labelled 7.10

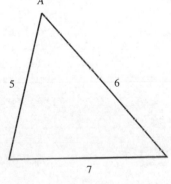

7.17

7.18

Task

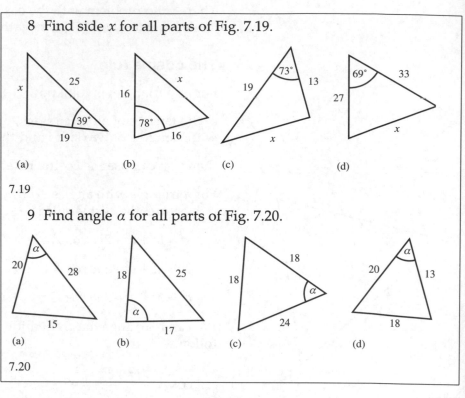

8 Find side x for all parts of Fig. 7.19.

(a)   (b)   (c)   (d)

7.19

9 Find angle α for all parts of Fig. 7.20.

(a)   (b)   (c)   (d)

7.20

SUMMARY

You should now be able to

- Name the sides of a right-angled triangle
- Define and use sine, cosine and tangent with right-angled triangles
- Know and use the sine and cosine rules
- Watch out for the ambiguous case

Chapter 8 Matrices

Matrices are useful in solving simultaneous equations with many unknowns and in probability theory when an experiment is repeated many times. They find applications in applied mathematics, physics, and computing.

The shape of a matrix

In mathematics a matrix is a rectangular array of numbers or letters. It is a way of presenting a collection of numbers, letters, or words as sets of rows and columns, where rows are horizontal and columns are vertical.

You first need to know how to identify the shape of a matrix.

An **$m \times n$ matrix** has m rows and n columns.

$\begin{pmatrix} 3 & -5 & 6 \\ -1 & 2 & 8 \end{pmatrix}$ is a 2×3 matrix.

$\begin{pmatrix} 7 & -4 & 9 & 2 \\ -3 & 2 & 1 & -5 \\ 6 & 7 & -8 & 2 \\ 0.5 & 1 & 7 & 1 \\ 11 & -2 & 0.8 & 10 \end{pmatrix}$ is a 5×4 matrix.

A **square matrix** has the same number of rows and columns.

$\begin{pmatrix} 8 & -3 \\ -4 & 2 \end{pmatrix}$ is a square, 2×2, matrix.

A **row matrix** has just one row and any number of columns.

$\begin{pmatrix} 8 & -3 & 2 & 5 & -6 \end{pmatrix}$ is a row, 1×5, matrix.

A **column matrix** has just one column and any number of rows.

$\begin{pmatrix} 7 \\ -8 \\ 3 \\ 0 \\ -6 \\ 10 \end{pmatrix}$ is a column, 6×1, matrix.

The **unit matrix** is any square matrix with '1's along the leading diagonal and '0's in all the other positions. The **leading diagonal** goes from the top left to the bottom right.

$$\begin{pmatrix} 1 & 0 & 0 & 0 & 0 \\ 0 & 1 & 0 & 0 & 0 \\ 0 & 0 & 1 & 0 & 0 \\ 0 & 0 & 0 & 1 & 0 \\ 0 & 0 & 0 & 0 & 1 \end{pmatrix}$$ is a 5×5 unit matrix.

The **zero matrix** has '0's in all the positions.

Task

1 Write down the shapes of the following matrices:

a $\begin{pmatrix} 1 & 3 & 7 \end{pmatrix}$

c $\begin{pmatrix} 7 \\ -2 \\ 8 \end{pmatrix}$

b $\begin{pmatrix} 5 & -4 & 2 \\ 4 & 3 & -1 \\ -2 & 9 & -2 \end{pmatrix}$

d $\begin{pmatrix} 9 & 6 & -1 \\ -5 & 3 & 7 \end{pmatrix}$

2 Write down the 2×2 unit matrix.

3 Write down any 1×6 row matrix.

4 Write down a 4×1 column matrix.

Adding and subtracting matrices

We can only add or subtract matrices of the same shape. The terms in corresponding positions in each matrix are then added or subtracted as required, to make a new matrix.

Addition

We add the terms in the corresponding positions.

For example,

$$\begin{pmatrix} 5 & 4 & -3 \\ -2 & 6 & 7 \end{pmatrix} + \begin{pmatrix} -8 & 2 & 5 \\ 2 & -1 & 9 \end{pmatrix} = \begin{pmatrix} 5-8 & 4+2 & -3+5 \\ -2+2 & 6-1 & 7+9 \end{pmatrix} = \begin{pmatrix} -3 & 6 & 2 \\ 0 & 5 & 16 \end{pmatrix}$$

Notice that both of the original matrices and the new matrix formed are 2×3 matrices.

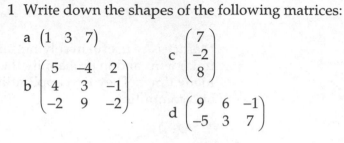

Task

5 Calculate the following:

a $\begin{pmatrix} 3 & 7 & 9 \\ 2 & 0 & 5 \\ 1 & 4 & 8 \end{pmatrix} + \begin{pmatrix} 2 & 6 & 4 \\ 1 & 3 & 8 \\ 5 & 0 & 7 \end{pmatrix}$

b $\begin{pmatrix} 2 & 5 \\ 3 & 7 \\ 1 & 9 \\ 6 & 4 \end{pmatrix} + \begin{pmatrix} -1 & 4 \\ 2 & -3 \\ -5 & 7 \\ -2 & 6 \end{pmatrix}$

c $\begin{pmatrix} 5 & -3 & -8 & 5 & 0 \end{pmatrix} + \begin{pmatrix} -2 & 1 & -3 & 3 & 5 \end{pmatrix}$

Subtraction

We subtract the terms in the corresponding positions.

For example,

$$\begin{pmatrix} 7 & 4 \\ -5 & 2 \end{pmatrix} - \begin{pmatrix} 3 & 2 \\ 1 & -6 \end{pmatrix} = \begin{pmatrix} 7-3 & 4-2 \\ -5-1 & 2-(-6) \end{pmatrix} = \begin{pmatrix} 4 & 2 \\ -6 & 2+6 \end{pmatrix} = \begin{pmatrix} 4 & 2 \\ -6 & 8 \end{pmatrix}$$

 Task

6 Calculate the following:

a $\begin{pmatrix} 2 & 5 & 7 \\ 9 & 6 & 4 \end{pmatrix} - \begin{pmatrix} 1 & 3 & 2 \\ 7 & 2 & 4 \end{pmatrix}$

b $\begin{pmatrix} 6 & -4 \\ -2 & 3 \end{pmatrix} - \begin{pmatrix} -1 & 5 \\ 0 & 1 \end{pmatrix}$

c $\begin{pmatrix} 5 & 6 \\ -2 & 3 \\ 1 & -4 \\ -9 & -8 \\ 10 & 7 \end{pmatrix} - \begin{pmatrix} 3 & -2 \\ 6 & -5 \\ -1 & -6 \\ 2 & 2 \\ 3 & 5 \end{pmatrix}$

d $\begin{pmatrix} 5 \\ -6 \\ 3 \\ -8 \end{pmatrix} - \begin{pmatrix} -8 \\ 7 \\ 3 \\ -10 \end{pmatrix}$

Multiplying matrices by a number

A matrix can be multiplied by a number. In this case all the numbers inside the matrix are multiplied, as if the matrix were a bracket in algebra.

For example,

$$3 \times \begin{pmatrix} 4 & 2 \\ -6 & 8 \end{pmatrix} = \begin{pmatrix} 12 & 6 \\ -18 & 24 \end{pmatrix}$$

The reason for this becomes clear if we add the three matrices together, i.e.

$$\begin{pmatrix} 4 & 2 \\ -6 & 8 \end{pmatrix} + \begin{pmatrix} 4 & 2 \\ -6 & 8 \end{pmatrix} + \begin{pmatrix} 4 & 2 \\ -6 & 8 \end{pmatrix} = \begin{pmatrix} 12 & 6 \\ -18 & 24 \end{pmatrix}$$

Multiplying matrices by each other

This time the shapes of the matrices are very important but in a different way. The number of columns in the first matrix must equal the number of rows in the second.

For example, a 4×3 matrix can be multiplied by a 3×2 matrix to give a 4×2 matrix as follows:

$$\begin{pmatrix} 7 & 5 & 6 \\ 2 & 8 & 1 \\ 3 & 9 & 4 \\ 5 & 1 & 8 \end{pmatrix} \times \begin{pmatrix} 1 & 4 \\ 3 & 9 \\ 8 & 7 \end{pmatrix} = \begin{pmatrix} 7 \times 1 + 5 \times 3 + 6 \times 8 & 7 \times 4 + 5 \times 9 + 6 \times 7 \\ 2 \times 1 + 8 \times 3 + 1 \times 8 & 2 \times 4 + 8 \times 9 + 1 \times 7 \\ 3 \times 1 + 9 \times 3 + 4 \times 8 & 3 \times 4 + 9 \times 9 + 4 \times 7 \\ 5 \times 1 + 1 \times 3 + 8 \times 8 & 5 \times 4 + 1 \times 9 + 8 \times 7 \end{pmatrix} = \begin{pmatrix} 70 & 115 \\ 34 & 87 \\ 62 & 121 \\ 72 & 85 \end{pmatrix}$$

Follow the pattern of this carefully as it is an unusual process.

1 To get the number in row 1, column 1 of the new matrix, multiply each number in the first row of the first matrix by the

corresponding number in the first column of the second matrix, and then add the results, as shown.

2 To get the new number for row 1, column 2, multiply each number in the first row of the first matrix by the corresponding number in the second column of the second matrix, and, again, add the results. This forms the top row of the new matrix.

3 Repeat this process for each of the other three rows.

You may find that it helps you to say to yourself *first row times first column* to get the multiplication started.

Multiply the matrix $\begin{pmatrix} 1 & 2 \\ 0 & 1 \end{pmatrix}$ by $\begin{pmatrix} 5 \\ 2 \end{pmatrix}$.

A 2×2 matrix can be multiplied by a 2×1 matrix to give another 2×1 matrix.

$$\begin{pmatrix} 1 & 2 \\ 0 & 1 \end{pmatrix} \times \begin{pmatrix} 5 \\ 2 \end{pmatrix} = \begin{pmatrix} 1 \times 5 + 2 \times 2 \\ 0 \times 5 + 1 \times 2 \end{pmatrix} = \begin{pmatrix} 5 + 4 \\ 0 + 2 \end{pmatrix} = \begin{pmatrix} 9 \\ 2 \end{pmatrix}$$

To work out whether two matrices can be multiplied, write down the number of rows and columns of each. The middle numbers must be the same and are eliminated in finding the size of the final matrix. So, for example, a 2×4 matrix multiplied by a 4×6 matrix produces 2×6 matrix.

Multiplication of matrices is *not* commutative, so $A \times B \neq B \times A$, for matrices A and B.

7 We have five matrices as follows:

$$A = \begin{pmatrix} 1 & 5 \\ 7 & 2 \\ 3 & 1 \\ 4 & 6 \end{pmatrix} \qquad D = \begin{pmatrix} -2 & 4 & -1 & 0 \end{pmatrix}$$

$$B = \begin{pmatrix} 4 & 2 & 1 \\ 3 & 9 & 5 \\ 1 & 6 & 7 \end{pmatrix} \qquad E = \begin{pmatrix} 2 & -6 \\ -1 & 3 \end{pmatrix}$$

$$C = \begin{pmatrix} 2 \\ 1 \\ 5 \end{pmatrix}$$

a Write down the number of rows and columns for each of the matrices A, B, C, D, and E.

b Which of the following products are possible to work out: $A \times D$, $D \times A$, $B \times C$, $C \times B$, $A \times E$, $E \times A$, $C \times D$, and $D \times C$?

c Work out the products that are identified as possible in b.

Division is not possible with matrices. However, it is possible to solve square matrix equations using the multiplicative **inverse** of the matrix. We need some new definitions:

Identity and inverse

Identity

In 'ordinary' arithmetic, $5 \times 1 = 5 = 1 \times 5$. In general, $1 \times y = y = y \times 1$.

We call '1' the **identity** under multiplication for ordinary arithmetic. The identity under a process is something that leaves the original unchanged.

Inverse

The multiplicative **inverse** of a number gives the identity when multiplied by the number. For example, in ordinary arithmetic, the multiplicative inverse of 3 is $\frac{1}{3}$ since $3 \times \frac{1}{3} = 1 = \frac{1}{3} \times 3$, and 1 is the identity.

The identity of a matrix

For any 2×2 matrix $\begin{pmatrix} a & b \\ c & d \end{pmatrix}$,

$$\begin{pmatrix} 1 & 0 \\ 0 & 1 \end{pmatrix} \times \begin{pmatrix} a & b \\ c & d \end{pmatrix} = \begin{pmatrix} a & b \\ c & d \end{pmatrix}$$

and

$$\begin{pmatrix} a & b \\ c & d \end{pmatrix} \times \begin{pmatrix} 1 & 0 \\ 0 & 1 \end{pmatrix} = \begin{pmatrix} a & b \\ c & d \end{pmatrix}$$

So the unit matrix $\begin{pmatrix} 1 & 0 \\ 0 & 1 \end{pmatrix}$ is the identity for a 2×2 matrix under multiplication. (It is the equivalent of 1 for ordinary multiplication in arithmetic.)

The inverse of a matrix

The inverse of a matrix gives the unit matrix $\begin{pmatrix} 1 & 0 \\ 0 & 1 \end{pmatrix}$ (the identity) when multipled by the matrix. The general formula for the inverse of a 2×2 matrix is

$$\frac{1}{ad - bc} \begin{pmatrix} d & -b \\ -c & a \end{pmatrix}$$

If we start with the matrix $\begin{pmatrix} a & b \\ c & d \end{pmatrix}$ and multiply by $\frac{1}{ad - bc} \begin{pmatrix} d & -b \\ -c & a \end{pmatrix}$

we get

$$\frac{1}{ad - bc} \begin{pmatrix} d & -b \\ -c & a \end{pmatrix} \begin{pmatrix} a & b \\ c & d \end{pmatrix} = \frac{1}{ad - bc} \begin{pmatrix} da - bc & db - bd \\ -ca + ac & -cb + ad \end{pmatrix}$$

$$= \begin{pmatrix} \dfrac{ad - bc}{ad - bc} & 0 \\ 0 & \dfrac{ad - bc}{ad - bc} \end{pmatrix} = \begin{pmatrix} 1 & 0 \\ 0 & 1 \end{pmatrix}$$

which is the identity for matrix multiplication.

To show that order doesn't matter (as required for the inverse), the identity is also obtained when the multiplication is performed for

$$\frac{1}{ad - bc} \begin{pmatrix} a & b \\ c & d \end{pmatrix} \begin{pmatrix} d & -b \\ -c & a \end{pmatrix}$$

So the inverse of the matrix $\begin{pmatrix} a & b \\ c & d \end{pmatrix}$ under matrix multiplication is

$\dfrac{1}{ad-bc} \begin{pmatrix} d & -b \\ -c & a \end{pmatrix}$, and this is the general format for the inverse of a 2×2 matrix.

> 8   Check that $\begin{pmatrix} 1 & 0 \\ 0 & 1 \end{pmatrix}$ is obtained from $\dfrac{1}{ad-bc} \begin{pmatrix} a & b \\ c & d \end{pmatrix} \begin{pmatrix} d & -b \\ -c & a \end{pmatrix}$.

Note that the inverse does not exist if $ad = bc$ in the original matrix, since this would make $(ad - bc) = 0$, and we cannot divide by 0.

Using the inverse matrix to solve simultaneous equations

Using our knowledge of matrix multiplication, we can represent any set of simultaneous equations in matrix form. For example, the simultaneous equations

$$a_1 x + b_1 y = c_1$$

$$a_2 x + b_2 y = c_2$$

can be written as the matrices

$$\begin{pmatrix} a_1 & b_1 \\ a_2 & b_2 \end{pmatrix} \begin{pmatrix} x \\ y \end{pmatrix} = \begin{pmatrix} c_1 \\ c_2 \end{pmatrix}$$

You can check that this works by performing the matrix multiplication.

Solving the equations

Find m and n such that $m - 2n = 1$ and $4m + 2n = 34$.

In Chapter 2, we found the solution to this problem to be $m = 7$, $n = 3$.

We can write these simultaneous equations in matrix form, as

$$\begin{pmatrix} 1 & -2 \\ 4 & 2 \end{pmatrix} \begin{pmatrix} m \\ n \end{pmatrix} = \begin{pmatrix} 1 \\ 34 \end{pmatrix}$$

To solve the equations we would like to end up with a simple matrix in the form $\begin{pmatrix} m \\ n \end{pmatrix} = \begin{pmatrix} a \\ b \end{pmatrix}$, which will tell us that $m = a$ and $n = b$.

To obtain the matrix $\begin{pmatrix} m \\ n \end{pmatrix}$ on its own, it would be useful to be able to divide both sides by the matrix $\begin{pmatrix} 1 & -2 \\ 4 & 2 \end{pmatrix}$, but we cannot divide matrices. Instead, we multiply both sides by the inverse of $\begin{pmatrix} 1 & -2 \\ 4 & 2 \end{pmatrix}$, which will have the same effect, i.e. since the matrix multiplied by its inverse is the unit matrix, this will leave $\begin{pmatrix} m \\ n \end{pmatrix}$ on the LHS.

Example

We know that the inverse of the matrix $\begin{pmatrix} a & b \\ c & d \end{pmatrix}$ is $\dfrac{1}{ad-bc}\begin{pmatrix} d & -b \\ -c & a \end{pmatrix}$.

In this case, $a = 1$, $b = -2$, $c = 4$ and $d = 2$.

$$\text{The inverse of } \begin{pmatrix} 1 & -2 \\ 4 & 2 \end{pmatrix} = \frac{1}{2-(-8)}\begin{pmatrix} 2 & 2 \\ -4 & 1 \end{pmatrix}$$

$$\frac{1}{2+8}\begin{pmatrix} 2 & 2 \\ -4 & 1 \end{pmatrix} = \frac{1}{10}\begin{pmatrix} 2 & 2 \\ -4 & 1 \end{pmatrix}$$

Now, multiplying both sides of the original equation by this inverse gives:

$$\frac{1}{10}\begin{pmatrix} 2 & 2 \\ -4 & 1 \end{pmatrix}\begin{pmatrix} 1 & -2 \\ 4 & 2 \end{pmatrix}\begin{pmatrix} m \\ n \end{pmatrix} = \frac{1}{10}\begin{pmatrix} 2 & 2 \\ -4 & 1 \end{pmatrix}\begin{pmatrix} 1 \\ 34 \end{pmatrix}$$

$$\begin{pmatrix} 1 & 0 \\ 0 & 1 \end{pmatrix}\begin{pmatrix} m \\ n \end{pmatrix} = \frac{1}{10}\begin{pmatrix} 2+68 \\ -4+34 \end{pmatrix} = \frac{1}{10}\begin{pmatrix} 70 \\ 30 \end{pmatrix}$$

$$\text{So } \begin{pmatrix} m \\ n \end{pmatrix} = \begin{pmatrix} 7 \\ 3 \end{pmatrix}$$

And we have the solution $m = 7$, $n = 3$, as before.

Task

9 Solve the following pairs of simultaneous equations (previously solved in Chapter 2) by using the inverse matrix.

a $5x + 7y = 27$
   $3x + 7y = 19$

d $2s + 9t = 1$
   $3s - 2t = 17$

b $2a + 3b = 24$
   $7a - 3b = 3$

e $5m + 3n = 60$
   $2m - 9n = 24$

c $p + 5q = 17$
   $3p + q = 9$

f $c - d = 8$
   $2c - 3d = 19$

Higher dimension matrices

It is usually simpler to solve two equations in two unknowns (i.e. equations in two dimensions) using the method in Chapter 2, but the matrix method is often used for higher dimensions. Computers and calculators can deal with these matrices and higher dimension equations. If you have a graphical calculator, investigate equations in three unknowns and use your calculator to solve Task 8 in Chapter 2.

Vectors

The vector from the origin to the point (3, 4) (see Fig. 8.1) is written in matrix form as $\begin{pmatrix} 3 \\ 4 \end{pmatrix}$ (see Chapter 4).

Transformations using matrices

Another use for matrices is in transforming (changing the direction and/or magnitude of) vectors.

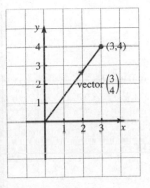

8.1

Example

For example, the vector $\begin{pmatrix} 3 \\ 4 \end{pmatrix}$ can be transformed by a 2×2 matrix to give a new vector.

A $\begin{pmatrix} 1 & 0 \\ 0 & -1 \end{pmatrix}\begin{pmatrix} 3 \\ 4 \end{pmatrix} = \begin{pmatrix} 3 \times 1 & 0 \times 4 \\ 0 \times 3 & -1 \times 4 \end{pmatrix} = \begin{pmatrix} 3 \\ -4 \end{pmatrix}$

This matrix has reflected the vector in the *x*-axis (see Fig. 8.2).

B $\begin{pmatrix} 5 & 0 \\ 0 & 5 \end{pmatrix}\begin{pmatrix} 3 \\ 4 \end{pmatrix} = \begin{pmatrix} 5 \times 3 & 0 \times 4 \\ 0 \times 3 & 5 \times 4 \end{pmatrix} = \begin{pmatrix} 15 \\ 20 \end{pmatrix}$

This has enlarged the vector by a factor of 5 (see Fig. 8.3).

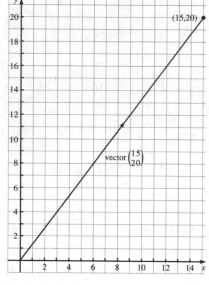

8.2

8.3

Task

10 Find the effect of each of the following matrices on the vector $\begin{pmatrix} 3 \\ 4 \end{pmatrix}$ and draw them on separate diagrams:

a $\begin{pmatrix} -1 & 0 \\ 0 & 1 \end{pmatrix}$ c $\begin{pmatrix} 1 & 4 \\ 0 & 1 \end{pmatrix}$

b $\begin{pmatrix} 0 & -1 \\ 1 & 0 \end{pmatrix}$ d $\begin{pmatrix} 2 & 0 \\ 0 & 5 \end{pmatrix}$

Transformations like these can be used to transform triangles and more complex shapes. 3×3 matrices can transform in three dimensions.

SUMMARY

You should now be able to

- Understand what is meant by the shape of a matrix
- Add, subtract and multiply matrices
- Recognise the identity of a square matrix
- Work out the inverse of a 2×2 square matrix
- Use matrices to solve equations
- Use matrices to carry out transformations

Glossary

Addition Putting numbers together by counting on from the first by the amount of the next. For example, $7 + 3 = 10$, and $7 + (-4) = 3$.

Algebra Branch of mathematics that generalises arithmetic by replacing numbers by letters.

Arithmetic Branch of mathematics dealing with numbers and operations on numbers.

Associative law The operation $\cdot$ is associative if $a \cdot (b \cdot c) = (a \cdot b) \cdot c$, for all a, b, c.

Asymptote If the graph of a function tends towards a line but never reaches it, that line is an asymptote of the function. For example, $y = \frac{1}{x}$ has $y = 0$ as an asymptote (see Fig. 1).

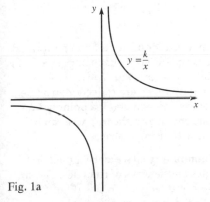

Fig. 1a

The axes are asymptotes to this rectangular hyperbola.

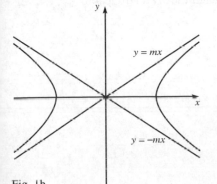

Fig. 1b

This hyperbola has asymptotes $y = mx$ and $y = -mx$.

Axes (singular, axis) Lines that enable us to refer to points in space. In two dimensions, we usually use two perpendicular lines as axes (the x- and y-axes) and in three dimensions we use three mutually perpendicular lines (the x-, y- and z-axes).

Commutative law The operation $\cdot$ is commutative if $a \cdot b = b \cdot a$, for all a, b.

Coordinates The position of a point referred to axes is given as a coordinate. For example, $(2, 3)$ refers to a point in two dimensions and $(5, -1, 6)$ refers to a point in three dimensions.

Cosine Trigonometric ratio given by the ratio of adjacent to the hypotenuse of a right-angled triangle. A cosine curve plots the cosine of an angle against all values of the angle, and is shown in Fig. 2.

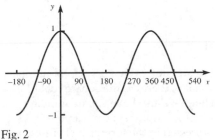

Fig. 2

Cube $n^3 = n \times n \times n$, where n is a number.

Division Arithmetical operation dividing a number into equal parts.

Equal sign $=$ shows that the quantities on either side are equal. The sign $\equiv$ means that the quantities on either side are identically equal, so that if $ax + b \equiv 3x + 7$, $a = 3$ and $b = 7$.

Equation Expression linked by equals sign, usually involving unknown or variable quantities.

Even number Any whole number (integer) that is exactly divisible by 2.

Formulae Equations that we can apply to a number of problems. They are either given in a book or list of formulae, or need to be remembered.

Fraction Part of a whole number.

Geometry Branch of mathematics that deals with shapes, such as the triangle, or the square.

Gradient The slope of a curve, obtained at a point by taking the ratio of the change in y to the change in x.

Graph A picture of an algebraic equation. In two dimensions, $y = mx + c$ is the equation for a straight line. The graph of this will be a straight line with gradient m and y-intercept $(0, c)$.

Identity Leaves a number unchanged under a certain operation. The identity for the addition of real numbers is 0, because $x + 0 = x = 0 + x$ for all x. The identity for multiplication of real numbers is 1, because $x \times 1 = x = 1 \times x$ for all x.

Index Number indicating a power. So the 3 in 5^3 and the 2 in x^2 are indices.

Infinity A concept, never to be treated as a number. We know that as x gets larger, $\frac{1}{x}$ gets smaller, and as x tends to infinity, $\frac{1}{x}$ tends to 0. Similarly, as x tends to 0, $\frac{1}{x}$ tends to infinity. The symbol for infinity is ∞.

Integer Positive or negative whole number.

Inverse Reverses a process. The process followed by its inverse gets you back to the identity for that process. For example, the inverse of 7 is -7 under addition, since $7 + (-7) = 0$ (which is the identity for addition — check that $x + 0 = x = 0 + x$). The inverse of 7 under multiplication is $\frac{1}{7}$ because $7 \times \frac{1}{7} = 1$, which is the identity under multiplication.

Matrix Way of arranging numbers within a bracket, and useful in algebra and geometry of any number of dimensions.

Multiplication Mathematical operation that abbreviates adding a number q to itself a number p times. Abbreviated as $\times$, or simply by writing one letter next to another, i.e. $p \times q = pq = p$ multiplied by q.

Number   An entity that the operations addition, subtraction, multiplication and division can be performed on. We can define different sets of numbers. Natural numbers, the integers and rational numbers are three examples. Each is an infinitely large set.

Odd number   Any number $2n + 1$, where n is an integer.

Permutation   Number of ways in which a set of objects or numbers can be arranged. The possible permutations of A, B and C are *ABC*, *ACB*, *BAC*, *BCA*, *CAB* and *CBA*. We generalise the result to find that n objects can be arranged in n factorial $= n! = n(n-1)(n-2)(n-3)\ldots 1$ ways.

Point   A specific place in space with no area. It is defined in any number of dimensions with reference to the appropriate axes. Examples of points are $(2, 7)$ in two dimensions and $(3, -1, 8)$ in three dimensions.

Power   A whole number power is the number of times a number is multiplied by itself, i.e. $5^4 = 5 \times 5 \times 5 \times 5$. Fractional powers are a root, i.e. $9^{\frac{1}{2}} = \sqrt{9} = 3$ and $8^{\frac{1}{3}} = \sqrt[3]{8} = 2$. Negative powers indicate reciprocals, i.e. $7^{-3} = \dfrac{1}{7^3} = \frac{1}{343}$.

Zero powers of any number except 0 are always 1; 0 raised to the power 0 is undefined.

Product   The product of two numbers m and n is mn (i.e. $m \times n$).

Pythagoras' Theorem   The square of the hypotenuse of a right-angled triangle is equal to the sum of the squares of the other two sides.

Quadratic equation   Equation of the form $ax^2 + bx + c = 0$, which can be solved in real numbers if $b^2 \geqslant 4ac$, either by factorising or using the formula

$$x = \frac{-b \pm \sqrt{b^2 - 4ac}}{2a}.$$

Rational number   Number that can be expressed as $\dfrac{p}{q}$ where p and q are integers with no common factor.

Real number   All numbers that do not involve the square root of a negative number. Numbers that do involve the square root of a negative number are

imaginary or complex numbers, and are always written in the form $a + bi$, where $i = \sqrt{-1}$.

Simple equation   Equation in the form (or able to be put in the form) $ax + b = c$, where x is the unknown and a, b, and c are given numerical values.

Simultaneous equations   More than one equation, where the solution satisfies all the equations. Generally, if there are n unknowns, n simultaneous equations are required in order to find a solution.

Sine   Trigonometric ratio given by the ratio of opposite to the hypotenuse of a right-angled triangle. A sine curve plots the sine of an angle against all values of the angle, and is shown in Fig. 3.

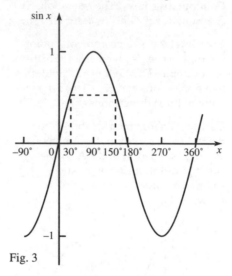

Fig. 3

Square root   When $y = x^2$, for numbers x and y, then x is the square root of y. Hence we also have square numbers, which are numbers that can be expressed in the form n^2, where n is a whole number (integer).

Tangent   Trigonometric ratio given by the ratio of opposite to the adjacent of a right-angled triangle. A tangent curve plots the tangent of an angle against all values of the angle, and is shown in Fig. 4. Also any line that just touches a curve (see Fig. 5).

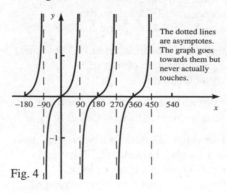

The dotted lines are asymptotes. The graph goes towards them but never actually touches.

Fig. 4

A tangent to a circle at P.

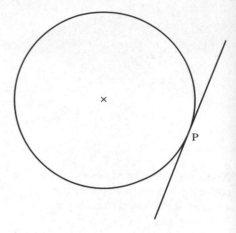

A tangent to a curve touches it at just one point and the gradient of the tangent gives the gradient of the curve at that point.

A tangent to a curve at Q.

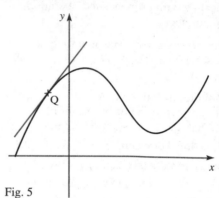

Fig. 5

Transformation   Operation performed to change the size, shape or position of a point, shape or solid. The main transformations are reflection in a line or place, rotation about a point or line, enlargement and shear. These can be dealt with using matrices.

Trigonometry   Geometry based on the angles and lengths of triangles. The sine, cosine and tangent graphs (Figs 2, 3 and 4) are the trigonometric graphs.

Vector   Line with both length (magnitude) and direction.

Answers

Chapter 1

1 a 2, 3, 5, 7, 11, 13, 17, 19, 23, 29, 31, …. . There are infinitely many prime numbers and no formula has yet been found for them. Although $6n + 1$ or $6n - 1$ seem hopeful, the numbers derived from these contain non-primes, i.e. $6 - 1 = 5$, $6 + 1 = 7$, $12 - 1 = 11$, $12 + 1 = 13$, $18 - 1 = 17$, $18 + 1 = 19$, $24 - 1 = 23$ *but* $24 + 1 = 25$, etc.

  b 1, 3, 5, 7, 9, 11 …; numbers not exactly divisible by 2.

  c 1, 4, 9, 16, 25, …, n^2, …; where n is a whole number.

  d 1.1, 1.2, 1.3, 1.4, 1.5 …; there are infinitely many.

  e …, 0.01, 0.1, 1, 10, 100, 1000, 10000, …

2 Even numbers – exactly divisible by 2.

  Rational numbers – numbers that can be expressed as $\dfrac{p}{q}$ where p and q are integers without a common factor.

  Irrational numbers – numbers that cannot be expressed as $\dfrac{p}{q}$ e.g. $\sqrt{2}$.

  Real numbers – the complete set of numbers, but not including roots of negative numbers, e.g. $\sqrt{-2}$.

  Imaginary numbers – numbers that are square roots of negative numbers.

  Complex numbers – numbers that combine real and imaginary numbers.

3 a, d and f

  b Equal when $x = 7$

  c & e Equal when $p = q$

4 a $4 \times 27 = 12 \times 9 = 108$

  b $-6 \times -16 = 12 \times 8 = 96$; yes it holds

5 a $5 \times 9 = 35 + 10 = 45$

  b $-2 \times -1 = -18 + 20 = 2$; yes it holds

6 Subtraction; check using possible values, say 5, 6 and 3.

  $5 - (6 - 3) = 5 - 3 = 2$

  $(5 - 6) - 3 = -1 - 3 = -4$

  These are not equal, so the associative law is not true for subtraction.

  Division; check using possible values, say 10, 6 and 2.

  $10 \div (6 \div 2) = 3\frac{1}{3}$

  $(10 \div 6) \div 2 = 1\frac{2}{3} \div 2 = \frac{5}{6}$

  These are not equal, so the associative law is not true for division.

  Addition; check using possible values, say 5, 6 and 3.

  $5 + (6 + 3) = 5 + 9 = 14$

  $(5 + 6) + 3 = 11 + 3 = 14$

  These are equal, so the associative law *could* be true for addition. One untrue result disproves a statement, but we can't say that a statement is generally true with any number of true results – a general proof is needed.

7 14

8 a 4   d −1

  b −10   e −6

  c 4

9 a −21

  b 16

  c −2

  d −8

  e $-3 \times -7 \div (-2) = 21 \div (-2) = -10.5$

10 a $p = 5$

   b $q = 3$

   c $m = -2$

   d $t = -2$

   e $g = -5$

   f $g = 8$

   g $m = 17$

   h $x = -1$

   i $5y + 4y = 90$, so $9y = 90$, so $y = 10$

11 a $x = -1$ d $y = 1$

   b $m = 2$ e $t = 37$

   c $p = 2$

12 a $y = 0.5$ f identity

   b $m = 2$ g $a = -8$

   c $p = 2$ h identity

   d $q = -3$ i $y = 4$

   e $h = 2$ j $x = 3$

Chapter 2

1 a $x = 4, y = 1$ f $c = 5, d = -3$

  b $a = 3, b = 6$ g $x = 2, y = -1$

  c $p = 2, q = 3$ h $h = 14, g = -9$

  d $s = 5, t = -1$ i $a = 2, b = 8$

  e $m = 12, n = 0$ j $70, -16$

2 a $(x + 3)(x + 2)$ d $(y - 5)(y + 3)$

  b $(x + 9)(x + 7)$ e $(m + 6)(m - 3)$

  c $(x - 5)(x - 2)$

3 a $x = -3$ or -1 f $q = -\frac{4}{3}$ or -1

  b $r = -5$ or -2 g $m = -\frac{2}{3}$ or $1\frac{1}{2}$

  c $x = 3$ or 4 h $h = 1.75$ or -1.5

  d $y = -3$ or 10 i $p = \frac{1}{5}$ or $-\frac{1}{5}$

  e $p = 8$ or 4 j $x = -\frac{7}{3}$ or $\frac{7}{3}$

Proof that the roots of $ax^2 + bx + c = 0$ add up to $-\dfrac{b}{a}$

The equation can be written $x^2 + \dfrac{b}{a}x + \dfrac{c}{a} = 0$

We also know that if m and n are the roots, it is true that $(x-m)(x-n) = 0$.

Multiplying out these factors, $x^2 - (m+n)x + mn = 0$.

Comparing the two forms of the equation, we know that the coefficients of x must be the same, so

$-(m+n) = \dfrac{b}{a}$

So $m+n = -\dfrac{b}{a}$.

Also notice that the product of the roots, $mn = \dfrac{c}{a}$.

Caution   Although the 'sum of the roots' property is a good quick check, the product must be checked too to make sure you have the right answer.

---

4 a 0.9231
   b 0.714
   c 0.18182
   d 0.2352941
   e 0.4

   f 4.80
   g 11.2694
   h 2.412
   i 9.1
   j 10.5

5 a -0.697 or -4.303
   b -0.129 or -3.871
   c 1.449 or -3.449
   d 0.804 or -1.554

   e -0.156 or -12.844
   f -0.119 or -1.681
   g 1.618 or -0.618
   h 1.554 or -0.804

   i $\sin\theta = -1$ or -1.4. The second value is greater than 1 and so is not a possible value for the sine of an angle. One value of θ is $-90°$ ($\sin^{-1}(-1) = -90°$), and the first positive value is $270°$.

   j $\tan\theta = 3.646$ or -1.646. Two values of θ are $74.7°$ or $-58.72°$.

In both i and j there are infinitely many possibilities for the angles and in examination questions you must look carefully for the range of values required in solutions to trigonometric equations. Also notice whether degrees or radians are asked for.

6 a 2 (-7 does not satisfy all the conditions of the problem)
   b 20 (the smaller number is -9)
   c 11 years old
   d $47°$
   e 11 m
   f 17 cm

7 a $x=3, y=8$ or $x=-8, y=-3$
   b $u=2, w=10$ or $u=1, w=7$
   c $m=-1, n=0$ or $m=5, n=3$
   d $p=5, q=1$ or $p=7, q=-1$
   e $t=2, v=11$ or $t=-12, v=-31$

8 a $x=5, y=0, z=1$
   b $p=2, q=-1, r=6$
   c $f=\frac{1}{2}, g=2, h=\frac{1}{4}$
   d $u=-2, v=3.5, w=-1$
   e $a=5, b=-1, c=-4$
   f $r=\frac{1}{5}, s=\frac{1}{2}, t=\frac{1}{3}$

Chapter 3

1 a $y = 7x - 4$

x	y	Coordinates
0	-4	$(0, -4)$
1	3	$(1, 3)$
2	10	$(2, 10)$

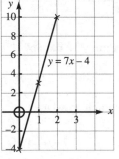

3.16

   b $y = 0.5x$

x	y	Coordinates
0	0	$(0, 0)$
2	1	$(2, 1)$
4	2	$(4, 2)$

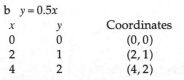

3.17

   c $y = 3x^2 + 2$

x	y	Coordinates
2	14	$(2, 14)$
1	5	$(1, 5)$
0	2	$(0, 2)$
-1	5	$(-1, 5)$
-2	14	$(-2, 14)$

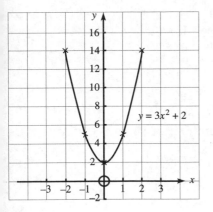

3.18

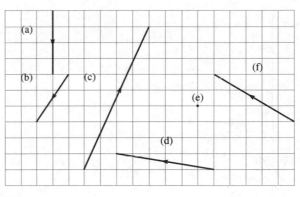

4.30

3 a $\begin{pmatrix} 15 \\ 10 \end{pmatrix}$ b $\begin{pmatrix} 7 \\ 15 \end{pmatrix}$ c $\begin{pmatrix} -9 \\ 6 \end{pmatrix}$ d $\begin{pmatrix} 13 \\ 3 \end{pmatrix}$

2 a A = (−1, 3) B = (1, 1), so the gradient = $\dfrac{1-3}{1-(-1)} = -\dfrac{2}{2} = -1$

   b A = (0, −3) B = (4, 3), so the gradient = $\dfrac{3-(-3)}{4-0} = \dfrac{6}{4} = \dfrac{3}{2}$

   c A = (−2, −2) B = (4, 1), so the gradient = $\dfrac{1-(-2)}{4-(-2)} = \dfrac{3}{6} = \dfrac{1}{2}$

3 a The line crosses the y-axis at (0, 1) so $c = 1$.

      Gradient = $\dfrac{3-1}{4-0} = \dfrac{2}{4} = \dfrac{1}{2}$, so $m = \dfrac{1}{2}$.

      The general equation of a line is $y = mx + c$, so the
      equation of this line is $y = \frac{1}{2}x + 1$.

   b The line crosses the y-axis at (0, 3) so $c = 3$.

      Gradient = $\dfrac{0-6}{1-(-1)} = -\dfrac{6}{2} = -3$, so $m = -3$.

      The equation of the line is $y = -3x + 3$, i.e. $y = 3 - 3x$.

   c The line crosses the y-axis at (0, −2) so $c = -2$.

      Gradient = $\dfrac{2-(-2)}{8-0} = \dfrac{4}{8} = \dfrac{1}{2}$, so $m = \dfrac{1}{2}$.

      The equation of the line is $y = \frac{1}{2}x - 2$.

4 a (1) and (3), (2) and (5), and (6) and (9)
   b (2) and (5)
   c (6) and (9)

5 a i $\frac{2}{3}$ ii 5
   b i −1   ii $-\frac{2}{5}$
   c i $\frac{1}{2}$ ii $-\frac{7}{4}$

6 a $x = 6$, $y = 20$
   b $x = 1$, $y = 5$
   c $x = 4$, $y = 10$
   d The lines $y = 2x + 3$ and $y = 2x + 1$ are parallel so there is
      no solution.

Chapter 4

1 a Don't move across and move four down
   b Move two left and three down
   c Move four right and nine up
   d Move six to the left and one up
   e Don't move
   f Move five to the left and three up

2 a $\begin{pmatrix} 2 \\ 6 \end{pmatrix}$ b $\begin{pmatrix} -4 \\ 1 \end{pmatrix}$ c $\begin{pmatrix} -1 \\ -7 \end{pmatrix}$ d $\begin{pmatrix} 2 \\ 1 \end{pmatrix}$ e $\begin{pmatrix} 3 \\ -7 \end{pmatrix}$

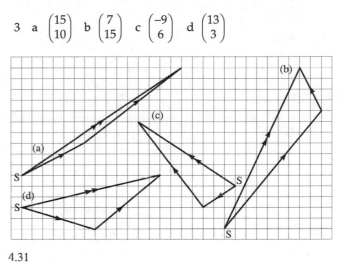

4.31

4 a $\begin{pmatrix} 6 \\ 6 \end{pmatrix}$ b $\begin{pmatrix} 3 \\ 3 \end{pmatrix}$ c $\begin{pmatrix} 6 \\ 12 \end{pmatrix}$ d $\begin{pmatrix} -1 \\ -6 \end{pmatrix}$

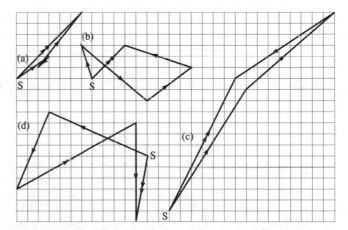

4.32

5 a $\begin{pmatrix} 4 \\ 2 \end{pmatrix}$ b $\begin{pmatrix} -7 \\ -3 \end{pmatrix}$ c $\begin{pmatrix} 2 \\ 5 \end{pmatrix}$ d $\begin{pmatrix} 1 \\ 1 \end{pmatrix}$

6 a $\begin{pmatrix} 16 \\ 20 \end{pmatrix}$ b $\begin{pmatrix} 18 \\ -3 \end{pmatrix}$ c $\begin{pmatrix} -18 \\ 12 \end{pmatrix}$ d $\begin{pmatrix} -20 \\ -15 \end{pmatrix}$

7 Any multiple of the original vector is parallel to it. So, for
   example, the vectors $\begin{pmatrix} -8 \\ 10 \end{pmatrix}$ and $\begin{pmatrix} -12 \\ 15 \end{pmatrix}$ are parallel to a.

8 a (9, 5), (9, 7), and (11, 7)
   b (2, −4), (2, −2), and (4, −2)
   c (−2, −2), (−2, 0), and (0, 0)
   d (−1, −2), (−1, 0), and (1, 0)

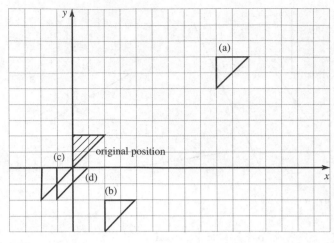

4.33

9 a $\frac{1}{2}a + \frac{1}{2}b$ b $\frac{1}{5}a + \frac{4}{5}b$ c $\frac{4}{7}a + \frac{3}{7}b$

10 a $\frac{4}{11}a + \frac{7}{11}b$ b $\frac{2}{7}a + \frac{5}{7}b$ c $\frac{3}{8}a + \frac{5}{8}b$

11 a $1\frac{1}{4}b - \frac{1}{4}a$ b $2\frac{1}{3}b - 1\frac{1}{3}a$ c $3\frac{3}{5}b - 2\frac{3}{5}a$

12 a 3.6, 56.3°   c 5, 126.9°
   b 8.49, 225°   d 9, 0°

13 a $\begin{pmatrix} x \\ y \end{pmatrix} = \begin{pmatrix} 1 \\ 4 \end{pmatrix} + a\begin{pmatrix} 4 \\ 5 \end{pmatrix}$ c $\begin{pmatrix} x \\ y \end{pmatrix} = \begin{pmatrix} 1 \\ 1 \end{pmatrix} + a\begin{pmatrix} 4 \\ 4 \end{pmatrix}$

   b $\begin{pmatrix} x \\ y \end{pmatrix} = \begin{pmatrix} 22 \\ 4 \end{pmatrix} + a\begin{pmatrix} -16 \\ 13 \end{pmatrix}$ d $\begin{pmatrix} x \\ y \end{pmatrix} = \begin{pmatrix} 21 \\ 13 \end{pmatrix} + a\begin{pmatrix} -18 \\ -4 \end{pmatrix}$

Chapter 5

1 a 40 353 607   d 0.015 625
  b 216   e 1
  c 130 321

2 a 5 764 801
  b 1 771 561
  c 43 046 721
  d 10 000 000
  e $3.906\ 25 \times 10^{-3} = 0.003\ 906\ 25$

3 a 7   d $161\ 051 = 11^5$
  b $1000 = 10^3$ e $0.125 = 0.5^3$
  c $81 = 9^2$

4 a $4^{-1} = \frac{1}{4} = 0.25$

  b $10^{-2} = \frac{1}{10^2} = \frac{1}{100} = 0.01$

  c $2^{-3} = \frac{1}{2^3} = \frac{1}{8} = 0.125$

  d $\frac{1}{8} = 0.125$

  e $\frac{1}{6^3} = \frac{1}{216} = 0.00463$ to 3 significant figures

5 a 2
  b $\frac{1}{16} = 0.0625$
  c $5^4 = 625$
  d $10^5 = 100\ 000$
  e $\frac{1}{125} = 0.008$
  f $\frac{1}{10^7} = \frac{1}{10\ 000\ 000} = 0.0000001$

6 a 5.67×10^9 f 1.53×10^{-5}
  b 7.69×10 g 4.12×10^{-3}
  c 4.36×10^{-3} h 1.98×10^4
  d 2.99×10^3 i 1.00×10^{-9}
  e 5.67×10^{-8} j 2.09×10^{-7}

7 a $(6^3)^{10} = (6^5)^6 = (6^2)^{15}$, etc.
  b $(5^2)^4 = (5^4)^2 = (5^{16})^{\frac{1}{2}}$, etc.
  c $(10^6)^4 = (10^8)^3 = (10^{12})^2$, etc.
  d $(y^{\frac{1}{4}})^3 = (y^3)^{\frac{1}{4}} = (y^{\frac{3}{2}})^{\frac{1}{2}}$, etc.
  e $(p^3)^{-4} = (p^{-3})^4 = (p^2)^{-6}$, etc.

8 a $2^3 = 8$ d $2^9 = 512$
  b $5^2 = 25$ e $25^{\frac{1}{2}} = 5$
  c $10^5 = 100\ 000$

9 e^x with $x = 1$ gives 2.718281828 as the value of e

10 a 6   d 0
   b 1   e −3
   c −1

11 a $y = 27.3$ d $t = 9.00$
   b $m = 16.0$ e $t = 4.57$
   c $q = 0.861$

12 a After 16 years (15.52)
   b After 10 days (9.97)
   c After 6 weeks (5.689)
   d After 7 weeks (6.64)
   e 0.936 to 3 significant figures
     i.e., $s \log 8 = t \log 7$
     $$\frac{s}{t} = \frac{\log 7}{\log 8} = \frac{0.84509804}{0.903089987} = 0.935784974 = 0.936 \text{ to}$$
     3 significant figures

Chapter 6

1 a Mean $= \frac{28}{7} = 4$, there is no mode (3 and 7 both occur twice), median $= 3$
  b Mean $= \frac{28}{8} = 3.5$, mode $= 8$, median $= 5$
  c Mean $= \frac{153}{9} = 17$, mode $= 25$, median $= 18$
  d Mean $= \frac{15}{5} = 3$, there is no mode, median $= 2$
  e Mean $= \frac{17}{5} = 3.4$, mode $= 1.9$, median $= 3.2$
  f Mean $= 100 + \frac{266}{7} = 100 + 38 = 138$ (notice that you can use this method for numbers that are not too widely spread, such as the age of a group of students, or the mean time for running a race), there is no mode, median $= 136$.

2 a It will be difficult if some children cannot reach the pegs, but a modal average will probably be best.
  b Mean.
  c A modal average would be best if times for large traffic flows are required.
  d The mean, approximately 23, although this would be too few for two of the groups.
  e The mean height of the male population plus a generous allowance. There are, in fact, regulations about the minimum height of doorways in new property, which is considerably above the mean height of the population but still leaves some very tall people having to know when to take care.

3 a Mean = 3, $\sigma = \sqrt{5.6} = 2.38$

  b Mean = 3, $\sigma = \sqrt{\frac{192}{10}} = 4.38$

  c Mean = 1.565, $\sigma = 1.785$

  d Mean = 232, $\sigma = 129.26$

  e Mean = 2.5, $\sigma = 7.632$

4 a Sum = 35.9, mean = 5.98, $\sigma = 2.36$, $\sigma^2 = 5.55$

  b Sum = 4500, mean = 900, $\sigma = 42.49$, $\sigma^2 = 1806$

  c Sum = 0.322, mean = 0.046, $\sigma = 0.0251$, $\sigma^2 = 0.000629$

  d Sum = 116, mean = 11.6, $\sigma = 62.09$, $\sigma^2 = 3855$

  e Sum = 438 580, mean = 109 645, $\sigma = 168\ 057$,
    $\sigma^2 = 2.8 \times 10^{10}$

5 a (H, H, H), (H, H, T), (H, T, H), (T, H, H), (H, T, T),
    (T, H, T), (T, T, H), (T, T, T)

  b $p(H, H, H) = \frac{1}{8}$

  c $p(2H, T) = \frac{3}{8}$, since order doesn't matter

6 a $p(G) = \frac{4}{10}$

  b $p(\text{2nd } G) = \frac{3}{9} = \frac{1}{3}$

7 $p(T, T, T, T, T) = \frac{1}{2} \times \frac{1}{2} \times \frac{1}{2} \times \frac{1}{2} \times \frac{1}{2} = \frac{1}{32}$

8 a $p(\text{both win}) = \frac{5}{6} \times \frac{3}{4} = \frac{15}{24} = \frac{5}{8}$

  b $p(\text{both lose}) = \frac{1}{6} \times \frac{1}{4} = \frac{1}{24}$

  c $p(\text{one wins, the other loses}) = (\frac{5}{6} \times \frac{1}{4}) + (\frac{1}{6} \times \frac{3}{4})$
    $= \frac{5}{24} + \frac{3}{24} = \frac{1}{3}$

  d The answers add up to 1. We could have anticipated
    that because the problems cover all the possible
    outcomes, with no overlap.

9 a There are five combinations that give a total of 8, i.e.
    $(5, 3)$, $(3, 5)$, $(4, 4)$, $(6, 2)$, and $(2, 6)$. Each die has six
    faces, so there are $6 \times 6 = 36$ total combinations. Hence,
    $p(\text{scoring 8}) = \frac{5}{36}$. (See also Fig. 6.2.)

  b 10 can be obtained from $(5, 5)$, $(6, 4)$, and $(4, 6)$, 11 can
    be obtained from $(5, 6)$ and $(6, 5)$, and 12 can be
    obtained from $(6, 6)$ so we have six possible
    combinations of numbers. Then $p(\text{10 or more}) = \frac{6}{36} = \frac{1}{6}$.

10 One head and two tails are obtained in the following
   combinations: (H, T, T), (T, T, H), and (T, H, T). So
   $p(2H, T) = \frac{3}{8}$ (8 ways in total, see 5a.)

11 $\frac{1}{7}$

12 $p(E) = \frac{1}{2}$ (half the numbers are even), so p(all five think
   of an even number) $= (\frac{1}{2})^5 = \frac{1}{32}$

13 $p(\text{one of each colour}) = \frac{15}{64} + \frac{15}{64} = \frac{30}{64} = \frac{15}{32}$

First draw   Second draw   Probabilities

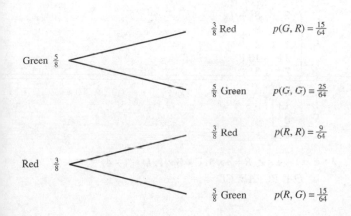

14 p(at least one A, K, Q, J in two draws)
   $= p(\text{A, K, Q, J in both draws})$
   $\qquad\qquad + p(\text{A, K, Q, J in first draw only})$
   $+ p(\text{A, K, Q, J in second draw only})$
   $= \frac{16}{169} + \frac{36}{169} + \frac{36}{169} = \frac{88}{169}$

   Consider also, $1 - p(\text{neither a picture nor A}) = 1 - \frac{81}{169} = \frac{88}{169}$

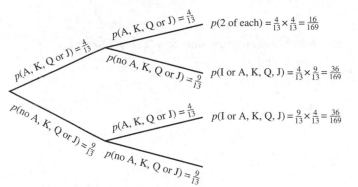

15 b $p(1C \text{ and } 1W) = \frac{2}{9} + \frac{2}{9} = \frac{4}{9}$

   c $p(2C \text{ and } 1W) = p(C, C, W) + p(C, W, C) + p(W, C, C)$
     $= \frac{2}{27} + \frac{2}{27} + \frac{2}{27} = \frac{6}{27} = \frac{2}{9}$

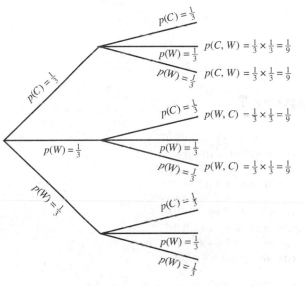

$p(\text{1 correct and 1 wrong}) = \frac{1}{9} + \frac{1}{9} + \frac{1}{9} + \frac{1}{9} = \frac{4}{9}$

16 a $p(M, I) = \frac{1}{2} \times \frac{1}{4} = \frac{1}{8}$

   b i $p(T \text{ or } G, \text{ not } I) = \frac{3}{35} + \frac{9}{70} = \frac{15}{70} = \frac{3}{14}$

     ii $p(M \text{ or } B, D) = \frac{3}{10} \times \frac{3}{7} + \frac{1}{5} \times \frac{3}{7} = \frac{9}{70} + \frac{3}{35} = \frac{3}{14}$

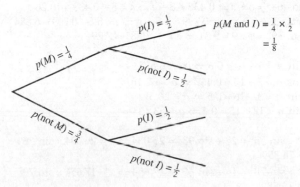

17 a $p(\text{all choose swimming}) = \frac{1}{3} \times \frac{1}{3} \times \frac{1}{3} = \frac{1}{27}$

   b $p(2F \text{ and } 1S) = p(F, F, S) + p(F, S, F) + p(S, F, F) = \frac{3}{27}$

18   a   3 628 800

     b 2.43×10^{18}

     c 2.63×10^{35}

19   a $4! = 24$

     b $\dfrac{4!}{2!} = 12$

     c   4

20   Number of arrangements of n 'a's, m 'b's and p 'c's is

     $\dfrac{(n + m + p)!}{n!m!p!}$

21   $\dfrac{6!}{4!} = 30$

22   $\dfrac{8!}{2!2!} = 10080$

23   $\frac{1}{26} \times \frac{1}{25} \times \frac{1}{24} \times \frac{1}{23} \times \frac{1}{22} \times \frac{1}{21} = 6 \times 10^{-9}$

24   $\frac{5}{12}$

25   a $\frac{11}{15}$ c $\frac{10}{15}$

     b $\frac{4}{15}$ d $\frac{8}{15}$

Chapter 7

1   a $\sin 45.0° = 4 \div 5.66 = 0.707$

    b $\sin 36.87° = 6 \div 10 = 0.6$

    c $\sin 63.43° = 4 \div 4.47 = 0.894$

    d $\sin 30° = 3 \div 6 = 0.5$

2   a $\cos 45° = 4 \div 5.66 = 0.707$

    b $\cos 36.87° = 8 \div 10 = 0.8$

    c $\cos 63.43° = 2 \div 4.47 = 0.447$

    d $\cos 30° = 5.2 \div 6 = 0.866$

3   a $\tan 45° = 4 \div 4 = 1$

    b $\tan 36.87° = 6 \div 8 = 0.75$

    c $\tan 63.43° = 4 \div 2 = 2$

    d $\tan 30° = 3 \div 5.2 = 0.577$

4   a $\cos 40° = a \div 11 \Rightarrow 0.766 = a \div 11 \Rightarrow a = 11 \times 0.766 = 8.426$

    b $\sin 55° = a \div 9 \Rightarrow 0.819 = a \div 9 \Rightarrow a = 9 \times 0.819 = 7.371$

    c $\cos 64° = 8 \div a \Rightarrow 0.438 = 8 \div a \Rightarrow a = 8 \div 0.438 = 18.26$

    d $\sin 53° = 5.5 \div a \Rightarrow 0.799 = 5.5 \div a \Rightarrow a = 5.5 \div 0.799 = 6.884$

    e $\tan 39° = a \div 9 \Rightarrow 0.81 = a \div 9 \Rightarrow a = 9 \times 0.81 = 7.29$

5   a $\sin \alpha = 6 \div 10 = 0.6 \Rightarrow \alpha = 36.87°$

    b $\cos \alpha = 7 \div 15 = 0.467 \Rightarrow \alpha = 62.18°$

    c $\tan \alpha = 8 \div 16 = 0.5 \Rightarrow \alpha = 26.57°$

    d $\sin \alpha = 12 \div 15 = 0.8 \Rightarrow \alpha = 53.13°$

6   a $x \div \sin 35° = 25 \div \sin 93° = 25.034 \Rightarrow x = 25.034 \times \sin 35°$

       $= 14.359$

    b $x \div \sin 70° = 16 \div \sin 65° = 17.654 \Rightarrow x = 17.654 \times \sin 70°$

       $= 16.589$

    c $x = 18.195$

    d $x = 39.089$

7   a $15 \div \sin \alpha = 28 \div \sin 85° = 28.107 \Rightarrow \sin \alpha = 15 \div 28.107$

       $= 0.534 \Rightarrow \alpha = 32.276°$

    b $25 \div \sin \alpha = 20 \div \sin 45° = 28.28 \Rightarrow \sin \alpha = 25 \div 28.28$

       $= 0.884 \Rightarrow \alpha = 62.13°$

    c $\alpha = 44.81°$

    d $\alpha = 62.738°$

8   a $x^2 = 25^2 + 19^2 - 2 \times 25 \times 19 \times \cos 39° = 247.71 \Rightarrow x = 15.74$

    b $x^2 = 16^2 + 16^2 - 2 \times 16 \times 16 \times \cos 78° = 405.55 \Rightarrow x = 20.14$

    c $x = 19.636$

    d $x = 34.34$

9   a $15^2 = 28^2 + 20^2 - 2 \times 20 \times 28 \times \cos \alpha \Rightarrow 225 = 1184 - 1120$

       $\times \cos \alpha \Rightarrow \cos \alpha = (1184 - 225) \div 1120 = 0.856$

       $\alpha = 31.13°$

    b $\alpha = 91.12°$

    c $\alpha = 48.19°$

    d $\alpha = 61.89°$

Chapter 8

1   a 1×3 c 3×1

    b 3×3 d 2×3

2   $\begin{pmatrix} 1 & 0 \\ 0 & 1 \end{pmatrix}$

3   $\begin{pmatrix} u & v & w & x & y & z \end{pmatrix}$

4   $\begin{pmatrix} g \\ h \\ i \\ j \end{pmatrix}$

5   a $\begin{pmatrix} 5 & 13 & 13 \\ 3 & 3 & 13 \\ 6 & 4 & 15 \end{pmatrix}$

    b $\begin{pmatrix} 1 & 9 \\ 5 & 4 \\ -4 & 16 \\ 4 & 10 \end{pmatrix}$

    c $\begin{pmatrix} 3 & -2 & -11 & 8 & 5 \end{pmatrix}$

6   a $\begin{pmatrix} 1 & 2 & 5 \\ 2 & 4 & 0 \end{pmatrix}$

    b $\begin{pmatrix} 7 & -9 \\ -2 & 2 \end{pmatrix}$

    c $\begin{pmatrix} 2 & 8 \\ -8 & 8 \\ 2 & 2 \\ -11 & -10 \\ 7 & 2 \end{pmatrix}$

    d $\begin{pmatrix} 13 \\ -13 \\ 0 \\ 2 \end{pmatrix}$

7   a $A = 4 \times 2, B = 3 \times 3, C = 3 \times 1, D = 1 \times 4, E = 2 \times 2$

    b DA, BC, AE, CD

c $DA = \begin{pmatrix} 23 & -3 \end{pmatrix}$, $BC = \begin{pmatrix} 15 \\ 40 \\ 43 \end{pmatrix}$, $AE = \begin{pmatrix} -3 & 9 \\ 12 & -36 \\ 5 & -15 \\ 2 & -6 \end{pmatrix}$

$CD = \begin{pmatrix} -4 & 8 & -2 & 0 \\ -2 & 4 & -1 & 0 \\ -10 & 20 & -5 & 0 \end{pmatrix}$

8 $\dfrac{1}{ad-bc}\begin{pmatrix} ad-bc & -ab+ab \\ cd-dc & -bc+ad \end{pmatrix} = \begin{pmatrix} 1 & 0 \\ 0 & 1 \end{pmatrix}$

9 a The inverse is $\dfrac{1}{35-21}\begin{pmatrix} 7 & -7 \\ -3 & 5 \end{pmatrix}$, and $x = 4$, and $y = 1$

b The inverse is $\dfrac{1}{-6-21}\begin{pmatrix} -3 & -3 \\ -7 & 2 \end{pmatrix}$, and $a = 3$, and $b = 6$

c The inverse is $\dfrac{1}{1-15}\begin{pmatrix} 1 & -5 \\ -3 & 1 \end{pmatrix}$, and $p = 2$, and $q = 3$

d The inverse is $\dfrac{1}{-4-27}\begin{pmatrix} -2 & -9 \\ -3 & 2 \end{pmatrix}$, and $s = 5$, and $t = -1$

e The inverse is $\dfrac{1}{-45-6}\begin{pmatrix} -9 & -3 \\ -2 & 5 \end{pmatrix}$, and $m = 12$, and $n = 0$

f The inverse is $\dfrac{1}{-3+2}\begin{pmatrix} -3 & 1 \\ -2 & 1 \end{pmatrix}$, and $c = 5$, and $d = -3$

10 a Moves to $\begin{pmatrix} -3 \\ 4 \end{pmatrix}$, reflection in the y-axis

b Moves to $\begin{pmatrix} -4 \\ 3 \end{pmatrix}$, rotation of 90° about $(0,0)$

c Moves to $\begin{pmatrix} 19 \\ 4 \end{pmatrix}$, a shear

d Moves to $\begin{pmatrix} 6 \\ 20 \end{pmatrix}$, a two-way stretch

(c)

8.4

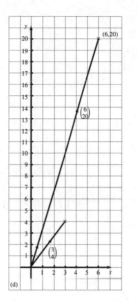

(d)

8.4

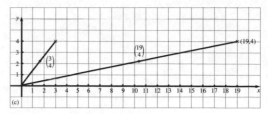

(a)

(b)

8.4

Contents

Map of the book

[1] Items in blue will be found in Part A.   [2] Items in black will be found in Part B.

Writing	Grammar	Vocabulary	Study skills	Pronunciation
	Verbs followed by the infinitive Verbs and common expressions followed by the -ing form	Adjectives followed by prepositions	Learning objectives	Short vowels
A notice	Verbs followed by the infinitive or the -ing form	(Positive descriptions)³	Spelling	Spelling and sounds
	Relative clauses Omission of relative pronouns and the position of prepositions	(Foreign words used in English)	Guessing meaning from context	Linking
An article	Future forms – will, shall, to be going to, present continuous, present simple Future forms – future continuous, future perfect, future perfect continuous, to be to, was/were going to	Two-part phrasal verbs	Fluency versus accuracy	Schwa /ə/ and weak vowels
A short story	Past tenses and the present perfect	Linkers Order of adjectives	Reading	
A formal announcement A letter of complaint	First conditional Variations of if	(Formal and informal vocabulary) Ways of asking for clarification		/b/ and /v/
	Second conditional Third conditional and mixed conditionals	Idioms of colour Word-building – nouns from adjectives and prefixes	Organising vocabulary	/s/ and /ʃ/ + /ʃ/ and /tʃ/
A review	wish, if only, would rather, it's time	Word-building – suffixes Adverb + adjective collocations	Learning grammar	Consonant clusters
	Modal verbs	Three-part phrasal verbs	Re-evaluating learning strategies	Word stress
A summary	The passive	Idiomatic expressions Countable and uncountable nouns	Speaking Summary writing	Sentence stress
Sentences from notes	Definite article or zero article? Definite, zero and indefinite articles	Word-building – word families Synonyms for smell Expressions with make and do	Listening	Silent letters
An article	Inversion	Compound words	Writing	(Stress in compound words)
	Indirect speech	Prepositions	Progress review	Chunking

³ Items in brackets will be found under a different section heading.

V

Acknowledgements

Author's acknowledgements

The author would like to thank colleagues at EF International Language School, Cambridge, in particular, Fiona Fallon, Jo Philips and Jill Stewart for their support. Special thanks to my editors, Charlotte Adams, Niki Browne and Erica Hall, who all gave invaluable help and support. On the home front, thanks to Robbie Burns for computer support and lots more.

The author and publishers would like to thank the following teachers for their help in testing and commenting on the materials and for the invaluable feedback they provided.

Mark Appleby, Spain; Anna-Marie Burke, UK; Henny Burke, Spain; Philip Devlin, Germany; Romayne Grangereau, France; Gökhan Gültek, Turkey; Jane Hann, UK; Joanne Lenthall, UK; Deirdre Mulrennan, Italy; Patricia O'Sullivan, UK; Aytül Özer, Turkey; Sandra Possas, Brazil; R S Pryor, UK; Roger Scott, UK; Mira Shapur, UK; Peter Watkins, UK; Clare West, UK.

The author and publishers are grateful to the following for permission to reproduce copyright material. It has not always been possible to identify the sources of all the material used and in such cases the publishers would welcome information from the copyright owners.

p. 3: *The Daily Mirror* for the text from 'The jungle bookworm' © The Mirror/Patrick Mulchrone (also by permission of MSI); p. 5: Mark Hancock for Stepping stones, adapted from an idea in *Pronunciation Games* © Cambridge University Press 1995; p. 9: *The Times* for 'Serious shopping – petrol stations' by Giles Cohen © Giles Cohen/Times Newspapers Limited, 16 November 1996; p. 11: *The Observer* for the text from 'Polynesian paradise host to a luxury hotel' by Catherine Field © *The Observer*; p. 14: *The Sunday Times* for the text from 'Bill Gates: net prophet' by Lesley White © Lesley White/Times Newspapers Limited, 12 November 1995; p. 15: Mario Rinvolucri and Paul Davis for Future chairs, adapted from an idea in *More Grammar Games* © Cambridge University Press 1995; p. 16: Stuart Krichevsky Literary Agency, Inc. for the listening text and extract by Michio Kaku, excerpted from 'Visions: How Science Will Revolutionize the 21st Century'; p. 19: *Focus* for 'What's so good about bug grub?'; p. 20: Angela Carter for 'The Werewolf' © Angela Carter 1979. Reproduced by permission of the Estate of Angela Carter c/o Rogers, Coleridge and White Ltd, 20 Powis Mews, London W11 1JN; p. 22: Mario Rinvolucri for Grammar auction, adapted from an idea in *Grammar Games* © Cambridge University Press 1985; pp. 28–30: Dorothee Mella for the charts, listening text adapted from *The Language of Colour* © Penguin; p. 31: *The Times* for 'Spectacular Northern Lights …' by Giles Whittell © Giles Whittell/Times Newspapers Limited, 15 March 1993; p. 34: *The Times Magazine* for the listening text adapted from 'The prom queen' by Joanna Pitman © Times Newspapers Limited, 24 May 1997; p. 34: *The Times Magazine* for the extract adapted from 'Truth or dare' by Ginny Dougary © Times Newspapers Limited, 4 January 1997; p. 35: *Time Out* for 'Absolute power' by Geoff Andrew © Time Out; p. 38: *The Times* for the text adapted from 'Stockbroker jailed for road rage assault' by Michael Horswell and Kathryn Knight © Times Newspapers Limited, 4 August 1999; p. 40: *The Independent* for the extracts adapted from 'Mouth burnt on pie? Join the rush to sue' by Michael Streeter © Michael Streeter/*The Independent*; p. 41: The BBC for 'I have always got even. It's so therapeutic' by Barry Wigmore, 1997; p. 42: Aileen Ballantyne (freelance medical/science journalist) for

'Battle of the sexes'; p. 46: Robert Tisserand for the listening text adapted from *Aromatherapy* © C W Daniel Company Limited; p. 49: Tony Hazzard for 'Problem solving dreams' from *Dreams and their Meanings* © Cassell and Company; p. 51: *The Times Magazine* for the extract from 'Style wars' by Lowri Turner © Times Newspapers Limited, 12 April 1997; p. 52: *The Sunday Times* for the text from 'The English butler' © Times Newspapers Limited; p. 53: *The Times* for 'Puppy love …' adapted from 'How suitable is that doggie in the window?' by James Allcock © James Allcock/Times Newspapers Limited, 29 November 1997; p. 54: *The Times Magazine* for 'Basic instinct' by Charlotte Uhlenbroek © Times Newspapers Limited, 18 October 1997; p. 55: limericks and illustrations from *An Explosion of Limericks* by Vyvyan Holland © Cassell and Company (now part of the Orion Group); p. 59: Stanton Newman and Susan Londale for 'Primary territory: our homes' from *Human Jungle* © Ebury; p. 63: *New Scientist* for 'An uncalculated risk'.

Fact file extracts in the Teacher's Book on Franklin Delano Roosevelt (p. 11), John Milton (p. 12), Bill Gates (p. 17), Aurora (p. 38) and Jan van Eyck (p. 45) are copyright (1990) (1991–1999) AND Data Ltd, Oxford, UK. All rights reserved.

Text permissions by Fiona Donnelly.

The author and publishers are grateful to the following illustrators and photographic sources.

Illustrators: Kathy Baxendale, Paul Davies, Phil Healey, Doreen McGuiness, David Micheson, Julian Mosedale, Martin Sanders, Jamie Sneddon, Natasha Stewart and Holly Swain.

Photographic sources: p. 2: Tracy Edwards: Sygma/M Polak, Mother Teresa: Sygma/A Fe Wildenberg, graduate: Tony Stone Images/Dan Bosler, Nelson Mandela: Sygma/Yves Wildenberg, Stephen Hawkins: Sygma/Jon Jones, sportsmen: Tony Stone Images/Bruce Ayres, Buzz Aldrin: Sygma/J Tizicu; p. 4: Rex Features Ltd; p. 6: Advertising Archives; p. 7: Junghans advert: Advertising Archives, Ulysse Nardin advert: Ulysse Nardin; p. 10: Rarotonga: Tony Stone Images/Glen Allison, Franklin D Roosevelt: Superstock; p. 14: Penguin/Trevor Clifford; p. 18: Tony Stone Images; p. 19: Rex Reatures Ltd; p. 20: *The Hobbit*: Collins/Trevor Clifford, *Cry, The Beloved Country*: Penguin/Trevor Clifford, *The Naked Ape*: Vintage/Trevor Clifford, *The House of Spirits*: Black Swan/Trevor Clifford, *Immediate Action*: Corgi/Trevor Clifford; p. 27: Tony Stone Images/Cosmo Cordina; p. 31: Science Photo Library; p. 32: Ronald Grant Archive; p. 34: *The Times*/Graham Wood; p. 35: Pictorial Press; p. 36: The Bridgeman Art Library; p. 42: Tony Stone Images/Jason Hawkes; p. 46: (1) and (3) Pictor International Ltd, (2) Superstock, (4) Rex Interstock; p. 50: (1) Tony Stone Images/Bob Torrez, (2) Camera Press London, (3) Tony Stone Images, (4) Robert Harding, (5) Tony Stone Images/Andy Sacs, (6) Popperfoto Ltd; p. 52: Superstock; p. 53: Bandai UK Ltd; p. 54: Rex Features Ltd; p. 60: Advertising Archives.

Picture research by Diane Jones.

Book design by Nick Newton and Dave Seabourne.

Book production by Gecko Limited.

Cover design by Mark Diaper.

The cassette which accompanies this book was produced by Martin Williamson, Prolingua Productions, at Studio AVP, London.

Introduction

Who *Advance Your English* is for

Advance Your English is a short course designed to take adult learners from upper-intermediate to advanced level. The material is suitable for learners who would like to further their English studies or communicate in English in a work situation or while travelling.

Advance Your English consists of this Coursebook and a Class Cassette, a Workbook and a Workbook Cassette, and a Teacher's Book.

The Coursebook and Class Cassette

The Coursebook provides approximately 40 hours of classroom activity in 16 units – 13 main units and three review units (Units 5, 10 and 16). The main units are broadly topic based and divided into two equal parts, Part A and Part B. The review units all feature activities and exercises to check that you have understood and remembered the work you have covered in the preceding units.

A comprehensive syllabus covers grammar, all four skills, vocabulary, pronunciation and study skills, the configuration of material varying from unit to unit. Tapescripts of all the listening material featured on the cassette (identified by ▣ in the units) are included on pages 64–74.

Grammar

Every unit has a strong grammar element. To maximise the benefit of this language work, it is recommended that you work in conjunction with a good grammar book, such as *Advanced Grammar in Use* by Martin Hewings (Cambridge University Press 1999). The course assumes upper-intermediate/FCE competence and it is important at this level not only to revise previously learnt structures, but also to improve, refine and learn new uses of grammar. For this reason, some grammar activities are designed to help you check what you already know, while others aim to develop and extend your knowledge and use of grammar.

The four skills

All four language skills – reading, listening, speaking and writing – are covered and the course offers a balance of individual skills work as well as integrated skills practice, although slightly less emphasis has been placed on writing. Reading texts from a variety of sources cover a range of topics of international interest. Varied listening material and extensive speaking opportunities offer ample scope for oral/aural practice throughout.

Vocabulary

An extensive lexical syllabus covers key areas such as phrasal verbs, compound words, prefixes, suffixes and collocation, as well as topic-related vocabulary. At the same time vocabulary learning skills are developed with activities which encourage guessing meaning from context, using dictionaries and keeping records.

Pronunciation

Despite the fact that this is a short course, pronunciation is such an important area that it is included in most units. Pronunciation activities, covering individual sounds, stress and intonation, are quite often practised using the cassette. A chart of phonetic symbols is included at the end the book.

Study skills

Most units have a study skills section where you are encouraged to analyse and develop your own learning strategies with a view to becoming an effective independent learner. This will help you continue your English studies on your own after you finish the course.

The Workbook and Workbook Cassette

The Workbook offers further practice and consolidation of the work in the Coursebook and, in some cases, development of Coursebook work. Accompanied by its own cassette, the Workbook runs parallel to the Coursebook with 13 main units and three review units, but the review units in the Workbook take the form of tests for self-assessment to help you check your progress.

You can use the Workbook independently, as full answers and tapescripts are included, or it can be used as additional classroom material. A special feature at the end of most units in the Workbook is *Reading for pleasure* or *Listening for pleasure*. This is literally what it says – a text or recording which is to be enjoyed. There is no exercise or activity arising from it.

The Teacher's Book

The Teacher's Book offers suggestions on how to approach, set up and in some cases extend Coursebook activities. There are also guidelines on which material to set for homework and on how to tailor the course to suit different classes.

1 Achievers

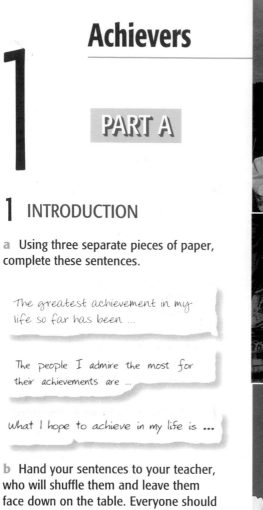

1 INTRODUCTION

a Using three separate pieces of paper, complete these sentences.

> The greatest achievement in my life so far has been ...

> The people I admire the most for their achievements are ...

> What I hope to achieve in my life is ...

b Hand your sentences to your teacher, who will shuffle them and leave them face down on the table. Everyone should pick up one piece of paper and walk around the class asking questions to find out who wrote the sentence. When you have found the writer, collect another piece of paper.

c As a class, discuss which achievements were the most interesting or unusual.

2 STUDY SKILLS Learning objectives

a What do you hope to achieve in your English language studies? Map out your English language objectives. Tick which situations apply to you now and in the future, and add extra information.

Studies	Work	Travel/Pleasure
Listening to the teacher/lecturer	Receiving information (e.g. instructions)	Receiving information (e.g. radio news, interviews, travel announcements)
Speaking to the teacher/lecturer	Explaining your product/ service Dealing with visitors	Asking questions Socialising with fellow travellers
Reading novels/textbooks	Reading letters, reports	Reading notices, travel guides
Writing essays/dissertation	Writing business letters, reports, emails	Writing personal letters, postcards, emails

b Compare your responses to **a** with a partner and discuss what knowing English will help you achieve.

c Rank these language skills in order of importance to you. 1 = very important, 5 = not important.

listening ☐
speaking ☐
reading ☐
writing ☐
learning more vocabulary ☐
learning and practising grammar ☐

d Discuss your ranking of the skills with a partner.

3 READING

a You are going to read an article about Miguel Hilario-Manenima and how he achieved his dream. Before you read, work in pairs and discuss different types of achievements, e.g. financial, emotional, technological or educational, and their relative importance to you and society in general.

b Read the article quite quickly and then, with a partner, decide on a suitable headline.

Miguel was born in a canoe and learned to survive life in the jungle by fishing for piranha and hunting armadillo. If he had told his tribal elders that one day he'd be studying at one of Britain's top universities, they'd have thought the youngster was possessed by the spirits. But Amazonian Indian, Miguel Hilario-Manenima, is doing just that. The 27-year-old has won a scholarship to Oxford to study politics and economics.

Miguel is the first member of his 30,000-strong semi-nomadic tribe ever to leave the Amazon jungle to study abroad. He was alerted to the razzamatazz of the world outside his remote village by a National Geographic magazine left in the rainforest by a missionary. Miguel was 13. The magazine pictures of New York skyscrapers and images of life in the West fascinated him and launched him on an incredible voyage of discovery. A keen musician, Miguel said, 'It made me realise there was a whole new world outside that I wanted to see with my own eyes.'

So he set off on a four-day boat journey to the jungle city of Pucallpa to find a school. From there he travelled to Peru's capital, Lima, where missionaries helped him study. Ironically, he was given the name Manenima – he who travels – because his mother gave birth to him in a canoe as she moved from village to village. Miguel's determination to broaden his horizons in Lima left him doing his homework under streetlights and living on leftover food from restaurants, but it also won him a scholarship to travel and study in Texas where he met Kim. Now he is married to Kim and they have a four-year-old daughter, Vanessa.

When Miguel first arrived in the USA he was staggered by the culture clash. His diet had consisted of monkeys, armadillos, fish and alligators so when he was first offered a dish of lettuce he was disgusted. Money was another source of fascination; with no form of currency, his tribe had relied on barter for trading. Now life has taken another dramatic turn as Miguel takes up his one-year scholarship at Mansfield College, Oxford. His fellow students will no doubt be fascinated to learn about Miguel's childhood in the rainforests; his college digs a far cry from the palm-leaf hut where he grew up in the Peruvian jungle. And what does Miguel think about all this? In his words, 'It's a dream come true for anyone but for someone from the Amazonian rainforest it's a chance in five million.'

c Work in pairs and discuss these questions.

1 Where and how did Miguel live until he was 13 years old?
2 What made Miguel decide to leave his tribe?
3 How did he go about achieving his aim?
4 How did he 'survive' in Lima, Peru?
5 Which aspects of culture shock are mentioned in the article?

d Choose a heading for each paragraph in the article about Miguel. There is one extra heading which does not fit.

A Miguel lives up to his name
B The high life
C Worlds apart
D The power of the image
E The unimaginable

e Discuss these questions.

1 Miguel achieved his aim but for many people their aim in life remains a dream. What makes the difference between fulfilling an aim and remaining a dreamer?
2 Have you ever suffered from culture shock? How did you feel and how did you cope with the situation(s)?

4 GRAMMAR Verbs followed by the infinitive

Certain verbs are always followed by the infinitive, e.g. in the article about Miguel we read *wanted to see*.

a Complete these sentences using the verbs in the list.

appears   begged   entitles   failed
helped   let   made   wanted

1 They .... to reach an agreement even after hours of debate.
2 She .... to have all the qualifications we need in someone.
3 They .... him wait for two hours at immigration.
4 The whole family .... to leave the city and live in the country.
5 Don't .... me forget to post that letter.
6 He .... her not to leave him.
7 This voucher .... you to take your meals in any of the hotel's restaurants.
8 They .... find the missing letter.

b In the sentences in **a** you can find examples of several verb patterns containing infinitives. What are they?

e.g. 1 = verb + *to* + infinitive

c Change these sentences into the passive and then, with a partner, discuss what changes occur in the verb pattern.

1 They saw him hand over the money.
2 They heard him whisper the answer.
3 They felt she was the best person for the job.

d What do these four sentences tell you about verb patterns after *help*?

1 They helped her to reach the shore.
2 They helped her reach the shore.
3 They helped reach the final agreement.
4 They helped to reach the final agreement.

3

PART B

1 LISTENING

a You are going to listen to a woman who has achieved success in a predominantly male area of the film industry. Before you listen, discuss these questions about work.

1 Do you believe most people can get the job they really want; it is only a question of determination?
2 How much importance do employers give to qualifications and how much to personality in finding the right person for the right job? Which do you think is the most important?
3 Are some jobs still exclusively male or female jobs? Which ones and why?
4 What is your impression of people who work in the film industry?

b 📼 Listen to Dot Evans talking about her job and complete these notes.

Job: 1

How she got into that particular line of work:
2

Two incidents when she sustained injuries:
3

4

Money: 5

New technology: 6

c 📼 Listen again and complete these sentences.

1 At first going up on top of the cable car was a .... experience, especially as the boats down below looked like ....
2 When she first went to the film studios it was as a .... , then they asked her to ride and, eventually, if she could ....
3 In order to be safe, she has to .... each job carefully. It is not always possible for women to .... but she does if she can.
4 She usually gets on really well with the actress she's .... for.
5 Her work often goes unnoticed, especially as she doesn't get a .... at the end of the film.
6 Her husband teases her saying she will become .... or .... in the future.

d Discuss these questions in small groups.

1 What sort of character do you think Dot is?
2 Do you think she was lucky to get her job so easily or do you think it is a pity she did not consider other options and come to a decision on her own?
3 What are the advantages and disadvantages of doing the same job as someone else in your family?

2 VOCABULARY Adjectives followed by prepositions

Some adjectives are commonly followed by certain prepositions, e.g. *Miguel is married to Kim.*

Put these adjectives into the appropriate column of the table. Some adjectives can go in more than one column, e.g. *qualified for a job* but *qualified in accountancy*.

aware good experienced responsible commensurate capable incompatible
liable adept lacking typical applicable qualified involved adequate eligible
expert worthy sensitive

in	of	to	at	with	for
qualified					qualified

3 PRONUNCIATION Short vowels

a 🔊 Listen and repeat these words, paying particular attention to the vowel sound.

sit /ɪ/	bench /e/
alley /æ/	bus /ʌ/
stop /ɒ/	could /ʊ/

b You are going to play *Stepping stones*. The object of this game is to cross the river using the words as 'stepping stones'. You are allowed to step vertically or diagonally. You can move to the next stepping stone by choosing a word with the *same short vowel sound* in the *stressed syllable* of the word. There are six routes across the river. In each line there are two words which do not contain a short vowel.

First mark the word stress on all the words with a short vowel in the stressed syllable (the first line has been done for you). Then find the other five routes across the river.

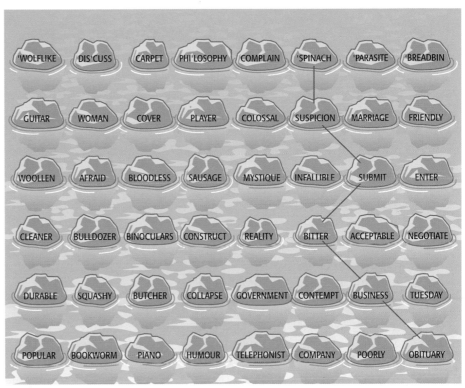

4 GRAMMAR Verbs and common expressions followed by the *-ing* form

Certain verbs are always followed by the *-ing* form, e.g. *She **avoids injuring** her head by wearing a padded wig.*

Prepositions are always followed by the *-ing* form, e.g. *She was **involved in looking** after her father's horses.*

Certain common expressions also take the *-ing* form, e.g. *It's **worth getting** a good education.*

Complete this profile of Dot Evans using the verbs in the list. You will have to put the verbs into the correct form.

consider   enjoy   imagine   mind
put off   look forward to   risk   resent
be used to   waste time

I'm the sort of person who has to be active every single waking hour, which is just as well considering my job. I can't ¹_____ having a job where I'd be sitting at a desk or something like that all day. I don't ²_____ getting up at the crack of dawn; I seem to be an early bird by nature. At first, I was ³_____ setting up a riding school but my involvement in training actors seemed to be leading naturally towards doing stunt work. I didn't ⁴_____ listening to people who told me how dangerous a job it was. In fact, I ⁵_____ being told that it was no job for a woman. Mind you, later I realised that women do ⁶_____ sustaining more injuries than men because we cannot wear so much padding under our clothes. When I met my husband-to-be I even ⁷_____ getting married for two months in order to finish a film I was working on. Now he ⁸_____ me taking off for weeks at a time to go on location. I think he rather ⁹_____ having a daredevil wife. Just as well because I'm ¹⁰_____ doing my next film which is being shot in Italy.

5 SPEAKING

Using verbs which take the *-ing* form, talk about:

1. what you are looking forward to doing later today, this month or this year.
2. what you enjoy doing most and what you used to enjoy doing as a child.
3. what you seldom waste time doing and what you resent doing.
4. what you are considering doing to achieve your dream in life and what you don't mind doing in order to achieve your aim.

2 Shop till you drop

PART A

GAP ATHLETIC

GAP

1 INTRODUCTION

a What do you think the expression *shop till you drop* means?

b Work in pairs. Look at the three advertisements and discuss these questions.

1 Do these advertisements make you want to buy the products? Give your reasons.
2 What do you like or dislike about the advertisements?
3 Who are the advertisements directed at and how do they hope to appeal to those people?

Drive the safest car in its class.

The New Mégane

RENAULT

FAIRLY PRICKLY.   FAIRY SOFT.

FAIRY

2 LISTENING

a You are going to listen to Rob talking to Anne about advertising. Before you listen, discuss these statements in pairs.

1 We are hugely influenced by advertising even if we don't want to admit it.
2 Advertising tells us about products we want to buy which otherwise we might never hear about.
3 Some products should not be advertised in any circumstances.
4 Sports events would not take place without sponsorship from advertisers.

b Listen and answer these questions.

1 Who has a more favourable opinion of advertising, Rob or Anne?
2 Who do you think has the stronger argument?
3 Do you think they resolve their difference by the end of the conversation?

c Listen again and note who expresses these views in the discussion. Put R for Rob, A for Anne and B for both of them.

1 It's immoral to sell people things they don't want. ☐
2 Advertisers mainly influence *which* product you buy not whether you buy it or not. ☐
3 Advertisers sell an image. ☐
4 Most people are easily led. ☐
5 The aim of fashion shows is to get the designers known. ☐
6 Advertising creates needs but doesn't offer satisfaction. ☐
7 Buying a product doesn't mean you'll get a certain lifestyle. ☐
8 People won't spend their money unless they want to. ☐
9 We're manipulated by advertising. ☐

d What are your own opinions about the points mentioned?

POWERED BY THE SUN.
RADIO SIGNAL CONTROLLED
TO BE ACCURATE WHEREVER
IT SHINES.

✦ **JUNGHANS**
ABSOLUTE PRECISION

The Junghans Mega Solar Ceramic Series. £495. The world's most technologically advanced watches. Synchronised with the atomic clock in Brunswick, Germany. Automatically corrected each day by radio beam to an accuracy of one second in a million years. Changes automatically between summer and winter time. Environmentally friendly solar powered. Ceramic cases. Absolutely unique. Range starts from £295.

A

1846   1996

An unbeaten record of Observatory honours

Since the company was founded in 1846, Ulysse Nardin of Switzerland have been the principal supplier of Marine Chronometers to the world's fleets despite the country being landlocked.

The reason for this paradox is the unbeatable reliability and unchallenged precision of Ulysse Nardin Marine Chronometers. More than 4,300 Observatory Prizes attest to this unique record and the Company's outstanding reputation.

Tribute to the past
To mark its 150th Anniversary, Ulysse Nardin pays tribute to its rich heritage. The legendary Marine Chronometer, with its power reserve and traditional oversized second hand display, has been re-designed as a wristwatch in a limited edition of 250 pieces in 18 carat yellow gold, rose gold or white gold.

(Also available in stainless steel).

Each case is individually numbered and is water-resistant to 200 meters.

ULYSSE NARDIN
since   1846

Marine Chronometer 18 ct Yellow Gold on strap, price £5,600.

Ulysse Nardin are available in the UK from a few select retail stockists
London: Harrods; The Watch Gallery, Fulham Road; Mappin & Webb, Heathrow
For details and a brochure please call 0171 371 6166 or contact Ulysse Nardin UK, PO Box No 12073, London W8 6GX.

B

3 READING

a Read these two advertisements for watches and decide which one appeals to you more. Then discuss your choice with a partner.

b Working quickly, find the answers to these questions.

1 Which watch advertisement emphasises the historical development of the company?
2 What information does each advertisement give about the accuracy of its watch?
3 Which advertisement gives more information about the look of the watch?
4 What is the price difference between the two watches?
5 Why is there a special edition of the Marine Chronometer?
6 How is the Junghans watch controlled and powered?

c Underline all the positive words and phrases in the two advertisements and check their meaning in an English–English dictionary, with your teacher or with a partner.

d Work in pairs.

Student A
Mark the word stress on the positive words and phrases in the Junghans advertisement, e.g. ʹaccurate. Then dictate the words and phrases to Student B, making sure that the word stress and pronunciation is clear. Change roles for the Ulysse Nardin advertisement.

Student B
Write down the words and phrases from the Junghans advertisement dictated by Student A. Mark the stressed syllable like this: ʹaccurate. Change roles for the Ulysse Nardin advertisement.

4 READING AND WRITING

a extra Turn to page 60. Read the advertisement there for Zoom Air Nike running shoes and describe its tone.

b Identify the key words and phrases which contribute to the tone of the advertisement.

c You recently left your pair of Zoom Air trainers in the changing room at a sports centre. Write a notice to put on the notice board. Say when you lost your trainers, what they look like and how you can be contacted. The sports centre is a small friendly place so your notice can be informal and, if you like, amusing.

5 STUDY SKILLS Spelling

a Discuss these questions in pairs.

1 Why is spelling difficult in English? Does your language have the same problem?
2 How important do you think it is to be able to spell correctly?

b Working in small groups, make a list of the things you can do to help improve your spelling in English.

c Write down five words which you have found difficult to spell and ask a partner to spell them.

PART B

1 GRAMMAR Verbs followed by the infinitive or the *-ing* form

Some verbs, e.g. *forget*, can be followed by either the infinitive or the *-ing* form, depending on the meaning of the sentence.

a Work in pairs and discuss the difference in meaning in these pairs of sentences.

1 a Did you remember to lock the door?
  b I don't remember hearing him say that.
2 a He told us he'd made a million; he then went on to tell us how he lost it!
  b She went on criticising the work even though she could see we were upset.
3 a I tried to tell her the truth but she wouldn't listen.
  b He tried putting the aerial on the garage roof and then the TV worked a lot better.
4 a In the end he stopped visiting us altogether.
  b She stopped to talk to her neighbour.
5 a Oh no, I meant to tell you; she phoned earlier.
  b If I take that job, it'll mean moving to Brussels.
6 a We regret to inform you that your application has been unsuccessful.
  b I regret saying that to her now.

b Complete this text using the infinitive or the *-ing* form of the verbs in the list.

tell spend get find think open buy (x 2) shop block see

SHOPAHOLICS

Some shops in Britain have announced that they plan [1]............... twenty-four hours a day. Great news for some of us, disastrous for those who can't bear [2]............... a good retail therapy experience go to waste – the shopaholics.

Research carried out at Oxford University has found around 700,000 people to be shopping addicts – two per cent of the adult population. According to the research, people are shopaholics when shopping has become central to their lives, like the woman who can vividly remember [3]............... every single bag (she's a handbag freak) but, as is often the case, simply forgot [4]............... her husband that she had run up thousands in credit card debts.

Shopping can start [5]............... out all other aspects of normal life to the point where, if people are not actually shopping, they are anxious or worried or full of excitement based on the next day's shopping.

Another indicator of a shopaholic is that they do not actually continue [6]............... any pleasure from the goods after they have bought them. It's quite common for a person (usually a woman) to find one nice pair of shoes and for her to go on [7]............... another six pairs of the same style shoe but in different colours. She didn't stop [8]............... whether she needed them or not. The shoes are then probably taken home and hidden in the back of the wardrobe. Perhaps that's guilt – realising that she didn't mean [9]............... so much money. But ask most shopaholics and they will tell you that they don't regret [10]............... . At the time it gave them the excitement they needed. Personally I think they should try [11]............... a less expensive hobby!

c Work in pairs and discuss the differences and similarities in structure and/or meaning in these sentences. Then complete statements A–E.

1 We don't allow running in the pool area.
  We don't allow children under eight to use the pool without an adult.
  Dogs aren't allowed to come into the pool area.

  He advised us to take the coastal route.
  We were advised not to invest in rural property.
  She advised taking the motorway.

A In active clauses, after the verbs *allow* or *advise* we use the .... form if there is no object. If there is an object we use the .... form. In passive clauses, we use the .... form.

2 I don't want you cluttering up the house with all that stuff.
  I don't want you to clutter up the house with all that stuff.

B *Cluttering* suggests we are talking about the *past/present/future*, while *to clutter* suggests we are talking about the *past/present/future*.
  delete as appropriate

3 I saw him taking the dog for a walk yesterday.
  I saw him leave the house at about 8am.

C The *-ing* form, *taking*, emphasises .... while the bare infinitive, *leave*, suggests ....

4 We'd like to play tennis.
  We like playing tennis.
  We like to play tennis.

D *Would like* is followed by .... *Like* can be followed by ....
  With *like*, the .... form is used to talk about enjoyment and the .... form to talk about choices and habits.

5 He learnt typing at evening classes.
  He learnt to type when he was 10.

E To talk about lessons or subjects of study we use the .... form, whereas the .... form is used to talk about the results of the study.

2 SPEAKING

In small groups discuss these questions. Try to use as many verbs which can take the infinitive or the *-ing* form as possible.

1 What would you advise a friend to do if you thought he/she was becoming a shopaholic?
2 What do you think the reason behind a shop window sign saying *Children under 14 are not allowed to enter without an adult* might be, and what do you think about it?
3 Can shopping be called a hobby?
4 Do you like shopping? What sort of things would you like to buy if you were very rich?
5 Do you like going with other people when they are shopping?
6 Have you ever seen someone shoplifting? What did you do or what would you do?

3 PRONUNCIATION Spelling and sounds

In English different letters can represent the same sound, e.g. the words *sun* and *son* have the same vowel sound /ʌ/, and some words have letters which are not pronounced, e.g. *castle* has a silent *t*.

a [image] Listen and write down the last word of each sentence you hear. The words have the same vowel sound but different spellings.

b Which vowel sound is represented in each of the words?

c [image] Listen and write down the words you hear. There is at least one silent letter in each.

d Put a line through the silent letter(s).

4 READING

a You are going to read an article about shopping at petrol stations. Before you read, discuss these questions.

1 What sort of shops do you like, small family-run shops or large department stores?
2 If there is a long queue either to pay or to try something on, how do you react?

b Read the article to find out in which paragraph the author:

1 feels irritated that he has been ignored.
2 criticises the concept of garage shops.
3 feels frustrated and impatient.
4 feels angry.
5 suggests that a system which works in one country does not necessarily work in another.

SERIOUS SHOPPING –
PETROL STATIONS

Sitting in the inside lane of a metropolitan dual carriageway, queueing behind 14 cars for the next available petrol pump, I often ponder
5 the emergence of the garage shop. A kind of road rage comes over me. I want to tailgate Mr Texaco for a couple of miles, flashing my lights and honking like a maniac, force him to
10 pull over, and then chew a hole in his windscreen with my teeth.

No jury of my peers would ever convict. They, too, would have known what it is to be late for work, next in
15 the queue for the pump, when the bloke in front fills up, puts the cap back on, takes his jacket from its hook in the backseat and disappears into the shop. Trapped by the queue behind you, you
20 can go nowhere. In front of his car the next two pumps have become vacant, but no one can get to them. You can see him in the shop, leafing through an amateur photography magazine. Then
25 he selects some frosted donuts and gets himself a coffee. The days tick by. He rummages through the display of cassettes. Eventually, he pays. The credit-card slip signed, he turns to go.
30 Then turns back and points at the cigarettes. The man behind the counter fetches him a packet. He has to pay cash now. They hold his note up to the light to check it. The till operator asks
35 his colleague if he has any twenties.

The man gets his change, and slides the notes into his wallet one by one.

He walks slowly back to his car sucking on a donut. He hangs his jacket in the back. He climbs into the
40 car. He dials a number on his mobile phone, switches on the ignition, and pulls gently away without so much as a raise of the hand.

It is time something was done. The
45 English being by nature a mistrustful, selfish race, this garage shopping simply doesn't work. On the Continent, where they have been doing it for years, people buy their petrol and then move
50 their car before going in to pay. English people can't be bothered with that, and if you do try it the staff come running out thinking you are a fuel-lifter. And anyway, there is nowhere to put the car.
55 That would waste retailing space.

Why do these shops exist? Because we are dealing with a breed of retailer that charges customers for air, and they know that those lead vapours
60 have not only long-term, but also short-term deleterious effects on your health. They drive you temporarily mad, and make you think you want to go shopping. It is the ultimate
65 statement in modern retail: chemically zombify your customer, then peddle him products that will either kill him, impoverish him, or make him both very unhappy and seriously ill.
70

c Match these words and phrases from the article to their definitions.

1 road rage (line 6)
2 tailgate (line 7)
3 honking (line 9)
4 peers (line 12)
5 bloke (line 16)
6 rummages (line 27)
7 fuel-lifter (line 54)
8 deleterious (line 62)

a someone who steals petrol
b a colloquial word for *man*
c drive very close to the car in front
d harmful
e anger while driving
f searches in a careless and hurried way
g sounding the car horn
h people of the same age and social status

3 Freedom

PART A

1 INTRODUCTION

a What does the word *freedom* mean to you?

> In the future days, which we seek to secure, we look forward to a world founded upon four essential freedoms.
> The first is freedom of speech and expression – everywhere in the world.
> The second is freedom of every person to worship God in his own way – everywhere in the world.
> The third is freedom from want …
> The fourth is freedom from fear …
>
> Franklin Delano Roosevelt [1882–1945]

b Work in pairs or small groups and discuss these questions.

1 Consider each of Roosevelt's four freedoms. What do you think is meant by them?
2 In your opinion which is the most important of these freedoms and why?
3 What other 'freedoms' would you like to suggest are important?
4 Which media do you think express freedom the best: speech, music, the novel, poetry or painting?
5 In our quest for freedom do you think that we may enslave or abuse others? Consider topics such as aid organisations, peace-keeping forces like the UN and even tour operators who buy up tropical beaches to be used exclusively by rich tourists.

2 READING

a Look at the photograph and discuss these questions.

1 What do you imagine it is like to live on a tropical island? What might be some of the advantages and difficulties?
2 Would you like to visit an island like this? Would you feel free? Would you like to live there permanently?

b Look at this newspaper headline and say what you think the article is about.

Polynesian paradise lost to a luxury hotel

c Read the article on page 11 and choose which sentence, A–D, best fills each gap, 1–4.

A Tourism is the Cook Islands' biggest industry.
B Each evening young and old islanders gather outside the construction site to chew over the changes looming in their lives.
C But the biggest worry facing the locals is that the hotel will destroy the unhurried Polynesian life.
D There are already signs of environmental damage.

Pa Teuruaa, who is a local guide, treks through Rarotonga's luscious forests each day showing tourists the fauna and recounting age-old Polynesian legends.
5 Miserably, he points to the glistening white cylinder that carries electricity cables to the new hotel.

The pipe cuts an ugly swathe through trees and bushes, snaking over a 1,355ft
10 hill and past a sacred site where the Polynesian god Tangaroa was worshipped. Voices become raised when Rarotongans look at the plans to divert the coastal road – 'The Sacred Way' – to give the hotel
15 access to the beach.

[1] They repeat that Tangaroa is so incensed with the sale of tribal land to the government that he struck the tribe's leader dead with a heart attack.
20 While a faded T-shirt on a boy's back proclaims 'The Cook Islands – Last Paradise on Earth', paradise, with its soft, white beaches and turquoise waves, is in trouble.
25 The government is pushing ahead with a large hotel complex that could swamp these 15 tiny islands with American tourists, endanger the fragile ecological balance and bequeath a debt burden for generations.
30 Seven artificial lagoons, lined with costly imported sand and complete with trapped tropical fish, are being built 50 yards from a real lagoon, which is rich with natural sealife and a real beach. [2].
35 Building workers are shifting hundreds of tonnes of red earth to landscape the hotel complex. Denuded of vegetation, soil is washing into the lagoon and killing fish. Repairing the damage will cost £690,000.

40 The hotel group argues the project is environmentally sound and will generate jobs. The director of the hotel group says: 'There is even a self-contained sewage treatment system that is above World Health Organisation standards.'
45

[3] Last year 50,000 tourists generated jobs for a third of the workforce and accounted for nearly a quarter of GNP. But the argument that the hotel is economically vital convinces few – the
50 money for the hotel is being raised as loans and the Prime Minister admitted last year that the debt was his greatest concern.

[4] Youngsters who traditionally became fishermen will find it easier to
55 become dishwashers. Songs and dances that are part of everyday life will die out, or perhaps survive in jokey 'Polynesian Nights' for gawking tourists.

d Did you predict the content of the article from its headline?

3 STUDY SKILLS Guessing meaning from context

a What do you usually do if you do not know the meaning of a word you read? Before you dash for your dictionary, look at these words in context in the article in 2. Ask yourself the questions and try to guess the meanings.

1 fauna (line 3)
What do you think tourists might look at as they walk through a forest?
2 swathe/to cut a swathe through (line 8)
What do you think the developers did in order to lay the electricity cables?
3 incensed (line 17)
How did the god of the island feel about the sale of the land?
4 bequeath (a debt burden) (line 29)
By accepting the development, what is the government doing to future generations?
5 denuded of (line 37)
If a person is *nude*, what does that mean? What do you think the ground will look like after tonnes of earth have been removed?

b Now guess the meaning of these two words from the context alone.

1 sound (line 41)
2 gawking (line 59)

c How successful were you? Try to apply this technique to guess the meaning of new words whenever possible.

4 SPEAKING

You are going to role-play a meeting between representatives of the hotel group and local residents to discuss whether the hotel development on Raratonga should go ahead.

a Work in pairs to prepare the role-play. First read the article again and make a note of the disadvantages to the island of building the hotel. If appropriate, use words from the article, but put them into your own sentences. Then think about the advantages which the hotel management can put forward to argue for the building of the hotel.

b Divide into two groups, one representing the hotel's interests and the other the islanders. The hotel group should read the notes in the box below and the islanders' group should look at their notes about the disadvantages to the island of building the hotel.

c Talk about and plan what you are going to say at the meeting. Decide who is going to represent which view(s). As many people as possible should have the chance to speak.

Hotel group

Financier
only interested in making money

Architect
genuinely believes the hotel will be beautiful and will not destroy the island at all

Human Resources Manager
convinced the hotel will benefit the island by providing jobs and consequently raise the islanders' standard of living

Public Relations Manager
wants photographs of the islanders/ island in the holiday brochure to help sell more holidays

PART B

1 GRAMMAR Relative clauses

a Work in pairs. Read these two sentences and decide which one has a defining clause and which one a non-defining clause. What do you notice about the punctuation?

1 The hotel, which is to have 250 rooms, will be completed by the end of the year.
2 The people who work in the hotel will have the chance to earn a lot of money.

b How would you explain the difference between a defining and a non-defining clause?

c Read the article on page 11 again and underline six examples of relative clauses. Are they defining or non-defining relative clauses?

d Match the beginnings (1–8) and ends (a–h) of these sentences to complete the definitions of the words in italics.

1 A *kibbutz* is
2 *Perestroika* is
3 A *rickshaw* is
4 *Hogmanay* is
5 A *gigolo* is
6 The *denouement* is
7 A *dacha* is
8 A *cul-de-sac* is

a the celebrations which take place on New Year's Eve in Scotland.
b a small two-wheeled vehicle for one or two passengers whose power comes from a man pulling or cycling.
c the period when the Soviet Union rebuilt itself politically.
d a Russian house in the country where people go to spend their weekends or summers.
e a street which has only one way in or out.
f a man who is paid to dance with a woman as her partner or to be her lover and companion.
g the end of a story when everything comes out right or is explained.
h a farm or settlement in Israel where many people live and work together.

e Which countries/languages do you think the words in **d** come from?

f Underline the relative pronoun in each sentence in **d**.

g Work out a definition for as many of these 'international words' as you can. Use relative clauses.

1 mall (North American)
2 siesta (Spanish)
3 ombudsman (Swedish)
4 borsch (Russian)
5 samba (Portuguese)
6 oasis (Arabic)
7 prima donna (Italian)
8 glasnost (Russian)
9 chaperone (French)
10 nirvana (Hindi)

2 SPEAKING

Work in pairs or small groups and discuss these questions.

1 Do you know any other foreign words used in English? What do you ask for in a restaurant to find out what they serve? What is the name for a playschool children go to before they start compulsory school?
2 Which foreign words have been adopted into your language?
3 What do you think about languages becoming more international? Is it an advantage or disadvantage?
4 How would you feel if English became the official language of your country?

3 GRAMMAR Omission of relative pronouns and the position of prepositions

In defining clauses, when the relative pronoun is the object of its clause, we can leave it out, e.g. *He's been to every country (**that**) we mentioned.*

In neutral and informal English, we often omit the relative pronoun and put the preposition at the end of the sentence or clause, e.g. *Who was the man you were talking **to**?* instead of *Who was the man **to** whom you were talking?*

a Complete these sentences with a preposition if it is necessary.

1 That must be the man you phoned ....
2 This is the office you'll be working ....
3 Here's some news you'll be interested ....
4 Is this the competition you've entered .... ?
5 The job he's applying .... is in Scotland.
6 Who's the student you're writing .... ?
7 When's that party you've been invited .... ?
8 Where's the hotel you're staying .... ?

b Write two sentences of your own like the sentences in **a**, leaving a gap for the preposition. Give your sentences to a partner to complete.

4 SPEAKING

Work in small groups and discuss these questions.

1 What are some of the ways we all get information every day?
2 How important is freedom of information?
3 Are there some cases where you think the press should not print information about people?
4 How true is it that the press can make or break a person?
5 Are people really interested in the private lives of film stars or members of royal families?

5 LISTENING

a In pairs or small groups, discuss these questions.

1 What do you think the news headlines are about today?
2 How much national and international news do you expect to hear on the TV or radio news?
3 What difficulties would a foreigner who could speak your language reasonably well have when listening to the radio news?
4 What advice would you give them so that they could understand more easily?

b You are going to hear the headlines at the beginning of the radio news. As you listen, note the answers to these questions.

1 How many headlines are there?
2 Which topics do they cover?
3 What are the key words in each headline?

c When you have agreed the key words in each headline with your teacher, try to guess what parts of speech the omitted words are, e.g. nouns, verbs, prepositions, articles.

d Listen again and complete the headlines.

6 PRONUNCIATION Linking

In spoken English some words are linked. This can make listening a little difficult sometimes unless you understand the mechanics of linking.

Type 1

When a word ending with a consonant sound is followed by a word beginning with a vowel sound, the words run together, e.g. *sat on* becomes /sæt ɒn/.

Type 2

When a word ending with a vowel sound is followed by a word beginning with a vowel sound we insert the sound /w/ or /j/, e.g. *he is* becomes /hiːjɪz/, *do it* becomes /duːwɪt/.

a Listen and mark the links in this extract from the radio news.

> Health watchdogs are preparing to name and shame Hollywood superstars whose films have been deemed to encourage young people to smoke.
>
> Doctors are worried that while smoking has been outlawed in most cinemas in Britain, the number of film scenes showing cigarette or cigar smoking has increased fourfold over the last eight years.
>
> This week the Health Education Authority will appeal to film directors to cut back on smoking scenes. It will also point the finger at actors with teen-appeal whose films or lifestyle may appear to make smoking glamorous.

b Listen again and note which sound is inserted in the Type 2 links.

4 2020

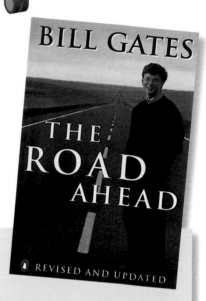

1 INTRODUCTION

Work in pairs and discuss what developments you think we will see in the future. You could start by talking about some of the topics in the list and then add some of your own.

communication   traffic/transport   food   technology
medical science   population

2 READING

a You are going to read an article about Bill Gates. Do you know who he is? What ideas for the future do you think he has?

b Read the article. Then work in pairs and make a list of all Bill Gates's ideas for the future.

BILL GATES

THE ROAD AHEAD

REVISED AND UPDATED

NET PROPHET

Staying ahead for Bill Gates means looking ahead, craning further and further into the unknown. He is bored by the temporal; he spends his life in the future, and he can't wait to get there, racing through his schedules, anticipating problems and questions, talking over the slow responses of people around him.

He details the miracles of the future in his book: the wonder of the wallet-sized PC that will make cash redundant; of telecommuters and video-conferencing; of hiring entertainment, ordering shopping, making friends, playing Scrabble without meeting another person; of pen-based computers that recognise handwriting and software that can 'remember' like an assistant.

This is a world where we will be able to select how the movie ends and speak to its characters; where electronic 'agents', like spirit guides, will lead us by the hand through cyberspace; where we can summon up a Picasso, hold a sick baby before a screen for diagnosis, commit our whole lives to the system so that when we are accused we can say, in Gates's words, 'Hey Buddy, I have a documented life.'

The Internet, he enthuses, will even vet our friends in a dangerous world; randomness will be a mere memory. 'I think this is a wonderful time to be alive,' Gates says. 'There have never been so many opportunities to do things that were impossible before. It is the best time ever to start new companies, advance sciences such as medicine that improve the quality of life.'

He wants the world to share his optimism and he sees his book as a way of inviting everyone to join the discussion 'about how we should be shaping the future'.

'The network will draw us together, if that's what we choose, or let us scatter ourselves into a million mediated communities. Above all, the information highway will give us the choices that can put us in touch with entertainment, information and each other.'

Most transforming of our personal lives will be the wallet PC, a combination of purse, credit card, universal entry ticket and best friend. We will no longer need to carry keys, cash, cameras, concert tickets, cellular phone – all will be contained in one small computer. 'Rather than holding paper money, the new wallet will store unforgeable digital money,' says Gates, who likens it to his boyhood Swiss army penknife. There will be no queues at airports, theatres or anywhere one is expected to show a ticket. The wallet will connect to the venue's system and prove that we have paid.

So where does Gates see himself when he's 70? He couldn't imagine. If the future is where he wants to be, old makes no sense to him. 'Are you asking where I'll be if I'm dead by then?'

Cyberheaven?

c Discuss these questions.

1 Which of Bill Gates's ideas do you think will become reality? (Use *will/won't be able to*.)
2 Are you as optimistic as he is about the future? Give your reasons.
3 What impression do you get of Bill Gates from the article?

3 GRAMMAR Future forms – *will*, *shall*, *to be going to*, present continuous, present simple

a Which future form is usually used:

1 to talk about personal arrangements and fixed plans, especially when the time and place have been decided.
2 to talk about an intention to do something.
3 to express obligation in formal English.
4 to forecast something on the basis of present evidence.
5 to give or ask for information about the future.
6 to make a promise, offer, request, threat.
7 to refuse to do something.
8 to make a prediction.
9 to talk about timetables or routines.
10 to make an offer using the question form with *I* and *we*.

b Complete these sentences with the most suitable form of the verbs in brackets.

1 Look at those children playing computer games; they .... the scientists of the future. (be)
2 Fiona says she .... an architect when she grows up. (become)
3 Do you think they .... life on another planet? (ever discover)
4 My flight is booked; I .... on October 6. (leave)
5 Don't worry. I .... you as soon as I get there. (ring)
6 The bus to London .... at 8 o'clock. (go)
7 What .... you this evening? (do)
8 One day we .... cash at all. (not need)
9 .... I .... the phone for you? (answer)
10 I .... my brother in Canada next summer. (visit)
11 I don't care what you think; I .... ! (not apologise)
12 .... you .... me? (marry)
13 The tenant .... six months' notice of intention to terminate the contract. (give)

c Work in pairs and answer these questions.

1 Why is the present simple used in the second part of this sentence?
   *I'll phone you as soon as I **get** back from my holiday.*
2 What other words or phrases are followed by a present tense when talking about the future?
3 Look at this sentence. Can you explain the use of *won't*?
   *Come back later, when I **won't** be so busy.*

d ☐ *extra* You are going to play *Future chairs*. Turn to page 60 for instructions.

4 VOCABULARY Two-part phrasal verbs

A two-part phrasal verb is made up of two components. There are two types:

Type 1   verb + preposition   e.g. *He **looked at** his watch.*
Type 2   verb + adverb particle   e.g. *She **came back** an hour later.*

A good dictionary will tell you which phrasal verbs are made up of prepositions and which are made up of adverb particles. A preposition expresses the relation between the word before and after it, whereas an adverb particle qualifies or modifies another word, especially a verb, adverb or adjective. This is an important distinction because it affects the sentence structure when we use phrasal verbs.

a Look at these sentences and, with a partner, work out the different sentence structure when we use verbs + prepositions and verbs + adverb particles.

1 My sister is looking after the children. (preposition)
2 My sister is looking after them.
3 She tried on the dress. (adverb particle)
4 She tried the dress on.
5 She tried it on.
6 Look out!

b Match these phrasal verbs to their definitions.

1	frown on	a	steal from or cheat someone
2	pick up	b	meet by chance
3	rip off	c	collect a person from a place
4	track down	d	employ
5	make out	e	disapprove of
6	take on	f	find by following signs or clues
7	get across	g	communicate/convey
8	bump into	h	manage to see

c Phrasal verbs are more common in informal English. Work in pairs and give a phrasal verb equivalent for these more formal verbs.

1	depart	4	cancel	7	support
2	cause	5	postpone	8	arrive
3	resemble	6	reduce	9	select

d Complete these sentences using phrasal verbs from b and c.

1 It was rather dark and I couldn't .... who was standing at the door.
2 Eventually we .... the missing report.
3 He really .... his grandfather.
4 It took me ages to .... a jumper as a present for my niece.
5 I hear the car factory is going to .... hundreds of new people.
6 He promised he'd .... me .... at 8 o'clock!
7 I'm sure I was .... by the taxi driver; he charged me £25.
8 We just couldn't .... it .... to her that we were trying to help.
9 Guess who I .... in town yesterday?
10 Will you .... me .... when I suggest we work flexitime?

PART B

1 LISTENING

a You are going to hear a description of a typical day in your life in the year 2020. Before you listen, work in pairs and discuss what you expect to hear. Go through a day from when you wake up to when you go to sleep.

b 🔊 Listen and answer these questions.

1 Who is Molly?
2 In what ways does 'she' help you? Write down at least five things that she can do for you.

c 🔊 Listen again and complete these sentences with a suitable word or phrase.

1 A relaxing picture of a .... soothes you as you sleep.
2 As you move through your house, ... turn themselves on.
3 The vacuum cleaner follows the lines of ....
4 A traffic-jam-free route comes up on your ....
5 As you drive past the .... , your account is debited.
6 Your .... is checked in order to verify your identity.
7 The virtual doctor is concerned about the clogging up of your ....
8 You know who people are at parties because a small camera .... the faces of the other party-goers.
9 An instrument on the .... will immobilise your car if you are over the alcohol limit.
10 Molly can even play the matchmaker by selecting .... single people in your neighbourhood.

d Would you like to live in 2020 as it is described on the cassette?

2 PRONUNCIATION Schwa /ə/ and weak vowels

When the letters *a, e, o* and *u* are pronounced in their weak form they are pronounced /ə/, e.g. *How was /wəz/ it done?*

a Look at this extract from the description of 2020 you have just heard and write /ə/ over the vowels which are or can be pronounced in their weak form. The first sentence has been done for you.

Molly is your 'intelligent agent', a computer program equipped with reason and common sense. She is your link to the 'Magic Mirror', the worldwide electronic membrane that holds all human knowledge. Before you leave home, you instruct the robot vacuum cleaner to get cracking. It springs to life and, sensing the wire tracks hidden beneath the carpet, begins its job. As you drive out of the city to your greenfield office in your electric/hybrid car, Molly has tapped into the Global Positioning System satellite orbiting overhead.

b 🔊 Listen and check which vowels are pronounced in their weak form.

c 🔊 Listen again and read the extract aloud in time with the cassette.

3 STUDY SKILLS Fluency versus accuracy

a Work in pairs and rank these points in order of difficulty for you when you speak English. 1 = the easiest, 7 = the most difficult.

maintaining grammatical accuracy ☐
using a wide range of grammatical structures accurately ☐
finding exactly the right word for what you want to say ☐
being able to communicate your ideas ☐
pronouncing individual sounds accurately ☐
using word stress and sentence stress accurately ☐
getting across your feelings with intonation and stress ☐

b Discuss these questions with your partner.

1 What can you do to develop fluency? And accuracy?
2 Is it possible to be good at both?

4 GRAMMAR Future forms – future continuous, future perfect, future perfect continuous, *to be to, was/were going to*

a Work in pairs and explain the form and use of the future in these sentences.

1 This time next week we'll be walking in the mountains.
2 I'm sorry, the marketing manager won't be available on Wednesday morning; he'll be having a meeting with the sales people.
3 Will you be having coffee, madam?
4 Look at all this work. There's no way I'll have finished it by 5 o'clock.
5 By the end of this term I will have been studying English for five years.
6 The Prime Minister is to meet leaders from other EU countries next Monday.
7 You can go to the cinema, but you're not to be back late.
8 I was going to go to Italy but it's all fallen through.
9 The Minister was to give a speech to the society, but he is ill.

b Complete these sentences using the most suitable future form of the verbs in brackets.

1 Now remember, you .... (brush) your teeth before you go to bed.
2 In a couple of years he .... (finish) his law studies.
3 My first job. Just imagine, this time next week I .... (stand) in front of a class of five-year-olds.
4 Yes, it's their silver wedding. In June they .... (be) married for 25 years.
5 We .... (build) an extension to the house, until we realised how much it would cost.

6 How .... (you pay), sir?
7 The prince .... (attend) a Charity Gala Night at the Royal Opera.
8 You .... (not say) that again. It's rude.
9 By May he .... (work on) that book for two years.
10 Where's John? Oh, I know, it's Tuesday. He .... (give) the sales team a pep talk.

5 READING

a Read this article about developments in science and choose the best paragraph, A–D, to fill each numbered gap. There is one extra paragraph which does not fit.

Three centuries ago, Isaac Newton helped to trigger a profound transformation in human society. With Newton's mechanics came powerful machines and eventually the steam engine, which reshaped the world by unleashing the industrial revolution and opening up entire continents with the railways.

Throughout the 19th and 20th centuries the pace of scientific discovery intensified. In the past decade, more scientific knowledge has been created than in all of human history. Computer power is doubling every 18 months. The Net is doubling every year. The number of DNA sequences we can analyse is doubling every two years. That epic phase of discovery is now drawing to a close, however, and an age of mastery is about to begin.

1 [ ]

The explosive growth of computer power is not limitless and 2020 is likely to be its high-water mark using the technology we have today. By then, science will have reduced microchip components to the limit roughly the size of molecules – and the fabled Age of Silicon will start to come to an end.

2 [ ]

Similarly, by 2020 biotechnology will be flooded with millions upon millions of genes whose basic functions are largely unknown. Only after this bottleneck in the DNA revolution is resolved – through computer development, perhaps – will we be able to tackle some of the most pressing chronic diseases.

3 [ ]

Confronted with potential upheaval on this scale, some voices say we are going too far, too fast. However, if we keep our eyes firmly on 2020 and the developments that are possible from current technology, we surely have two extraordinary and enjoyable decades ahead.

A Scientists are already looking at other forms of technology to overcome this problem: optical computers, molecular computers or quantum computers. If they succeed, we may see the entrance after 2020 of true robot automatons that have common sense, can understand human language, can recognise and manipulate objects in their environment and can learn from their mistakes.

B The technology already exists. The only drawback is the cost. But by 2020 the price of a chip will have fallen from hundreds of pounds to a penny. This is what will make the year 2020 so significant, the advent of dirt-cheap microprocessors.

C With such a breakthrough, we may also isolate the 'age genes' enabling us to extend the human life span. And even learn how to design new life forms and to orchestrate the physical and mental makeup of our children.

D We are on the cusp of the transition from passive observers of nature to its active choreographers. The period from now until 2020 is one of the most exciting to be alive. So what will the future look like?

b What do these reference words in paragraph A refer to?

1 this (line 3) 3 their (line 11)
2 they (line 5)

6 WRITING

a You have been asked to write an article called 'The Way Ahead' for an English magazine for young people. Before you write your article, read these tips.

Tips for writing a good article

Give your article an attention grabbing headline.
The first paragraph in particular must interest the reader.
Divide the article into paragraphs with distinct and clear topics.
Involve the reader by asking questions.
Avoid boring words like *nice*, *get*, etc.
Be emphatic even dramatic.
Vary the length of your sentences.
Finish the article with a significant or thought-provoking statement or question.

b Write your article using about 200–250 words.

5

1 INFINITIVE OR *-ING* FORM?

a Complete this text about a man who has fulfilled his ambition and become an expert on snakes. Put the verbs in brackets into either the infinitive or the *-ing* form as appropriate.

Snakes alive!

Mark O'Shea, 41, has been interested in snakes since he first held a boa constrictor at Dublin Zoo when he was eight years old. From that moment on he never even considered ¹......................... (do) anything else but his dream job – being an expert on snakes (official name: herpetologist). Mark divides his time between looking after captive snakes as curator of reptiles at West Midland Safari Park and trying ²......................... (track down) wild ones in more exotic locations.

What's involved: When I'm working in the Park I help the keepers ³......................... (check) the cages and then they usually want me ⁴......................... (clean) them out! Throughout the day, the phone will be going. On a typical day I might have enquiries from journalists, documentary producers or the Red Cross. I spend quite a bit of time persuading people ⁵......................... (not have) a snake as a pet. Or someone may have a snake in their garden which needs ⁶......................... (identify).

I spend anything from five weeks to five months a year away from the UK, working out in the field in places like Belize, Brazil and Borneo. Sometimes I do an inventory of the snakes in a national park or I have to catch snakes to milk them for their venom; sometimes I advise companies how ⁷......................... (develop) eco-tourism if a tour operator wants to start ⁸......................... (bring) tourists into a natural environment.

Best aspects of the job: I like ⁹......................... (be) away in the Tropics and love ¹⁰......................... (be) in my own little laboratory under a tarpaulin or in a village hut. There's nothing better than the wet season; all I need ¹¹......................... (have) is my hurricane lamp, microscope and specimens, a few bottles of beer and a tropical storm. It's great. I don't even mind ¹²......................... (be bitten) by leeches. I'm always looking forward to ¹³......................... (go) on the next trip.

Worst aspects of the job: I'm very fond of my animals so I do miss them when I go away. I also hate being in hospital with snake bites or malaria. I've never stopped ¹⁴......................... (count) how many times I've been bitten but I've caught malaria several times, have been stung by scorpions and bitten by tarantulas. I don't relax well and I'm always itching to get back to my snakes. The last time I was in intensive care I made someone ¹⁵......................... (prop) me up in bed so that I could do the crossword!

b Some people do jobs which may seem strange to us, like steeplejacks, window-cleaners of skyscrapers, astronauts, lighthouse-keepers or chicken farmers. Work in pairs and discuss what's involved and the best and worst aspects of those jobs. You can, of course, talk about different jobs.

2 TWO-PART PHRASAL VERBS

a In this word box there are 15 two-part phrasal verbs written as one word. How many can you find?

```
G I V E U P P U T O F F
P A S I F I O T S E T U
B C A B A C K U P D O G
R U T W O K R T O O B C
I H S E T O F F P L U U
N A P K L U O E M P M T
G O O N E T U R N U P D
A R L O O K L I K E I O
B S O O N W Y P T U N W
O A L M A K E O U T T N
U O C A L L O F F K O C
T A K E O N R F D U L D
```

b Make your own phrasal verb word box. Work in small groups. Make a list of 10 two-part phrasal verbs. Write them as one word and then link them as in **a**, adding other letters to complete the box. Give your word box to another group to find your phrasal verbs.

3 RELATIVE CLAUSES

a Rewrite these sentences using relative clauses to combine the individual sentences into one longer sentence.

1   Martin Luther King Jr was born in 1929 in Atlanta, USA.
    He became known as a civil rights campaigner.
2   He later lived in Alabama.
    He set up his first ministry in Alabama.
3   As a leader of the civil rights movement he showed his great oratorical skills.
    The civil rights movement was known for its policy of passive resistance.
4   He had great success in challenging the segregation laws of the South.
    After that he turned his attention to social conditions in the North.
    The conditions in the North were less tractable.
5   He was assassinated in Memphis.
    His assassin was James Earl Ray.
    Ray was arrested in London.
    Ray was sentenced in Memphis to 99 years.

b In Unit 3 of your Workbook you listened to a talk about Gandhi and you have just read about Martin Luther King. Do you know of any other people who are famous for their connection with civil rights, freedom, peace or charity work? Tell a partner about that person. Try to use relative clauses where appropriate.

4 ADJECTIVES FOLLOWED BY PREPOSITIONS

Complete this text with the correct prepositions.

What's so good about bug grub?

Insects could become a major source of food in the 21st century as long as we are capable ¹........................ overcoming our culturally programmed horror of eating creepy crawlies. Many insects are high ²........................ protein and have a multitude of nutritious vitamins and minerals. It seems that insects may even offer a type of fatty acid, similar ³........................ that which makes oily fish like mackerel and salmon so good ⁴........................ our health. Many insects are a perfectly wholesome form of food and the only problem is that they are not compatible ⁵........................ our psychological profile. Children, less sensitive ⁶........................ cultural norms, are quite adept ⁷........................ popping worms or caterpillars into their mouths but are usually stopped by cries of 'Put that down, it's dirty' by horrified parents.

There's a fundamental paradox going on here too. Think about it for a moment: why are prawns so much more acceptable ⁸........................ us than locusts? Insects are actually closely related ⁹........................ things like lobster and prawns. In fact, insects are often far safer to eat than seafood. Oysters, for example, are molluscs or filter feeders, which means they will suck up whatever is in the water – and you can probably imagine the kind of nasties that are floating around our polluted shores. Once we are aware ¹⁰........................ that fact, insects may suddenly seem more appealing!

5 FUTURE FORMS

a Complete these statements about future forms.

1   We use .... to make a prediction.
2   .... expresses obligation in formal English.
3   We use .... to talk about timetables or routines.
4   .... expresses our intention to do something.
5   We use .... to refuse to do something.
6   Using .... suggests that the arrangements are fixed.
7   To forecast something on the basis of present evidence, use ....
8   We use .... to make a promise, offer, request or threat.
9   To give or ask for information about the future, use ....
10 We use .... to talk about what will be happening in the future.
11 For official plans and engagements, use .... when you want to be formal.
12 We use .... to say how long something will have continued by a certain time in the future.
13 To ask or say something politely and formally, we use ....
14 We use .... to refer to things taking place as a matter of course.
15 Use .... to give orders.

b Work in pairs and write an example sentence for each statement in **a**.

Once upon a time

6

1 INTRODUCTION

Work in pairs and discuss these questions.

1 Where do you think you would see or hear the phrase *Once upon a time* … ?
2 What sort of stories do you like reading and why?
3 What makes a good story?

2 SPEAKING

Work in pairs and discuss these questions.

1 Have you read or heard of any of these books? If you have, what was it about and did you enjoy it?
2 Look at the title and cover of the books you do not know. What do you think these books are about?
3 Which of these books would you like to read?

The Werewolf
by Angela Carter

It is a northern country; they have cold weather, they have cold hearts.

Cold; tempest; wild beast in the forest. It is a hard life. Their houses are built of logs, dark 5 and smoky within. There will be a crude icon of the virgin behind a guttering candle, the leg of a pig hung up to cure, a string of drying mushrooms. A bed, a stool, a table. Harsh, brief, poor lives.

10 To these upland woodsmen, the Devil is as real as you or I. More so; they have not seen us nor even know that we exist, but the Devil they glimpse often in the graveyards, those bleak and touching townships of the dead where the 15 graves are marked with portraits of the deceased in the naïf style and there are no flowers to put in front of them, no flowers grow there, so they put out small, votive offerings, little loaves, sometimes a cake that the bears come lumbering 20 from the margins of the forest to snatch away. A midnight, especially on Walpurgisnacht, th Devil holds picnics in the graveyards and invite the witches; then they dig up fresh corpses, an eat them. Anyone will tell you that.

25 Wreaths of garlic on the doors keep out th vampires. A blue-eyed child born feet first on th night of St John's Eve will have second sigh When they discover a witch – some old woma whose cheeses ripen when her neighbours' d 30 not, another old woman whose black cat, o sinister! *follows her about all the time*, they stri the crone, search for her marks, for th supernumerary nipple her familiar sucks. The soon find them. Then they stone her to death.

35 Winter and cold weather.

Go and visit grandmother, who has been sic Take her the oatcakes I've baked for her on th hearthstone and a little pot of butter.

The good child does as her mother bids – fiv 40 miles' trudge through the forest; do not leave th path because of the bears, the wild boar, th starving wolves. Here, take your father'

3 READING

a *The Werewolf* is a variation of the fairy story *Little Red Riding Hood*. **Work with a partner and retell the story of *Little Red Riding Hood*. If you do not know the story, find a partner who does and ask him/her to tell you the story.**

b Read *The Werewolf*. Then work in pairs and answer these questions.

1 When do you think *The Werewolf* was written?
2 What does the author's choice of vocabulary add to the story?

c Can you find words in the story with these meanings (the paragraph number is given in brackets)?

1 asks (7)
2 tramp/trek (7)
3 a long loud wailing cry (8)
4 confronted (8)
5 grey (9)
6 cut (9)
7 the noise in the throat when air is swallowed (10)
8 a noisy intake of breath when crying (10)
9 running awkwardly and not very fast (10)
10 scent/trace (10)
11 prevented from being seen (10)
12 restless (11)
13 a pad of cloth pressed on a patient to relieve fever, pain, etc. (11)
14 making a loud, harsh cry (usually a frightened or excited bird) (13)
15 showing signs of infection (13)

d Find five more interesting words in the story and look them up in an English–English dictionary. Give your definitions to a partner and ask him/her to find the words in the story.

e Work in pairs and discuss these questions.

1 How would you describe the style of this story?
2 In what way does the style help to evoke the atmosphere?
3 Can you detect a hint of sarcasm or satire at any point(s) in the story?
4 What do you think of the story?

nting knife; you know how to use it.
The child had a scabby coat of sheepskin to
ep out the cold, she knew the forest too well
fear it but she must always be on her guard.
hen she heard that freezing howl of the wolf,
e dropped her gifts, seized her knife and
rned on the beast.
It was a huge one, with red eyes and running,
izzled chops; any but a mountaineer's child
ould have died of fright at the sight of it. It
ent for her throat, as wolves do, but she made
great swipe at it with her father's knife and
ashed off its right forepaw.
The wolf let out a gulp, almost a sob, when it
w what had happened to it; wolves are less
ave than they seem. It went lolloping off
sconsolately between the trees as well as it
uld on three legs, leaving a trail of blood
hind it. The child wiped the blade of her knife
ean on her apron, wrapped up the wolf's paw
the cloth in which her mother had packed the
tcakes and went on towards her grandmother's
ouse. Soon it came on to snow so thickly that

the path and any footsteps, track or spoor that
might have been upon it were obscured.

⁷⁰ She found her grandmother was so sick she
had taken to her bed and fallen into a fretful
sleep, moaning and shaking so that the child
guessed she had a fever. She felt the forehead,
it burned. She shook out the cloth from her
basket, to use it to make the old woman a cold
compress, and the wolf's paw fell to the floor.

⁷⁵ But it was no longer a wolf's paw. It was a
hand, chopped off at the wrist, a hand
toughened with work and freckled with old
age. There was a wedding ring on the third
finger and a wart on the index finger. By the
⁸⁰ wart, she knew it for her grandmother's hand.

She pulled back the sheet but the old woman
woke up, at that, and began to struggle,
squawking and shrieking like a thing possessed.
But the child was strong, and armed with her
⁸⁵ father's hunting knife; she managed to hold her
grandmother down long enough to see the cause
of her fever. There was a bloody stump where her
right hand should have been, festering already.

The child crossed herself and cried out so
⁹⁰ loud the neighbours heard her and came
rushing in. They knew the wart on the hand at
once for a witch's nipple; they drove the old
woman, in her shift as she was, out into the
snow with sticks, beating her old carcass as far
⁹⁵ as the edge of the forest, and pelted her with
stones until she fell down dead.

Now the child lived in her grandmother's
house; she prospered.

4 VOCABULARY Linkers

Linkers – conjunctions, relative pronouns and adverbs – play an important part in narrative texts. Conjunctions add to the coherence of the plot, relative pronouns introduce clauses which give more information and adverbs indicate attitude or feelings.

a Complete this summary of *The Werewolf* using the words in the list.

and   and what's more   as   as soon as   at the end   because of (× 2)   but
calmly   despite   however   in the end   just then   obediently   so (× 2)   so … that
such … that   where   who

> The child and her family lived in a cold bleak place ¹............. the people were superstitious. One day, the child's mother asked her to visit her grandmother ²............. had been sick ³............. take her some food. ⁴............. , the child started out through the wood. She had taken her father's hunting knife ⁵............. the wild animals, ⁶............. , she knew how to use it. ⁷............. , she heard the howl of a wolf, ⁸............. she took out the knife. ⁹............. the wolf attacked her, she slashed off one of its paws. ¹⁰............. , the wolf ran off. ¹¹............. , the child picked up the paw, wrapped it in a cloth and continued to her grandmother's house. Her grandmother was ¹²............. sick .... she had gone to bed. ¹³............. the child was taking the cloth out of the basket to make a cold compress, the paw fell out. ¹⁴............. , it was no longer a paw, ¹⁵............. a hand; her grandmother's hand. ¹⁶............. her grandmother's fever, the child pulled back the sheets and saw her grandmother's hand had been cut off. The child screamed with ¹⁷............. force .... the neighbours came in. ¹⁸............. the wart on the hand they knew the grandmother was a witch ¹⁹............. they drove her out of the house and killed her. ²⁰............. of the story, the child lives in the house and is doing very well.

b Put these linking words in the correct column of the table. Four have been done for you.

~~first~~   ~~also~~   now   ~~in conclusion~~   overall   ~~since~~   furthermore   last but not least
in addition   therefore   to summarise   as a result   moreover   first and foremost
finally   consequently   what is more   to conclude   in brief   hence

Sequencing	Adding	Expressing cause and result	Summing up
first	also	since	in conclusion

c Think of a story you know and briefly tell a partner what it is about. Use as many of the linkers from **a** and **b** as you can.

5 WRITING

a Work in pairs and summarise what for you are the key features of a good story.

b Prepare to write a short story of about 300 words, bearing in mind all the points discussed in **a**. You can choose one of these openings or you can make up your own.

1
> We were walking through Central Park in New York under a sky unscarred by clouds …

2
> 'What are you gaping at?'
> 'It's Clarissa, isn't it?'

3
> No one knew where she came from, or why she had sought refuge among us.

c Outline your plot and characters. Note some good vocabulary to use. Then write your story.

PART B

1 GRAMMAR Past tenses and the present perfect

a You are going to hold a *grammar auction*. Work in pairs or in small groups. Read through these sentences and decide which are grammatically correct and which are incorrect. In the auction you are going to bid for correct sentences. You have a total of £4,000. Write down in the budget column how much you are willing to bid for each sentence. The minimum bid is £150. The winners will have bought the most correct sentences and have the most money left.

	Budget	Bought

1 I studied English before I had read the book.
2 Jorge went on an English course in Australia because he had been accepted on a Creative Writing course in Sydney.
3 The book had been made into a film last year.
4 Charlotte was having a flat in Paris for several years.
5 We were trying to listen to the story while the students next door were listening to music.
6 Tony asked if he can borrow the book to read on holiday.
7 I finished the last chapter of the book just as the children were coming home from school.
8 In the story the murderer was almost getting away with it but his ex-wife was alerting the police.
9 The end of the story left you feeling confused.
10 He read that book for six months!
11 The author was owning a cottage in Greece; that's why many of her stories had been set there.
12 The main character slowly poisoned her twin sister; that's why no one suspected foul play.
13 Have you been reading a lot lately, your eyes look red?
14 The beginning of the book was seeming very boring, that's why I didn't finish it.
15 Are you sure the butler committed the murder? I thought it had been the cook.
16 Since he came to live in the village, I've only seen him once.
17 It's the first time Lucy rides a horse.
18 He had been acting on stage for years before he was discovered by Hollywood.

b Correct the incorrect sentences in **a**.

c Work in pairs. For each of these sentences write another with nearly the same meaning, using the present perfect simple or continuous.

e.g. *They are at home now.*
*They **have come back** home.*

1 Your children look bigger.
2 He isn't here.
3 I can't remember the phone number.
4 The dishes are still dirty.
5 You look in good shape.
6 Your hair looks shorter.
7 It's wet outside.
8 The cat is hungry.
9 The TV still doesn't work.
10 You sound breathless.

2 READING

You are going to read a modern fairy story by Archibald Marshall. His stories were written for both children and grown-ups, and he called them *Simple Stories*, perhaps because they are always short and have very little punctuation. This one tells of a Prince who *didn't* want to marry the Princess, and what the Princess did about it.

a Read the story and then in small groups choose one of these topics to work on.

1 unexpected turns in the plot and unexpected personality traits of the main characters
2 the style of the language
3 references to the setting and culture

b Underline the parts of the story which are relevant to the topic you have chosen. In your group discuss the meaning and significance of the parts you have underlined. Then prepare to present your analysis to the rest of the class.

c In small groups think up the plot of a modern Prince and Princess story. How would their characters be different from the traditional Prince and Princess and how would the plot be different?

Once there was a Prince who went to his father and said I want to marry Rose.
His father said who is Rose? and
5 he said she is the girl I want to marry.
And his father said why do you want to marry her? and he said because I like the shape of her
10 face.
So his father said well you can't, and he said why not?
And his father said because I have just arranged for you to
15 marry a very nice Princess.
And he said what Princess?
His father said I forget her name but she is the daughter of a King who is very rich and I owe him
20 some money.
So the Prince went away very sad, and when he had gone the King clapped his hands together and his *caitiff came to him and
25 touched the ground with his forehead and said Salaam.
And the King said bring me my *hookah, and when he had brought him his hookah he said
30 do you know a girl called Rose? and he said yes.
And the King said well put her in a dungeon.
So the caitiff touched the
35 ground with his forehead again and said *Amen and went out.

3 STUDY SKILLS Reading

Work in pairs and discuss these questions.

1 What is the difference in reading techniques between scanning and skimming? Can you give examples of when you would use either of these two skills?

2 When you read for pleasure, how do you read and why?

3 How is it different when you read for pleasure in your own language and when you read for pleasure in English?

4 Do you look up all unknown words when you read in English or do you just try to understand the general meaning?

5 What can you do to extend your reading in English?

6 How do you think reading in English contributes to other areas of your English studies, e.g. vocabulary and grammar?

4 VOCABULARY Order of adjectives

Descriptive writing is often loaded with evocative adjectives. Generally speaking, adjectives which give an opinion go before adjectives which give facts.

a Look at this phrase and work out the order of adjectives.

a lovely big new yellow Spanish cloth beach bag

b Put these adjectives in the most usual order.

					Noun
1	frightening	south-westerly			gale
2	interesting	weather-beaten	hunter's		face
3	woollen	grey	threadbare	winter	coat
4	ancient	Chinese	tiny		carving
5	Spanish	mottled	ceramic	blue	attractive	tiles
6	oak	Victorian	slightly damaged	huge	chest of drawers
7	green	breath-taking	English		countryside
8	faded	sombre	18th-century	Dutch landscape	painting
9	plastic	cycling	uncomfortable	white	helmet
10	Italian	delicious	colourful	spicy	evening	meal

Well that evening the Prince went to Rose's house and asked for her, and her mother said she is not here, and he said where is she? and she said I don't know.

So the Prince was very sad, and that night at the banquet he could not eat any of the rich and delicate *viands but drank a little iced sherbert flavoured with pineapple because his father was looking at him.

And after the banquet he went out into the garden which was very lovely and had a million roses in it and a great many bulbuls which was what they called nightingales. And they were all singing and it was very lovely, but the Prince said I would rather hear Rose's bulbul than any of those, I think I will go indoors.

Now Rose had a tame nightingale which she had taught to speak, and directly the Prince had said I think I will go indoors he heard a voice, and it said Rose is here.

So he knew it was Rose's nightingale and he said where?

And it said in the dungeon.

So the Prince rescued Rose out of the dungeon and he put her on his swift Arab steed and fled with her into the desert.

Well they came to a small oasis where there was a well and a palm tree with some dates on it, but when they had eaten all the dates they were still very hungry, and the Prince said if somebody doesn't come soon we shall die.

And Rose was very brave and she said oh well never mind.

Well just as they were going to die they saw a caravan coming with lots of camels and dromedaries, and it was the caravan of the Princess who was coming to marry the Prince.

The Princess was a little old but she was very nice. The Prince did not tell her who he was at first but he told her that he wanted to marry Rose and his father wouldn't let him so he had fled with her into the desert.

And the Princess said quite right too and you shall marry Rose, I will see to it.

The Prince said thank you, and the Princess said I like weddings and used to play at them when I was a little girl, and I have brought my private clergyman with me and if you don't mind my religion being a little different he can marry you now if you like, I expect it will count but if not you can be done again when you get home.

So the Prince was married to Rose and the Princess gave him a lovely *kaboosh with rubies and emeralds for a wedding present, and she gave Rose a shawl to go on with and said she would give her something more when her camels were unpacked.

So the next day the Prince told the Princess who he was, and she said oh well it can't be helped now and you are a little young for me, perhaps I can marry your father, it would be a pity not to marry somebody as I have come so far.

So the Princess married the King, because his wife was dead and anyhow he was allowed by his religion to have as many wives as he liked if he didn't have too many and was kind to all of them.

And he forgave the Prince for marrying Rose, and he said she is very nice and I don't think you could have done better.

caitiff slave
hookah a pipe of oriental origin for smoking tobacco, with a long flexible tube connected to a container of water, through which the smoke is drawn from the tobacco
Amen an expression of agreement (archaic)
viands food (archaic)
kaboosh jewellery box

7 P's and Q's

PART A

1 INTRODUCTION

a Do you think this extract is easy to understand? If not, what makes it difficult?

> In the event of loss or damage, you are asked to produce this certificate as proof of posting. You may be able to claim compensation for a lost or damaged item sent inland provided it was sent in accordance with Royal Mail requirements. No compensation will be paid in respect of money or jewellery sent in the ordinary post.

b Work in pairs and discuss the meaning of these terms. Try to come up with an example to illustrate the meaning of each term and say in what sort of situation it might be used.

1 jargon
2 gobbledygook
3 small print
4 everyday English
5 a complex sentence
6 a colloquialism
7 an idiom
8 formal English

2 SPEAKING

a Look again at the extract in 1. Work in pairs and answer these questions.

1 What sort of document do you think this extract comes from?
2 Who has produced this document?
3 Who might need to have such a document?
4 How would you say this if you were talking to a friend?
5 What are some of the main differences between formal and informal English?

b Work in pairs and explain in everyday English what these formal phrases mean.

1 Please settle your account …
2 Available at most retail outlets.
3 We value your custom …
4 Please forward all correspondence to:
5 Expiry date:

c Where might you come across each phrase in **b**? Can you think of any other common examples of similar phrases?

3 GRAMMAR First conditional

a Look at these two sentences. Work in pairs and answer the questions.

> If the job is not completed within three months, a penalty clause will come into effect.

> Provided your order reaches us by the 30th of the month, the goods can be dispatched within 14 days.

1 What sort of document do you think each sentence comes from?
2 What grammatical structure is being used in these sentences?
3 What word can we use instead of *if … not*?
4 What other expressions can replace *provided*?
5 What other ways are there of saying *can be*?
6 What are the rules for this grammatical structure?
7 What variations of the structure do you know?

b Work in pairs and explain what will or can happen in these situations.

4 READING AND SPEAKING

Read this document about fitting extra electrical gadgets to a new car. Work in pairs and answer the questions which follow.

WARNING

ADDITIONAL ELECTRICAL ACCESSORIES

The electrical system of your vehicle is designed to operate correctly with all standard optional equipment.

5 Before having additional electrical equipment fitted to your vehicle, please consult your dealer for advice.

Some electrical accessories can 10 by their nature, or as a result of the way they are fitted, adversely affect the operation of the electrical system of your vehicle.

If electrical accessories of any 15 sort are not correctly installed, with due regard to the size of cables used, their routing, and the fuse protection circuits, the safety of your vehicle may be put 20 at risk.

The company declines any responsibility for malfunctions and costs incurred arising from the installation of accessories 25 not approved by it or not installed as recommended by it.

1 Comment on the structure and style of the document. Look, in particular, at the paragraphing, sentence length, punctuation and vocabulary.
2 Who has produced this document and why?
3 If the document is difficult to understand at first, why do you think that is?
4 Are there any words you do not understand? If there are, can you guess their meaning?
5 Reformulate each paragraph into less formal English, using first conditional forms as often as possible.

5 PRONUNCIATION /b/ and /v/

a 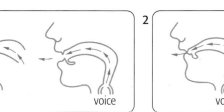 Listen and circle the words you hear.

| 1 | very | berry | 3 | vigour | bigger | 5 | vow | bow |
| 2 | vanish | banish | 4 | vote | boat | | | |

b Look at these two diagrams. Which represents the sound /b/ and which represents /v/?

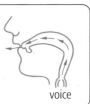

c Listen and repeat these words.

| 1 | bat | vat | 3 | bolt | volt | 5 | buy | vie |
| 2 | bend | vend | 4 | beer | veer | | | |

d Work in pairs.

Student A
Say one of the words in each pair.

Student B
Circle the word you hear.

| 1 | vest | best | 3 | very | berry | 5 | vigour | bigger |
| 2 | van | ban | 4 | vote | boat | 6 | vanish | banish |

6 GRAMMAR Variations of *if*

Complete this dialogue between a secretary and her boss with words from the list.

given   if so   unless   otherwise   provided/as long as

ROD Could I just go through some of the things we need to sort out today?

ANGELA Yes, of course.

ROD First of all we've got to send Simpsons that information about our new range of furniture.

ANGELA Yes, I'll send them a fax; [1]................ they won't get it until next week. Oh, by the way, do you know there's going to be a rail strike. The new desks might have to be rerouted to Birmingham; [2]................ we'll have to arrange to have them picked up by truck.

ROD Yes, could you look into that? [3]................ the demands of the union, I'm pretty sure the strike will go ahead.

ANGELA Have you signed the contract with Dempsters?

ROD No, and I'm not going to [4]................ they agree to clauses 4 and 5.

ANGELA OK. Anything else?

ROD Yes, we need the new leaflets announcing the new range by the end of the month. Will they be ready?

ANGELA Yes, [5]................ we get the proofs to the printers by Friday, we'll have the leaflets by the 23rd.

ROD Great!

PART B

1 READING AND WRITING

Read this informal note from a colleague. Then use the information it contains to complete the formal announcement which follows with a maximum of three words per gap.

```
┌──────────────────────────────────────────────────────┐
│ Normal    [📖][🖨][📄][🗑][📎][📋][ABC][OFF][SEND]       │
│ ┌────────────────────────────────────────────────┐   │
│ │ FROM:                                           │   │
│ │   TO:                                           │   │
│ │   CC:                                           │   │
│ │   BCC:                                          │   │
│ └────────────────────────────────────────────────┘   │
│ ┌────────────────────────────────────────────────┐   │
│ │ Message                                         │   │
│ └────────────────────────────────────────────────┘   │
```

I've just managed to get all the information we need for the conference at Manchester University in April. As I'm off on holiday tomorrow, I won't have time to make up the announcement to send out. Could you do it for me? It's from the 14th until 16th and Professor James Levington is going to run the whole thing. He's going to start off with a sort of welcome cum introduction and that's going to be followed by a talk on the role of English in international business by Svetlana Spassova. Various companies who have language training and translators/interpreters are going to have all their stuff out in the central lobby in the Renold building. There'll be workshops on different things to do with language, like audio-visual aids, computers, etc., so people can find out more about their special areas. And this is the time when people get the chance to chat together. The whole thing will be rounded off with a light-hearted look at cultural differences. Mark Chapman's going to do that. He's really funny and he's called his talk 'I'm sorry, I didn't realise …'. People will have to pay £450 which includes accommodation and food. Not bad! They have to make out their cheques to Manchester University.

Manchester University **MU**

Conference: The role of the English language in international business

On Wednesday 14th April the main conference begins with a welcome address by Professor James Levington and the [1]........................ by Svetlana Spassova, who will [2]........................ 'The role of English in international business'. In the central lobby in the Renold building you will find [3]........................ offering you the chance to find out what is [4]........................ from various companies. A variety of workshops will [5]........................ to find out more about areas of special interest to you. This is also an ideal opportunity to [6]........................ , renewing old acquaintances and making new [7]........................ . The closing plenary [8]........................ by Mark Chapman with his light-hearted talk on cultural differences, [9]........................ 'I'm sorry, I didn't realise …'. The [10]........................ of the conference, [11]........................ accommodation and full board, is £450. Cheques should be [12]........................ to Manchester University.

2 VOCABULARY Ways of asking for clarification

When you come across complicated language which you don't understand, you need to be able to ask for clarification, simplification or repetition.

a Work in pairs. Look at these phrases you can use to ask for clarification and divide them into two groups – more formal and less formal.

1 I'm sorry?
2 Wait a minute, I'm not sure I see what you mean.
3 Do you think you could possibly go through that again for me?
4 I'm not quite sure what that means. Is it that … ?
5 Are you telling me that … ?
6 I wonder if you could explain what that means exactly.
7 Would you mind explaining that part? I don't think I've really understood.
8 I'm totally lost now. Can you go over it again?
9 I can't make head nor tail of this.
10 I didn't get that at all.

b 🚗 Listen and repeat the phrases in **a**, paying particular attention to the intonation.

c Can you think of any other phrases you could use? Are they formal or informal?

3 SPEAKING

a Work in pairs and take turns to ask for and give an explanation of the words in italics in these phrases. When you are asking for an explanation, try to use some of the phrases from 2. When giving an explanation, use less formal language.

1 We will *endeavour* to …
2 *In the event of* …
3 *Prior to* your departure …
4 Prior to the repair being *undertaken* …
5 Your deposit will be *retained*.
6 *Due to adverse weather conditions* …
7 We will do our *utmost to assist* …

b Make sure that you have found a synonym for each of the words and phrases in italics in **a**.

c Work in pairs and take turns asking for and giving an explanation of the booking conditions in these extracts from the small print of a holiday brochure. When you are asking for an explanation, use some of the expressions from 2. When you are giving an explanation, use less formal language.

1

In the event of unforeseen delay you should notify the hotel of your intended arrival time at the earliest opportunity.

2

Should you have a complaint, immediately inform the relevant supplier (e.g. hotel) who will endeavour to put things right. In the event of being unable to resolve the problem you must obtain written confirmation which you should submit to us within 28 days of your return.

3

Bookings made within six weeks of departure must be accompanied by full payment.

4

If you cancel more than 10 days before travel, you will be charged 50% of your final balance. Thereafter no refunds can be made.

4 WRITING

You are at the end of the first week of a four-week trip organised by a company called Voyager. You have lots of complaints about the holiday but your requests to get things put right have got nowhere. The staff at the hotel say there is nothing they can do and that you will have to write to the head office. You decide to write a letter of complaint saying what you will do if the situation does not improve in the next three weeks. You are determined to have a good holiday and will take matters into your own hands if necessary.

Read the advertisement for the holiday with your own comments added. Then write a letter of complaint. Use the first conditional form to say what you will do if things do not improve.

VOYAGER

A holiday of a lifetime travelling to exotic locations

The groups are huge, must be divided up.

Exploration in small groups to experience local history and culture

Fully equipped coaches, comfort guaranteed

Evening lecture programme by experts

Old uncomfortable coaches, ours broke down! I refuse to go in them again.

Service awful – not enough waiters.

Five-star luxury hotel with air-conditioned rooms, en-suite facilities, phone and TV

Dining excellence to make evenings an unforgettable experience

Not in my room. I'm going to move.

Pool has no water. I'm going to ask for a refund.

Swimming pool and sports facilities equal to none

All inclusive – no extras

Ha! At the end of the first week I got a bill for breakfast. I'm not paying it.

The language of colour

8

1 INTRODUCTION

Work in pairs. Look at the colour chart and discuss these questions.

1 Which colour do you identify with most strongly; which one is 'you'?
2 Which colours make you feel calm, secure, romantic or excited?
3 Which colours leave you indifferent?
4 Which one is your 'yuk' colour, the colour you dislike the most?

| Pink | Red | Yellow | Maroon | Gold | Orange | Brown |

| Grey | White | Peach | Apple Green | Mint Green | Light Blue |

| Black | Green | Blue Green | Dark Blue | Silver | Mauve | Purple |

2 SPEAKING AND READING

a Look at the colours in 1 again. If you were a colour, what colour would you be? (Think of what colour represents you. Don't be concerned about what colour you might wear all the time, but choose a colour that expresses you.) Do not tell anyone which colour you have chosen yet, just make a note of it.

b Choose two other people in the class and guess which colour they will choose for themselves. Do not tell anybody about your choices yet, just make a note of them.

c e/tra Now turn to page 61 and read about your colour choices.

d Find out if the colour you chose for two other people in the class is the same as the one they chose for themselves. Do you all agree with the interpretations of the colours?

e According to colour analysts, when we are wearing certain colours we are giving out particular messages. To what extent do you believe this is true? Can you think of any examples?

f In small groups, discuss which colour(s) would be suitable for a person who wanted to say:

1 Look at me, I'm physical and emotional.
2 Let's communicate, I like to share.
3 I like to express my feelings and have others recognise how great I am.
4 I love to be the boss and the decision-maker.
5 I hear what you say but I don't want to be involved.
6 I like to be by myself, even in a crowd, for I need my own space.
7 Let me show you how creative yet analytical I am.
8 I'm charitable, kind and like to be involved.
9 I like to love, be loved and care for others.
10 Don't tell me what to do, for I know best.

g e/tra Now check your suggestions on page 61.

3 VOCABULARY Idioms of colour

Complete these sentences using the expressions in the list. Make any necessary changes to the verbs.

black and blue   black eye
black sheep   a grey area
to catch someone red-handed
in black and white   out of the blue
a red herring   to see red
to see the world through rose-coloured spectacles

1 Now that Helen is in love she ....

2 I was so angry at what he said, it made me ....

3 Did you read about the burglar who was watching TV in the house where he had just stolen all the jewellery when the police .... ?

4 Luckily Simon wasn't seriously injured in the accident but he's .... all over.

5 I know it looks as if someone has hit me, but really, this .... is the result of walking into a lamp-post.

6 We're not entirely sure how we stand legally; it seems to be a bit of .... in the law.

7 I won't believe I've got the job until I see it ....

8 I hear the Wheelers are having trouble with their son again; he's really turned out to be the .... of the family.

9 It was brilliant seeing Jill after all these years; I just couldn't believe it when she turned up .... like that.

10 I think the council is using this issue as .... to divert our attention from the main point.

4 GRAMMAR Second conditional

a Work in pairs and explain the grammar and situations in these sentences. Contrast a and b in 1–7 and explain the use of *would* in both clauses in 8.

1 a If I wear red, everybody will notice me.
   b If I wore red, everybody would notice me.
2 a Is it all right if I leave now?
   b Would it be all right if I left now?
3 a If I won first prize, I would never forget it.
   b If I won first prize, I should never forget it.
4 a If you get there before me, will you pick up the tickets?
   b If you should happen to get there before me, would you pick up the tickets?
5 a If the principal dancer were to fall ill now, the whole show would have to be cancelled.
   b Were the principal dancer to fall ill now, the whole show would have to be cancelled.
6 a If it weren't for his pot-belly, James would be quite attractive.
   b If James didn't have a pot-belly, he would be quite attractive.
7 a I wouldn't be surprised if she got the lead role because she's brilliant.
   b I wouldn't be surprised if she didn't get the lead role because she's brilliant.
8 I would appreciate it if you would return the documents within 14 days.

b Work in pairs and discuss how you could combine colours to change your image according to the chart, e.g. *if you wanted to come across as businesslike, you should wear dark blue with light pastels*. Remember to use the second conditional form.

Desired image	Colours
dramatic	Bold, vivid, primary colours, strong contrasts.
romantic	Pink, rose reds and pastels of all red and violet shades.
executive	Dark shades of blue, grey, brown, wine and purple. All blacks with light pastel blouses or shirts.
secured	Earth tones and dark shades of all colours. Combine earth tones or deep shades of colours with bright accents of gold, ivory or white.
sensual	All warm colours (except yellow); light, bright and dark shades, especially reds
holistic	Greens, violets, yellows and earth tones with rainbow colours.

5 VOCABULARY Word-building

a Write the nouns from these adjectives, which all appeared in 2.

1 ambitious
2 energetic
3 sympathetic
4 competent
5 gentle
6 dexterous
7 modest
8 innovative
9 sensitive
10 impatient

b An easy and quick way to find the opposite of an adjective is to add a negative prefix when possible. In English the negative prefixes are: *un, in, im, non, dis, ir, il*. Which prefix goes in front of the adjectives in these sentences?

1 I don't know how you came to that conclusion: it's completely ......logical.
2 Wearing striking colours shows a(n) ......conformist attitude.
3 Even though he's 16 he's still quite ......mature for his age.
4 To throw out all the clothes in her wardrobe was a(n) ......rational reaction
5 It was so rude to make such a(n) ......tasteful comment in front of everyone.
6 I couldn't live there; it's such a(n) ......hospitable climate.
7 He gave his ......wavering support throughout the ordeal.
8 They praised his ......reproachable character.
9 Her ......penetrable defences meant that no one understood her true personality.
10 I'm afraid we've got a(n) ......satisfied customer here.

c Work in pairs and match these prefixes (1–10) to their meanings (a–j) and at the same time find a word as an example.

1	out	a	badly, wrong
2	arch	b	across
3	counter	c	not, without
4	hyper	d	against
5	mal	e	under
6	a	f	for, in favour of
7	pro	g	chief, main, highest ranking
8	pseudo	h	false, pretended
9	sub	i	exceeding, surpassing
10	trans	j	extremely, too

PART B

1 LISTENING

a You are going to hear a colour analyst talking about colours and the effect they can have on people. Before you listen, work in pairs and try to predict the effects of the six colours in the table. How do you think they make people feel?

Colour	Predicted effect	Effect according to speaker
1 red		
2 blue		
3 orange		
4 green		
5 yellow		
6 mauve		

b Listen and note the actual effect of the colours in **a** according to what you hear.

c Work in pairs and discuss how close your own ideas are to those of the colour analyst.

d Think of some other colours, e.g. black, beige, brown, and discuss what effect they might have on us.

e Listen to the same colour analyst talking about colour itself. According to what you hear, complete these sentences.

1 Colour is .... light.
2 Humans can see .... of the rainbow of colour.
3 Colour penetrates our bodies through our eyes and our .... , sending signals to our ....
4 Strong energy is present in all .... and warm colours.
5 The intensities of blues and pastel colours are lesser in .... and ....
6 Colour is a .... of passive solar energy.

2 GRAMMAR Third conditional and mixed conditionals

a Check that you know the forms of the third conditional by putting the verbs in brackets into the most appropriate form. Some of the sentences will sound better if you use a continuous form.

1 If she .... (wear) a darker colour at the interview, she .... (get) the job.
2 If we .... (arrived) five minutes later, we .... (miss) the train.
3 He .... (not make) such a serious mistake if he .... (pay) attention to his work.
4 If you .... (tell) me you were going out, I .... (have not) invited my sister round.
5 If I .... (not win) that money, I .... (never buy) such an extravagant present.
6 If he .... (go) any faster, he .... (kill) himself.

b Write two sentences about yourself in the third conditional, one using the present perfect simple and the other the present perfect continuous.

c Work in pairs and explain how and why these two sentences are 'mixed conditionals'.

1 If you didn't finish that job last night, you'll have to do it this morning.
2 If I had got the earlier train, we wouldn't be in such a rush now.

d Match the two halves of these sentences.

1 If you plant these in spring,	a you wouldn't be so confident.
2 If I had listened to her advice,	b you'll be feeling sick in a minute too.
3 If you read a review in the paper,	c the dog would still be here!
4 If you had been at yesterday's meeting,	d you'll get fruit this summer.
5 If you had written it down in the address book,	e you wouldn't be doing resits.
6 If you ate the same as me for lunch,	f we wouldn't be searching the house for the scrap of paper.
7 If we ordered the parts last month,	g it'll soon be dry.
8 If you'd worked harder for your exams,	h I wouldn't be in so much trouble now.
9 If you painted the door two hours ago,	i they will be here this week.
10 If he'd closed the door,	j it must mean the film will be on general release soon.

e Write two sentences of your own using mixed conditional forms.

3 STUDY SKILLS Organising vocabulary

Read these ideas from learners about what they do to remember and organise their vocabulary. Which of them do you already do and which do you think would help you? Work in pairs.

1 After the class I write all the new words I have learnt in a special vocabulary book.
2 I write new words in a sentence.
3 I write the translation next to the word in my Coursebook.
4 I think if I need a word again and again, I'll remember it.
5 I have a file divided into topic areas and I write the word in it.
6 I record new words in sentences onto a cassette and listen to it as often as possible.
7 I make a card with the new word on it and stick it somewhere prominent in my room, for example on my mirror!
8 I make a mind map like the one on page 61. I think a visual stimulus helps.
9 I like drawing, so I try to draw the word or a symbol for it. It's more memorable.
10 The teacher is the most important thing. When the teacher mimes or demonstrates a word, especially if it's funny, it's easier to remember.

4 PRONUNCIATION /s/ and /ʃ/ + /ʃ/ and /tʃ/

a 🔊 Listen and repeat these words.

1 see   she
2 saw   shore
3 sake   shake
4 socks   shocks
5 sour   shower

b Work in pairs.

Student A
Circle one of the words in italics in sentences 1–4, e.g. *shelling*, and dictate the sentences with the words you have chosen to Student B. Then listen and circle the words you hear Student B say in sentences 5–8.

Student B
Circle one of the words in italics in sentences 5–8, e.g. *gas*. Listen to Student A dictate sentences 1–4 and circle the words you hear. Then dictate your sentences to Student A.

1 He's *selling/shelling* nuts.
2 He has been *shaving/saving* since he was 12.
3 The *parish/Paris* I knew as a child has gone.
4 I like those green *bushes/buses*.
5 It was a dangerous *gas/gash*.
6 We took a little *ship/sip*.
7 We'll have to buy some *seats/sheets*.
8 It was the *same/shame*.

c 🔊 Listen and repeat these words.

1 share   chair
2 sheep   cheap
3 sheer   cheer
4 shoes   choose
5 washing   watching
6 wish   which

d Work in pairs.

Student A
Circle one of the words in italics in sentences 1–4, e.g. *watching*, and dictate the sentences with the words you have chosen to Student B. Then listen and circle the words you hear Student B say in sentences 5–8.

Student B
Circle one of the words in italics in sentences 5–8, e.g. *ships*. Listen to Student A dictate sentences 1–4 and circle the words you hear. Then dictate your sentences to Student A.

1 I'm busy *washing/watching* something.
2 I couldn't *cash/catch* the cheques.
3 He's got a bruise on his *shin/chin*.
4 That's not my *chair/share*.
5 She doesn't like *chips/ships*.
6 There were three *wishes/witches*.
7 It's *sheepish/cheapish*.
8 It's best to *mash/match* them up.

5 READING

a It is believed that light can affect people in different ways. Read the article about the Northern Lights, or aurora borealis as they are also known, and answer these questions.

1 What has generally been thought to be the cause of depression in the Far North?
2 What connection does Dr Bush claim her research has revealed?
3 What alarming trend does Dr Bush cite?
4 What does Dr Bush believe about reported SAD patients?
5 Why does she suggest some people should wear dark glasses?
6 How has Professor Hallinan reacted to her proposition?

Spectacular Northern Lights linked to suicidal depression

Alaska's tragically high suicide rate may be related to cosmic storms and the Northern Lights (aurora
5 borealis), according to an expert in the study of brainwaves.

Depression in the Far North has in general been
10 attributed to the deep gloom of its long, dark winters. But Dr Anita Bush, who specialises in electro-encephalography, has
15 complicated matters by discovering a link between solar flares and brainwave activity in two sets of Alaskans she has studied
20 for the past five years.

The tiny electric impulses were concentrated in an area of the brain known also to trigger seasonal
25 affective depression (SAD), the condition hitherto blamed for dozens of suicides each year in the remote Alaskan hinterland.
30 Suicide levels among the state's 15 to 24-year-olds have risen sharply in recent years, to six times the national average, says Dr Bush.   35

She has not yet demonstrated a link between heightened brainwaves and suicidal tendencies but she 40 thinks existing data on supposed SAD cases may in fact include cases of suicide induced by geomagnetism. For now 45 she has suggested that special dark glasses, worn against solar flares and the Northern Lights, might boost morale 50 among the suicidal.

Some of her colleagues are sceptical. Professor Tom Hallinan, one of a team studying the aurora, 55 recently insisted that the most serious health risk in watching the Alaskan night sky was a cricked neck.   60

b Find words in the text which mean:

1 near darkness
2 signals
3 cause something to happen
4 until now (formal)
5 an area of land behind a piece of coastline
6 increased or intensified
7 improve or lift
8 painful and stiff

9 Time out

1 INTRODUCTION

Work in pairs and discuss these questions.

1 *Time Out* is a British magazine. What sort of information do you think it contains?
2 What do you like doing in your free time?
3 What events have you been to recently? What were they like?
4 Do you think people should have to pay to go into art galleries and museums?
5 What is the maximum you would be prepared to pay to go to different events in your country?

2 READING

a Work in pairs. Quickly scan the advertisements from *Time Out* and find which event(s) these statements refer to.

1 There are over 100 performers.
2 On one afternoon performances are cheaper.
3 Children under 10 do not have to pay.
4 There will be a talk followed by a film.
5 There are special arrangements for people who want a box.
6 You can only see this event on one day.
7 The money from this event will go to charity.
8 This event has won an award.
9 You do not have to pay a booking fee.
10 This event is held outside.
11 Tickets are cheaper for the unemployed, students and club members.
12 This event has no sponsorship.

b Work in pairs and discuss these questions.

1 If you were in London for a couple of weeks, which event(s) in **a** would you choose to go to and why? What other things would you like to do or see in London?
2 If you were organising a summer festival for the town where you live, what events would you include?

3 GRAMMAR *wish, if only, would rather, it's time*

a Work in pairs. Which grammatical structures follow *wish*, *if only*, *would rather* and *it's time* in these sentences?

1 I wish that show would come to Oxford.
2 I wish I had time to go and see it.
3 I wish I had booked earlier; tickets are sold out now.
4 I wish to inform you of our decision.
5 If only that were true!
6 If only that man would shut up; I can't hear the film!
7 If only I had phoned earlier!
8 Jane would rather go to a night club than to the cinema.
9 I'd rather we met at 6.30pm.
10 I'd rather not spend so much money on a ticket.
11 I'd rather you didn't repeat what I'm going to tell you.
12 It's time to go home.
13 It's time we went home.

b Work in pairs and, by looking at the sentences in a, complete these 'rules'.

1 .... and .... are followed by the same structures when talking about a past regret.
2 .... is a stronger way of expressing *wish*.
3 .... and *would rather* + clause are followed by the same structures.
4 To talk about a present desire, we use *wish* + ...
5 To express a regret about something that happened in the past, we use *if only* + ...
6 *Would rather* + clause is followed by ....
7 *It's time* with no clause is followed by ....
8 *Would rather* with no clause is followed by ....
9 We use *wish* + ... to talk about what we would like people (not) to do. This often expresses dissatisfaction or annoyance.

c You are going to hold a *gripes auction*. Your teacher will explain how the auction works. To prepare for it, first think about which group of people or situation you have the most to complain about. Is it your relatives, your school, your job or your town? Choose one of these or add your own idea. Then, in pairs or small groups, talk about your complaints using *I wish, If only, I'd rather* and *It's time*.

4 STUDY SKILLS Learning grammar

a Learning grammar is part and parcel of learning a foreign language and in some cases your own language. Work in pairs and discuss these questions about grammar.

1 Do you think it is useful to learn grammar?
2 Do you like learning it? Why/why not?
3 In what ways is English grammar different to the grammar of your language and in what ways is it similar?
4 How grammatically accurate do you think your speaking and writing is?
5 Do you use a wide range of grammatical structures? Why/why not?
6 Do you find it easier to write or speak in grammatically correct English?
7 What do you do to improve your grammar?
8 What new ways of improving your grammar can you suggest?

b Work in pairs and give examples of these grammatical terms.

1 an adverb particle
2 an auxiliary verb
3 a conjunction
4 a contraction
5 a determiner
6 a phrasal verb
7 a reflexive pronoun
8 an adverb + adjective collocation
9 a question tag
10 ellipsis

5 PRONUNCIATION Consonant clusters

Consonant clusters are two, three or four consonant sounds occurring together, e.g. *three* /θr/. Consonant clusters can occur at the beginning, middle and end of words.

a Look at the phonetic symbols at the end of the book and familiarise yourself with the transcriptions of the consonants. Then, working in pairs, listen and repeat these words, paying particular attention to the two consonant clusters at the beginning. Check each other's pronunciation. Mark with a cross any words which you find difficult to pronounce.

1 plant
2 break
3 dreadful
4 clash
5 grated
6 quickly
7 frequent
8 thrill
9 swallow
10 shrimp

b If there are any words in **a** which you found difficult to pronounce, write the word in a sentence and practise saying it again. Ask your partner if it sounds correct.

c Working in pairs, listen and repeat these words, paying particular attention to the three consonant clusters at the beginning of 1–5 and at the end of 6–14. Ask your partner if your pronunciation sounds correct.

1 splash
2 spread
3 strength
4 scratch
5 squeaks
6 sixth
7 mixed
8 months
9 announced
10 revenged
11 thanked
12 tourists
13 tasks
14 fifths

d Write the phonetic transcription of the words in **c**. Then write a sentence for any word which is difficult for you to pronounce and practise saying it. Ask your partner if your pronunciation sounds correct.

e Can you think of any words with four consonant clusters?

6 VOCABULARY Word-building

a *extra* You are going to play *Snap*. Turn to page 62 for instructions.

b Complete these sentences using the words in the list.

accusatory   allergic   amiable
cupful   expiry   interviewee   liar
lifelike   plumpish   customary
soundproof   monumental

1 He is an .... sort of person, everybody likes him.
2 She's .... to strawberries; when she eats them she comes out in spots.
3 I wouldn't believe everything little Johnny says, even his mother says he's a ....
4 The .... had a tough time evading the probing questions of the personnel manager.
5 There was a .... crash as the mirror fell to the floor.
6 It was .... for lawyers to tie up their papers in red tape or ribbon.
7 Have you seen the new portrait of the queen? I must say it's extremely ....
8 She's a .... girl with striking green eyes.
9 My neighbours' son has just bought some drums; I hope he has a .... bedroom.
10 What is the .... date of your driving licence?
11 Her .... tone left no one in doubt as to who she suspected.
12 Add one .... of rice per person.

c Make two sentences of your own, leaving a gap for a word with a suffix, and then give them to a partner to complete.

PART B

1 LISTENING

a Work in pairs and discuss these questions.

1 If you had an artistic talent, would you rather be a singer, dancer, actor or something else?
2 Looking back at your own childhood, are there any skills you wish you had developed more? Which?
3 What do you think it must be like to be a child prodigy? Have you heard or read about any child prodigies?

b You are going to hear a radio feature on a young US violinist, Leila Josefowicz, who was a child prodigy. As you listen, make notes to answer these questions.

1 Describe Leila's family background.
2 How does she feel about her summer schedule?
3 When did Leila start playing the violin and how did people react to her?
4 How did Leila and her family try to make her life as normal as possible?
5 What does Leila say about being a serious musician?
6 What is one of the reasons for her maturity?
7 What do you think 'stardust poisoning' means?
8 What do some recording companies force young stars to do?
9 What does Leila say about being on stage?
10 How do audiences react to her now?

c Discuss your answers to **b** in pairs.

d Work with a different partner and discuss these questions about Leila.

1 Do you think Leila missed out on anything in her childhood?
2 What sort of character has she got?
3 What do you think her life will be like in the future?

2 READING AND EDITING

A newspaper journalist is describing her first meeting with the novelist Jeanette Winterson. They meet in the street before going to Jeanette's new house to do an interview.

Read the text carefully. In most lines there is one unnecessary word. Write the word at the end of the line. If the line is correct, put a tick against the line number. When you have finished, compare answers with a partner.

Our day, which has been meticulously mapped out by the	1 ✓
interviewee, which starts with a rendezvous in a London station.	2 which
From here we walk down through curving back lanes to the	3 ....
writer's new home. We are both looking for a red-headed women,	4 ....
but when I approach to her she feels the need to establish my	5 ....
identity. Her own writing forms such an intimate bridge between	6 ....
her and her readers that she is too warily accustomed to fans	7 ....
greeting her as a long-lost friend.	8 ....
She would not only naturally stand out in a crowd were her features	9 ....
not so recognisable: and the skittish tilt of the nose, the freckled	10 ....
cheeks with their hamsterish tendencies and her fine brown eyes.	11 ....
A full-length military coat threatens her to overwhelm her slight frame.	12 ....
She talks as much she walks, at a cracking pace, her face	13 ....
animated, wanting me to share her enthusiasm for her new habitat.	14 ....
The outside exterior of the house is obscured by scaffolding.	15 ....
The interior is so submerged in shadow that it is so hard to see	16 ....
where you are going to. We enter a room which someone has	17 ....
been prepared for our interview. There is a rug, two chairs and a	18 ....
well-stoked fire. It is as theatrical, in this empty, derelict house, as	19 ....
a stage set.	20 ....

3 READING

a You are going to read a review about a film called *Absolute Power*. Judging by the title, what do you think the film is about?

b Read the article, then work in pairs and answer these questions.

1 What sort of film is *Absolute Power*?
2 What is the outline of the plot?
3 Make two lists, one of the positive points about the film and one of the negative points, according to the critic. Use your own words.
4 What do you think of the way this review is written? How would you improve it?

Absolute power

When ultra-secretive master-burglar Luther Whitney (Clint Eastwood) breaks into a mansion owned by politically influential millionaire Walter Sullivan (EG Marshall), he expects the house to be empty. So he's surprised not only by the sudden arrival of Sullivan's wife, but – as he discovers while hiding in a closet behind a two-way mirror – by the fact that she's carrying on with one Alan Richmond (Gene Hackman), President of the USA. Worse, after their drunken shenanigans turn nasty, Whitney witnesses both a murder and a deliberate cover-up by the presidential staff. While he successfully makes his escape, not only does the detective Seth Frank (Ed Harris) deduce that only a thief as ingenious as Whitney could have found his way into the Sullivan residence, but the President's men are soon on his trail. Surely, the best defence is attack …

If it's impossible to rank this light, partly comic Hitchcockian thriller, scripted by celebrity hack William Goldman from a novel by Daniel Baldacci, among Eastwood's best work as actor-director, there's no denying it's solidly enjoyable entertainment.

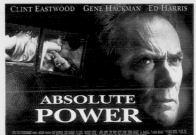

For one thing, pleasure can be had from seeing a superior cast at work. For another, while the script is conspicuously bereft of any proper political analysis or comment, it's hard to take against a contemporary Hollywood movie which forefronts a cowardly, cynical, philandering president. True, the plot has its fair share of implausibilities and contrivances (especially towards the end), and a strand involving Whitney's daughter threatens to slip into sentimentality. But Eastwood's sense of pace, irony and action somehow holds it all together. Flawed, for sure, but fun.

c Reviews usually include a mix of facts and opinion. How many of these points are included in the review in **b** ?

1 essential information about the plot
2 who directed and produced it
3 who stars in it
4 where and when it is set
5 where it was filmed
6 what the film is an adaption of
7 the reviewer's own opinion of the film
8 a recommendation for the viewers

4 VOCABULARY Adverb + adjective collocations

a These adverb + adjective collocations are all taken from film reviews. Work in pairs and decide whether they probably refer to the characters, photography, acting, plot or film as a whole. Some could be used for more than one category.

1 compellingly thrilling
2 simplistically portrayed
3 audaciously imaginative
4 immensely assured
5 marvellously credible
6 perfectly matched
7 eminently forgettable
8 brilliantly inventive
9 deftly assembled
10 occasionally amusing
11 gleefully cinematic
12 relentlessly innovative
13 highly original
14 surprisingly successful
15 distinctly unconventional
16 vastly enjoyable
17 faithfully adapted
18 unbearably bleak
19 visually sumptuous
20 emotionally powerful

b Which of the phrases in **a** could have a negative implication? If you feel some are ambiguous, say why.

c Compare your favourite phrases from **a** with those of a partner.

5 WRITING

a Work in pairs and choose a film, video, TV programme, concert or sporting event you have seen recently to review.

b Look again at 3 and the points in **c** which can be included in a review and plan the paragraphs of your review, deciding what you will include in each paragraph.

c Decide whether your review is going to be mainly positive or negative and then, before you start writing, note down as many positive/negative adjectives and adverb + adjective collocations as you can which will be relevant to your review. Can you use any from 4?

d Write your review in pairs in class or on your own as homework.

10

1 LINKERS

a Read this formal letter of complaint about a music festival and use the linkers in the list to complete it.

also (× 2)   although   as   as for   because of   consequently   despite
finally   firstly   furthermore   to sum up   in addition to   secondly   so (× 2)
so that   thirdly   until   when   with regard to   yet

Jan van Eyck (c. 1390–1441)

> 78 Long Lane
> Leeds LS6 1AB
> 15 Aug 2000
>
> The Festival Organiser
> TWR Concerts
> PO Box 2052
> London W1A 1HH
>
> Dear Sir,
>
> I am writing ¹................. the two-day festival held in Hylands Park on 11/12 August. ²................. , ³................. ordering and paying for our tickets over the phone well in advance, the tickets did not get to us ⁴................. the day before the festival. ⁵................. the worry this caused, it ⁶................. meant that we were unable to travel to Hylands the day before ⁷................. we had originally intended.
> ⁸................. , ⁹................. we arrived at Hylands Park in good time, we stood in a queue for one hour for a security check before entering the park. ¹⁰................. we finally got to the park gate, there was only one person checking the hundreds of people entering the park, ¹¹................. the queue was inevitable. More staff should have been made available ¹²................. people could enter the park quickly and safely.
> ¹³................. , the audience was kept ¹⁴................. far away from the stage that it was almost impossible to see the bands. ¹⁵................. , we were extremely disappointed to find that Paul Weston, the main attraction, only played for half an hour.
> ¹⁶................. , the facilities in the park were very poor; ¹⁷................. the hot weather people wanted to buy drinks, ¹⁸................. again it meant queueing for a long time. The rest area and toilet facilities were ¹⁹................. inadequate for the number of people attending the festival.
> ²⁰................. , you did not organise the festival carefully enough and ²¹................. the performances of the band we feel that we did not get our money's worth. ²²................. we are asking you to refund part of the £150 that we paid for three people to attend this event.
> We look forward to your prompt reply.
>
> Yours faithfully,
>
> *J. Lyons*
>
> Mrs Jane Lyons

b Imagine you wrote the formal letter in **a**. Read it through again and highlight the complaints. Then work in pairs and practise using linkers with less formal language to tell each other what happened.

c Work in pairs. Have you ever been to a large festival or anything like that? Tell your partner about it. If you have not been to a big event, tell your partner about the last time you went out to a film or restaurant. Remember to use linkers.

2 CONDITIONAL FORMS

a Match the beginnings (1–10) and ends (a–j) of these sentences about colour.

1 If a woman chose a white wedding dress in ancient China,
2 As long as people work in green environments,
3 If you put your food on a blue plate,
4 If babies are put in bright yellow rooms,
5 If you had lived in 15th-century Europe,
6 If you had a red car,
7 If you had used a softer yellow in the kitchen,
8 If you use a red wallet,
9 If the Japanese Emperor, Hirohito, hadn't loved his garden so much,
10 If you had put a blue light in your fridge,

a you will probably never be rich.
b do you think you would have more accidents?
c you would lose your appetite.
d her parents may not have approved.
e you would have been able to stick to your diet.
f I'm sure we wouldn't be having so many arguments.
g your wedding dress would probably have been green.
h they have fewer stomach aches.
i his birthday wouldn't be celebrated as 'Green Day'.
j they will cry more.

b In Unit 6 you were asked to recall the story *Little Red Riding Hood*. Work in pairs and use these prompts to say what would/would not have happened if things had been different, e.g. *If her grandma hadn't been ill, Little Red Riding Hood wouldn't have gone to visit her.*

1 Red Riding Hood so kind/she offer to visit her grandma.
2 Red Riding Hood obey mother/she go straight to grandma's house.
3 Red Riding Hood speak to wolf/he know where she go.
4 Red Riding Hood take wolf's advice/she get to house more quickly.
5 The wolf get to house before Red Riding Hood/she take so long.
6 The wolf sound like Red Riding Hood/grandma invite him in.
7 The wolf hear the sound of a gun/he eat grandma.
8 Red Riding Hood scream/grandma bang on wardrobe.
9 Hunter enter cottage/wolf run away.
10 Red Riding Hood do what her mother say/this never happen.

3 ORDER OF ADJECTIVES

a Work in pairs and put the adjectives in these phrases in the right order. The first and last words are in the right place.

1 a checked upholstery new linen beautiful fabric
2 a youth provocative theatre American female company
3 a round renovated fantastic open-air theatre
4 a Peruvian money highly decorated gold ancient box
5 a hamburger trendy brightly coloured American new restaurant

b Make five sentences of your own with three to five adjectives. Jumble up the adjectives and give your sentences to a partner to rewrite correctly. Don't forget that it is quite unusual to have so many adjectives together, so don't overdo it when you are writing!

4 PREFIXES AND SUFFIXES

a Complete this crossword using the clues to help you find the missing adjectives and nouns.

Across

1 reliable and responsible
6 kind, mild and pleasantly calm in character and behaviour
7 quite high
8 able to sense something is true, even though you have no proof
9 able to stop all sound getting in or out
11 unhappy because you don't have any friends
12 the amount which one cup can hold
13 not based on logical reason or clear thinking
15 the end of something's validity (e.g. legal documents, etc.)
16 you become ill or develop a rash when you come into contact with certain things

Down

2 concerning the emotions
3 friendly, pleasant to be with
4 you do not make people feel welcome or do not like guests
5 against the law
9 a lack of something that is needed
10 a new beginning
14 someone who does not tell the truth

b Work in small groups and look back to Units 8 and 9 to find other words with prefixes or suffixes. Either write definitions and give them to another group to find the word, or make a crossword puzzle or word box.

5 PAST TENSES

You are going to play *Consequences*. You will each need a large piece of paper. Your teacher will ask you to write about certain things. After each sentence, fold the paper so that no one can see what you have written, and then pass it to your neighbour to write the next sentence. Always pass the paper to the person on your left. When you have finished, read out your 'story' for the class.

11 Doing time

PART A

1 INTRODUCTION

a *Doing time* is associated with crime and criminals. What do you think it means?

b Work in pairs and write down all the types of crimes you know. Put a circle round the crimes which you consider to be the most serious.

c Compare lists with another pair. Then discuss what the punishments should be for two of the very serious crimes and two of the less serious crimes.

d Talk about the reasons people commit crimes and what can be done to combat crime.

2 READING AND SPEAKING

a Look at the headline of this article and discuss what it might be about.

b Have you heard of any road rage incidents? If you have, tell the class about them.

c Read the article and then, in pairs, choose the option – a, b or c – which you think is the most likely to complete each numbered gap.

1 a fined £500
   b jailed for five months
   c put on probation for one year
2 a had her licence confiscated for one year
   b had her car confiscated
   c has to take more driving lessons
3 a led to the cells
   b reunited with her husband
   c ordered to pay the costs of the trial
4 a who was ordered to apologise to Wade
   b who was ordered to pay him £200 in compensation
   c who was ordered to pay him £400 in compensation and was disqualified from driving for four years
5 a reckless driving
   b dangerous driving
   c driving without due care and attention
6 a common assault
   b grievous bodily harm
   c mugging
7 a defacement of property
   b vandalism
   c criminal damage

d In pairs discuss what you think of Mrs Cernuschi's sentence. Do you think that people like Mrs Cernuschi must be punished severely or do you think the judge needn't have been so harsh?

Stockbroker found guilty of road rage assault on cyclist

A woman stockbroker who exploded with 'road rage' and ran down a cyclist for clipping the wing mirror of her car was [1]................ yesterday.

Frances Cernuschi, 47, who swerved towards the bicycle 5 of Alexander Wade, a medical student, to teach him a lesson for scratching her Rover saloon, also [2]................ .

Judge Peter Fingret told the Crown Court: 'It was a deliberate assault by you, using your car as a weapon on an innocent road user.'

10 Cernuschi, dressed in a bright blue skirt and jacket suit, who earns £60,000 a year at a London stockbrokers, looked shocked as she was [3]................ . Her husband gasped with surprise.

Joe Cernuschi, 60, a retired BT engineer, said later: 'I don't want to talk about it. It's disgusting.' The couple, married for 24 15 years, have no children. Friends say she has been under strain at work and from caring for her husband, who is in poor health.

Mr Wade, 21, who suffered cuts and bruises, was knocked from his bicycle and just missed being hit by the car. His assailant, [4]................ , sped off but was pursued by a 20 motorcyclist, who alerted the police. Cernuschi admitted [5]................ , [6]................ and [7]................ .

Anne Darlow, for the prosecution, said: 'The defendant pulled up to a set of red traffic lights at the same time as Mr Wade's bike passed her car, overtaking her on the nearside. 25 He clipped her wing mirror, causing a scratch. The defendant sounded her horn and Mr Wade mouthed the word "Sorry" to her.'

But as the cyclist moved forward when the lights changed, Cernuschi swerved into the back of his bicycle and he was 30 flung into the road. 'She then drove over his rear wheel, narrowly missing Mr Wade's legs.'

Cernuschi told police she acted in a flash of temper and bitterly regretted her actions.

e Find words in the article which mean:

1 hit and injured a person with a vehicle
2 hitting someone or something with a light blow
3 changed direction suddenly
4 a family car that holds four or more people
5 intentional
6 took a short quick breath in through his mouth
7 pressure
8 attacker
9 drove away quickly
10 slowed down and stopped the car

3 GRAMMAR Modal verbs

a Work in pairs and discuss the meaning of the modal verbs in these sentences. Choose a meaning from the list for each one. You can use the meanings more than once.

(no) obligation   (no) necessity
advisability   prohibition   (in)ability
permission   willingness   probability
certainty   (im)possibility

1 Mr Wade couldn't ride his bike for two weeks because of his injuries.
2 Mrs Cernuschi could lose her job.
3 Can the jury talk to the press during the trial?
4 She can't have been imprisoned.
5 Could you help me with these papers?
6 I must drive more carefully.
7 That man must be her husband.
8 She had to hand over her driving licence.
9 She shouldn't have lost her temper.
10 If he left the court at 2pm, he should be home by now.
11 They might take her good character into consideration.
12 Mr Wade didn't have to go to hospital.
13 We didn't need to go to the police station.
14 We needn't have gone to the police station.
15 She might well have told the truth.
16 She might as well have told the truth.
17 The jury must not discuss the case outside the court.
18 You may refer to your statement.
19 If you will come this way.
20 Do you think the defendant might sit down, your Honour?

b Explain the difference in the situations in sentences 13 and 14 in **a**.

c Explain the difference in meaning in sentences 15 and 16 in **a**.

d Complete these sentences.

1 You only started that job an hour ago; you .... already!
2 I told you your toothache would get worse; you .... to the dentist's yesterday.
3 Emma .... me the money; I found my purse in the car.
4 Oh no, I haven't got my umbrella; I .... it in the café.
5 We've been waiting for an hour; you .... to let us know you would be late.
6 Thank goodness you've only got a broken arm; you .... in an accident like that.
7 Sam's car was in the drive last night; he .... from holiday yesterday.
8 You .... the washing up; I was going to do it myself later.
9 They .... the letter by now, but I'm not sure.
10 Paul .... better marks if he had tried harder.

4 PRONUNCIATION Word stress

a Mark the stressed syllable in these pairs of words.

e.g. 'criminal   crimi'nology

1 confiscate   confiscation
2 disqualified   disqualification
3 precede   precedent
4 confer   conference
5 commit   committal
6 reform   reformation
7 compensate   compensation
8 environment   environmental
9 legal   legality
10 judgement   judgemental

b What changes take place, if any, in the vowel sounds of each pair?

c Practise saying the words. Work in pairs and take it in turns to say the words and listen to each other's pronunciation.

5 LISTENING

a You are going to hear reports of two court cases from a local radio news broadcast. Corresponding newspaper headlines were 'Hotelier in the soup over foreign crab' and 'Prison threat for bird-feeding pensioner'. What do you think the reports will be about?

b [image: cassette] Listen and complete the table.

	Report 1	Report 2
1 Accused name and occupation		
2 Spouse name and occupation		
3 Reason for court appearance		
4 Court ruling		
5 Facts of the case		
6 Name(s) of people interviewed		
7 View(s) expressed		

PART B

1 SPEAKING

a Work in pairs and discuss whether these cases should have been taken to court.

1 A woman who tried to 'dry' her dog in a microwave sued the microwave manufacturers because they had not displayed a warning not to put pets in it.
2 A woman who tripped over the New York newspaper on her doorstep sued the publisher for making the newspaper too thick.
3 A woman sued a bar owner after she fell out of the bar drunk and hurt herself.
4 A film director was sued by the 'copycat' victim of a violent crime in one of his films.

b Have you heard of any similar cases? Tell a partner or the class about them.

2 READING AND SPEAKING

a Read these reports about some people who successfully took their cases to court and try to guess how much compensation each 'victim' got. Choose an amount from the list to complete each gap. Then compare answers with a partner.

£4,000   £750   £3,000

b What is your opinion of the cases you have just read about? What do you think should have happened?

c Find words in the reports with these meanings (the number of the report is given in brackets).

1 burnt by liquid or steam (1)
2 came to an arrangement between themselves rather than letting the court decide (1)
3 not admitting responsibility (1)
4 a person who rents a piece of land in order to grow vegetables or flowers (2)
5 someone who enters a place in order to commit a crime (2)
6 shocking or offensive (3)
7 triumphantly described (3)

1

THE CASE OF THE SCALDING APPLE PIE

Darren Miles, aged 28, won .... compensation from McDonald's after the hot filling from an apple pie fell out and scalded his arm.

Mr Miles fears he may be permanently scarred as a result of the accident. His lawyer said the pie had not been fit for its purpose – to be eaten immediately after sale. 'Had a child been injured in this way, it could have been a lot more serious.' McDonald's settled out of court without accepting liability.

2

The case of the burglary victim

A burglary victim was told by a court to pay .... damages – to the burglar.

Allotment holder, Ted Newbery, 82, shot an intruder in his shed. The intruder was later jailed for the burglary but he then sued Newbery for damages, claiming that the injuries had been traumatic and had 'ruined his life'. A judge awarded the damages saying that the amount would have been larger if the burglar had not been partly to blame. The judge commented: 'To poke a shotgun through a hole and fire it with the knowledge that there are people outside constitutes negligence to the point of recklessness.'

3

The case of the holiday pests

Two British women were awarded .... damages and costs after they were pestered and sexually harassed by staff at a hotel in Tunisia.

What made the case unique was that the two women, who were awarded the money for 'psychological injury', had sued the tour operators. Both tourists were on their first trip abroad and said they had to put up with unwanted attention and an obscene gesture.

Lawyers for the women hailed the case as forcing tour operators to be more careful in their choice of accommodation however, the operators are now wondering just how far their liability extends.

3 VOCABULARY Three-part phrasal verbs

a Match these three-part phrasal verbs (1–10) with their correct collocations (a–j) and definitions (i–x).

1	get away with	a	the competition	i	end a relationship
2	get round to	b	promotion	ii	apply for
3	live up to	c	a crime	iii	meet/fulfil
4	put (you) down for	d	our expectations	iv	enter
5	put (it) down to	e	doing my homework	v	discover something secret
6	be in for	f	the football team	vi	escape without punishment
7	go in for	g	your girl/boyfriend	vii	eventually do something you have been avoiding
8	be on to	h	the murderer	viii	record your name as intending to do something
9	put in for	i	a shock	ix	be going to experience something
10	split up with	j	his aristocratic upbringing	x	to believe something is caused by

b Use the verbs in the list, in their correct form, to complete the three-part phrasal verbs in these sentences.

come   get   have   make   stand

1 You'll have to learn to .... up for yourself when you leave home.
2 Most people do in fact .... on with their in-laws.
3 It was Brian who .... up with that brilliant idea.
4 I think my boss .... it in for me; he's always making things difficult.
5 Damages, even of £1 million, cannot .... up for the injury.

c Use the prepositions and adverbial phrases in the list to complete these sentences.

forward to   off with   up with   out with   over to

1 I'll have to have it .... Sam to get to the bottom of this rumour.
2 I'm looking .... seeing all my school friends at the party.
3 I hear that Mary Black has gone .... her husband's brother!
4 Do you remember when Britain went .... decimal currency?
5 I've been off sick for two weeks; it's going to be difficult to catch .... the rest of the people on the course.

d Work in pairs and paraphrase the phrasal verbs in **b** and **c** to explain their meaning.

4 READING

a You are going to read part of a newspaper article about a man called Philip Seldon. Look at the headline and, in pairs, discuss what you think the article is about.

b Read the article and complete it by putting one word in each gap.

'I have always got even. It's so therapeutic'

When Philip Seldon was a small and skinny schoolboy, he was the first child all the others picked on. A callow youth [1]............... buck teeth, in the playground he was bullied. [2]............... love, he was laughed at.

Philip started leaving embarrassing notes, [3]............... in his adversaries' handwriting and [4]............... with their names [5]............... the teacher would find them. Young Philip soon discovered [6]............... he believes to be an inarguable fact of [7]............... : revenge is [8]............... .

He moved on to [9]............... cunning ploys. [10]............... a teenager he [11]............... report, anonymously, toes who crossed [12]............... to the police for traffic violations, [13]............... as lights not working on their cars. He knew the lights did not work because he had [14]............... the bulbs.

Seldon has been getting even [15]............... since. In fact he has [16]............... a mini career of it. Now he lectures [17]............... the subject in the world's biggest battleground for getting even – New York. There is no [18]............... of willing disciples wishing to [19]............... his evening classes and learn from his experiences.

From dumped spouses to angry mothers-in-law and sacked workers, they [20]............... round the block to attend his high altar of revenge.

c In small groups discuss these questions, giving reasons for your opinions.

1 Is revenge a natural instinct?
2 Do you think revenge can usually be justified?
3 Do you agree with Philip Seldon that most people feel good after getting their revenge?
4 Have you heard of any cases of people getting their revenge? What happened and why?

5 STUDY SKILLS
Re-evaluating learning strategies

It is a good idea once in a while to stop and think about the way you are studying. This can help you make the best of your time and help you get the most out of your studies.

a Work in pairs and discuss these questions.

1 What sort of notes have you made in your Coursebook? Are they easy to read and are they helpful?
2 What sort of notes have you got in a note book or file? How is your file organised?
3 How often do you look back at the notes in your Coursebook or look ahead to the next unit?
4 How often do you look at your notes in your file?
5 How much time, in addition to your lessons, do you spend studying English? How much of this time is homework set by the teacher and how much is time spent on studying something you have chosen?
6 Work out how much free time you have and how much of it you would like to spend studying English.
7 What do you think is the best way for you to spend time on your own study?
8 What additional books have you got to help you?
9 What other facilities, like a language laboratory, computer or videos, have you got access to?
10 Which areas of the language do you think are improving well and which areas do you think you need to spend more time on?

b Make a timetable for a week or a month of your English studies; include lessons, homework and free study.

1 INTRODUCTION

a Have you ever been in a maze? What do you think the phrase *a moral maze* means?

b Work in pairs and discuss these moral questions.

1 Do you think people should be able to 'select' the sex of their children?
2 Should cigarettes be advertised on TV, in cinemas and in the street?
3 Would you buy a product if you knew that the people who had made it had been exploited or even injured?

c Think of two other 'moral' issues which you are interested in and discuss them with a partner.

2 READING

a You are going to read a newspaper article with the headline 'Battle of the Sexes'. What do you think the article is about?

b Read the article quite quickly in order to answer these questions.

1 Who is Julia?
2 Why has she gone to Naples?

BATTLE OF THE SEXES

Julia is a 34-year-old actress. She has three beautiful, bright little boys and a large house in London. Last week she and her husband, Oliver, flew to Naples, where, she hopes, she will become pregnant. If she does, she will know with absolute certainty that she is carrying the baby girl they have always longed for.

The reason for her certainty is that scientists will check whether the three-day-old, eight-cell embryo they are to implant into Julia's womb is a boy or a girl. They will do this by removing a single cell when the embryo is no bigger than the full stop at the end of this sentence. It may sound like science fiction, but it's not. The new technique which makes this possible is based on existing test-tube technology and works by creating more embryos than are needed for a pregnancy – usually around six. Then, using a method known as pre-implantation diagnosis, doctors remove the single cell and make millions of 'photocopies' of the genetic material in that cell, by a process known as Polymerase Chain Reaction (PCR). This makes it possible to check if the resulting child from that embryo would be a boy or a girl. All that remains is for the embryo of the 'right' sex to be transferred to the mother's womb.

Julia does not wish to be known by her real name because she believes some people would criticise her for having the treatment. It costs £10,000 for the first attempt, with only about a one in three chance of taking home a baby. She believes she is very fortunate to be able to afford it. 'We live in a lovely big house; we have three adorable boys and a brilliant nanny who helps to make a large family a lot less of a strain. But we do want a fourth child because otherwise the baby could easily become very spoilt because we all dote on him so much.

'We don't just want a girl as a sort of "fashion accessory". I am really into clothes and dressing up, which girls love, but I also just think I would be a good mother to a girl. I think we'd regret it in ten years' time if we didn't take the chance to use this new technique.'

Julia and Oliver have to go to Naples for treatment because the test-tube watchdog body in Britain, the Human Fertilisation and Embryology Authority, has refused to license embryo sex selection for purely social reasons.

'Given that I already have three wonderful children, I do wonder if I'm pushing my luck by fiddling around with nature. My GP was most disapproving when I approached him about it. This is a very new treatment and some people are very odd about it. For that reason we have told only some very close friends. We haven't even told our parents.'

She stresses, however, that the desire to have a girl or a boy if you already have a large number of children of the opposite sex can be all-consuming. 'I know women who are desperate to have a son and have gone on having daughter after daughter until they are quite worn out by the pregnancies. We don't have any inherited money but we are very lucky that my husband has worked hard and has a skill that allows him to have a highly paid job in the City. But I don't think treatment like this should just be available for those who can afford it.'

c According to the article are these statements true or false?

1 Julia's main aim is to have a larger family.
2 It is certain that Julia's baby will be a girl.
3 Julia is rather reluctant to tell people about what she is doing.
4 The treatment has a 100% success rate.
5 Julia admits it is difficult to give all her children her full personal attention.
6 She wants a girl so that she can indulge her own love of fashion.
7 She does have some concerns about interfering with nature.
8 Her doctor was not encouraging about the idea.
9 She acknowledges that the desire to have a child of a certain sex can become an obsession.
10 She accepts that this treatment should be paid for by the individual, not the state.

d Find words or phrases with these meanings in the article (the paragraph number is given in brackets).

1 wanted very much (1)
2 the part inside a woman's body where a baby grows before it is born (2)
3 show a great deal of love, perhaps an excessive amount (3)
4 something pretty and trendy to be seen with, like a new hat or handbag (4)
5 putting on your best clothes (4)
6 a committee whose job it is to make sure that companies do not act illegally or irresponsibly (5)
7 if you take into account that (6)
8 taking a risk (6)
9 messing/playing with (6)
10 more important to you than everything else (7)

e In small groups discuss these questions.

1 What impression does the author give of Julia's character?
2 What do you think about the fact that she is doing something which has been declared unethical by her country?
3 What might happen if people are allowed to choose the sex of their children?
4 How would you feel about being able to choose the physical and mental characteristics of 'your' baby?
5 What do you think about the way the article is written?

3 LISTENING

a 🔊 You are going to hear two doctors discussing sex selection. Listen and discuss these questions in pairs.

1 Which doctor, Victor Bridges or Janet Rainer, is for selecting the sex of children and which is against?
2 Are the doctors discussing the ethics or the science and technology of the treatment or both?
3 Why is the question of culture raised?

b 🔊 Listen again and, according to what you hear, complete these sentences.

1 Janet hasn't chosen this line of work in order to become famous or a ....
2 She argues that the .... is so strong that women should have the right to choose the sex of their child.
3 The fees for the treatment are calculated on a ....
4 If a woman has three treatments the success rate can be up to ....
5 Sex selection has developed from .... treatment.
6 In the past some people in Britain found it hard to accept that babies would be made in a ....
7 Victor argues that the treatment is .... because some embryos are thrown away.
8 In societies which prefer boys, a girl baby may be .... or may even die.
9 The risk is that in some cultures there will be a(n) .... in the sexes in the population.
10 In Europe about .... of people prefer a girl.

c Summarise Janet's argument for sex selection treatment.

d What is your own opinion? Talk about the issue in small groups considering the arguments for and against.

4 VOCABULARY Idiomatic expressions

a In the discussion in 3 Janet said *It just so happens that our clinic is the first to grasp the nettle.* What do you think the expression *grasp the nettle* means?

b Match the two halves of these other idiomatic expressions and then discuss what they mean with a partner. When you have checked their meaning with your teacher, write a sample sentence to provide a context for five of the expressions.

1 take the bull   a close to the wind
2 don't look a gift horse   b running
3 can't see the wood   c with the flow
4 hit the ground   d in the mouth
5 come up   e against the tide
6 turn over   f by the horns
7 to go   g smelling of roses
8 walk   h a new leaf
9 sail   i a fine line
10 swim   j for the trees

PART B

1 SPEAKING

Sometimes when we are discussing moral questions, it is necessary to be tactful in the way we give our opinion, disagree or make a suggestion.

a Rank these expressions for making a suggestion in order of tactfulness. 1 = the most tactful, 6 = the least tactful.

I don't see why you can't … ☐
Have you ever thought about … ? ☐
You should just … ☐
I think you ought to … ☐
Well, looking at it from that point of view, it might be better to … ☐
The best thing to do is … ☐

b Work in pairs and make a list of phrases you could use for expressing disagreement. Then rank them in order of tactfulness (1 = the most tactful).

c These situations are all based on real cases and involve some sort of moral consideration. Work in pairs and choose two of the situations. One of you should take the part of the person in question while the other tactfully gives their opinion, disagrees or makes suggestions.

1 Your great-grandfather, who is now 104 years old, still drives a car. He is very proud of the fact that his name is going to be put in *The Guinness Book of Records*. He has never taken a driving test because they weren't invented when he started driving. He has never had an accident and his only offence has been to get a parking ticket. He gets up at 5am, goes to work for three hours a day and works six days a week.

2 Your friend, a teenage girl, smokes. She smokes as a way to control her weight. She says nicotine is an appetite suppressant and it also relieves stress. You think she is being influenced by supermodels who are thin and glamorous. You've just been reading about the increase in lung cancer in young women.

3 A friend of yours is an art student but he's not very good. He got (stole) a great idea from another student about making a collage for a competition. Putting together this collage does not really require much artistic talent but it's a brilliant idea. He's going to enter the competition where the prize is £5,000. He is almost sure to win.

4 Your friend's father is a surgeon. Your friend is 15 years old and wants to go into the operating theatre with her father and help him with an operation. She can always get her own way with her father. You're a bit concerned about your friend doing this. What if something goes wrong? Who is ultimately responsible for the operation? What would be the consequences for her father if someone objected? How would the patient feel about this?

2 PRONUNCIATION
Sentence stress

a Read these sentences and underline the word(s) that would be stressed if you were trying to be tactful and persuasive. All the sentences relate to the situations in 1. Think about intonation and tone of voice.

1 You might have reached the age where it's perhaps better not to drive so much.
2 Well, you could always try to cut down on the number of cigarettes you smoke.
3 I think you really ought to use one of your own ideas.
4 Have you thought about the fact that this could have serious consequences for your father?

b ▢ Listen to the sentences in **a** to see if you were right.

c Practise saying the sentences.

d ▢ You are going to hear six sentences. Listen to them one by one and answer the question with the same number. When answering, pay particular attention to which words are stressed and where the pauses are.

1 Did she put her career first?
2 Do you know the nationality of the teacher?
3 Was Anne laughing?
4 Had Tony told everyone the same thing?
5 Was he almost sure that Simon would turn up?
6 Is he pleased or annoyed?

3 STUDY SKILLS Speaking

a Put a tick (✓) for the areas you feel reasonably confident about while speaking and a cross (✗) by the things you feel a little unsure about.

1 individual sounds ☐
2 the stress on individual words ☐
3 stressed and unstressed words in a sentence ☐
4 intonation ☐
5 speed/fluency ☐
6 extended sentences ☐
7 grammatical accuracy ☐
8 grammatical variety ☐
9 appropriate vocabulary ☐
10 linkers and fillers ☐
11 range of vocabulary ☐
12 communicative ability ☐

b Compare lists with a partner and discuss how you feel about speaking in English.

c Make a plan of how you are going to work on your speaking. First consider what materials and opportunities are available to you to practise speaking English.

d Using 'fillers' is a good way of giving yourself time to think without sounding as though you are hesitating. English-speaking people often say things like *Well, So, Let me think, Then* and *Anyway,* when they want to fill a few seconds' gap. Can you think of any more fillers? Work in small groups and make a list.

e You are going to play *Just a minute*. Choose a topic from 1 on page 42 or, if you prefer, choose a topic of your own and prepare to speak on that topic for one minute. If possible, record your talk and analyse it afterwards for strengths and weaknesses.

4 VOCABULARY Countable and uncountable nouns

a Give an example of a countable noun and an uncountable noun.

b Which of these words are countable?

accommodation	advice	baggage
equipment	furniture	illness
information	means	news
premises	progress	research

c In many cases we use a phrase when we want to make the countable form of an uncountable word, e.g. *a bar of soap*. Match these phrases (1–15) and nouns (a–o).

1 a ball of
2 an item of
3 a shot of
4 a clove of
5 a pad of
6 a slice of
7 a dab of
8 a pint of
9 a splash of
10 a head of
11 a reel of
12 a blade of
13 a hunk of
14 a round of
15 a roll of

a water/soda
b news/clothing
c paper
d beer
e grass
f bread
g hair/lettuce
h film
i lemon
j toast/bread
k perfume
l garlic
m wool
n whiskey
o cotton

5 STUDY SKILLS Summary writing

a How would you go about writing a summary of a text? Put these points in the best order.

1 Consider how you can put across the points in your own words.
2 Make a rough draft of the summary.
3 Edit your rough draft; expand or contract.
4 Finally, check for appropriate content, grammar, spelling, vocabulary and length.
5 Highlight the relevant points in the text.
6 Read the text for the first time.
7 Think about which linking words will be appropriate.
8 Write the final version of the summary.
9 Highlight the key words in the instructions for the summary.
10 Check the number of words in your summary.
11 Group the points from the text.

b extra Keeping in mind the points from **a,** read the text on page 63 and write a summary of about 70–90 words outlining the advantages and disadvantages of xenotransplantation. Don't worry if you don't know what that is – it is explained in the text.

6 GRAMMAR The passive

a Look again at the text on page 63 and underline all the examples of the passive form in the text. The first one is *But **it is feared** it could* … (lines 2–3).

b Look at your summary of the same text. Are there any sentences which use the passive form? Can you change any of your 'active' sentences into the passive?

c Put these sentences into the passive form.

1 They entered his name in *The Guinness Book of Records*.
2 They believe him to be a dangerous driver.
3 They made him stop driving.
4 They say nicotine is an appetite suppressant
5 We believe thousands of very young girls smoke.
6 He should give the money to the other student.
7 Someone has ruined the collage.
8 They thought he had acted unprofessionally.

13 Feel-good factors

PART A

1 INTRODUCTION

Work in pairs and discuss these questions.

1 Do you have some days when you feel low, down in the dumps or just lethargic and others when you feel on top of the world? Can you figure out why you sometimes feel like that?

2 What would you do to treat yourself, to make yourself 'feel good', if you felt:
   a as if you were getting a cold?
   b stressed?
   c as if you had too much nervous energy?
   d apathetic?
   e as if you couldn't concentrate?

2 LISTENING

a You are going to hear an aromatherapist talking to some new students on an aromatherapy course. What do you think she looks like? What do you think her voice will sound like? Choose which woman you think is the aromatherapist. Give reasons for your choice.

b Before you listen, work in pairs and look at the notes in **c**. Try to predict as many answers as you can.

c ▭ Listen and, according to what you hear, complete these notes.

> Aromatic oils used in three types of product:
> 1 _____
> 2 _____
> 3 _____
>
> Essential oil from oranges can be seen by:
> 4 _____
>
> Important factors when picking plants:
> 5 _____
> 6 _____
> 7 _____
>
> Sources of harm to essential oils:
> 8 _____
> 9 _____
> 10 _____ and moisture
> Not all plants used in herbal medicine are aromatic
> only: 11 _____
> Pheromones are: 12 _____
> Plants can have 'animal' characteristics, e.g.:
> 13 _____

d Discuss these questions.

1 Did you learn anything new about plants from the aromatherapist?

2 Do you know of any other examples of plant extracts being good for the body or certain conditions like sunburn?

3 Do you think plants can communicate? Do you know anyone who talks to their plants?

3 VOCABULARY Word-building

The words in this table were used by the aromatherapist in 2. Check that you understand what they mean, then fill in the other forms.

	Verb	Noun	Adjective
1	evaporate	evaporation	evaporated/evaporating
2	ignite		
3	perceive		
4	exhibit		
5	—		carnivorous
6	repel		

4 GRAMMAR Definite article or zero article?

a Work in pairs and underline the definite articles and words with zero (no) article in these sentences. Then choose an explanation for the use of the articles from A–K.

1 She's studying the history of aromatherapy.
2 The weather can have a profound effect on our personality.
3 The ancient Egyptians had a thorough knowledge of essences.
4 Some very ornate boxes and stone jars were recovered from the Egyptian tombs. The boxes were probably used for cosmetics.
5 Who invented the microscope?
6 It has been suggested that Cleopatra was in fact not a great beauty but her power and seduction was accomplished by her lavish use of perfumes.
7 Please pass the salt.
8 Yes, she met *the* Anthony Hopkins, the actor.
9 Oil of clove is one of the best ways to relieve toothache.
10 Perfume has always played an important part in society.
11 Where have you put the book I lent you?

A We have already mentioned it/them.
B We know who or what we are talking about.
C With proper names.
D We want to say something/someone is well known.
E We are talking in general about a plural or uncountable noun.
F With superlatives and *only*.
G When only one exists.
H With the natural environment.
I We say which one(s) we mean.
J In generalisations with singular countable nouns to talk about a class of things.
K When a description with *of* follows a noun.

b Summarise the rules for using the definite article and zero article by putting a tick (✓) by the explanations in **a** (A–K) where we use the definite article and a cross (✗) where we do not.

c Complete these sentences by putting either *the* or *0* (zero article) in the gaps as appropriate.

1 .... most people do not have a very keen sense of smell.
2 .... knowledge of perfumes was passed from .... Egyptians to .... Greeks.
3 .... cosmetics often contain .... antiseptics.
4 René-Maurice Gattefossé, a Frenchman, was .... first to coin the word, ... 'aromatherapy'.
5 Gattefossé lived and worked in .... area around Grasse, in .... southern France.
6 During .... Great Plague, in .... Middle Ages, fires made of .... pine wood were lit in an attempt to combat .... disease. Strangely enough, perfumers of the time were almost immune to .... disease.
7 When I get home from .... college, I put .... lavender and geranium oil into a burner.

d Work in pairs and put these places in the appropriate column of the table according to whether they take the definite article or zero article. Give an example for each. Two have been done for you. What are the exceptions to the places marked with an asterisk?

most towns/cities*   ~~hotels~~   seas   most streets*   continents
most countries*   lakes   cinemas   states/counties deserts
most mountains*   mountain ranges rivers   island groups   theatres

the	zero article
hotels (The Hilton)	most towns/cities (York)

5 WRITING

You are going to combine the work you did on the definite article with other language skills to expand these notes from 2 into full sentences. You will need to put the verbs into the correct tense and add articles, prepositions, etc. – everything to make one complete sentence.

e.g. aromatic oils – use – medicine – not only flavouring – also therapeutic ingredients
Aromatic oils are used in medicine not only as flavouring agents but also as therapeutic ingredients.

1 essential oils – highly volatile – means – readily evaporate – air
2 they – different – fatty oils – consistency – more water – oil
3 presence – oil in oranges – demonstrate – squeeze peel – lighted match
4 oil droplets – spray out – ignite – pass through flame
5 while in plant – essences – change – chemical composition
6 oils – keep – cool, dry conditions
7 all animals – inc. humans – own characteristic smell
8 commonly – not aware – own smell – other people's
9 scent of plant – attract – insects – move – plant to plant – fertilisation – take place
10 essences – many plants – natural defence mechanism – repel insects – otherwise – harm – plant

6 VOCABULARY Synonyms for *smell*

a Work in pairs and divide these nouns, which all mean *smell*, into two groups – positive and negative. Two of the words can go in both groups. Think about what you associate with the word and this may help you decide if it has a positive or negative connotation, e.g. the *aroma* of coffee. Say which one of the words is informal.

aroma   fragrance   odour   perfume   pong   scent   smell   stench   stink   whiff

b What exactly do the words mean? How many of them have an adjectival form and what is it?

c What does the expression *to smell a rat* mean?

PART B

1 STUDY SKILLS Listening

a Work in pairs and discuss what you find easy and what you find difficult about listening to English.

b 🎧 You are going to hear six extracts from different speakers. Listen and number the pictures to say what each extract is about.

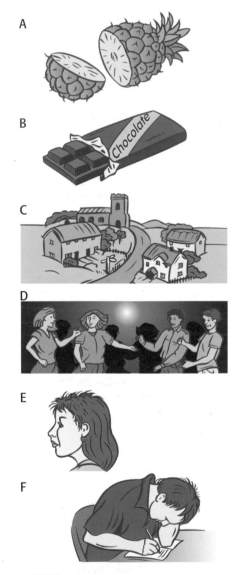

A

B

C

D

E

F

c 🎧 Listen again and say which speakers you found easy to understand, which more difficult. Why were some difficult and others easy to understand?

d What would you say to the speakers in 1, 2, 4 and 5 so that you could understand them better?

e What could you do to improve your listening skills in the areas you have identified as being difficult?

f 🎧 Look at these pictures and predict what the interactions are about. Then listen and predict the rest of the conversations.

2 PRONUNCIATION Silent letters

Working on your pronunciation can help you understand spoken English. Understanding pronunciation can explain why it sometimes sounds as if people are 'swallowing' words or sounds.

a Work in pairs. How are these words pronounced and how many syllables are there?

e.g. *chocolate /tʃɒklət/ is pronounced with two syllables*

1 chocolate	4 difference	7 preferable	10 vegetable
2 cholesterol	5 interesting	8 medicine	
3 comfortable	6 literature	9 temperature	

b 🎧 Now listen and repeat the words in **a**.

c 🎧 Listen and write down the number of words and the number of syllables in each phrase you hear. You will hear each phrase twice.

d 🎧 Now listen and repeat the phrases from **c**.

3 GRAMMAR Definite, zero and indefinite articles

For many people a really good way to relax, solve problems, get over the stresses and strains of the day is to get a good night's sleep. Our body can rejuvenate itself, hence the phrase *I must get my beauty sleep*, and sometimes we work out our problems in our dreams.

a Discuss these questions about dreams.

1 How often do you dream?
2 Do you dream in colour?
3 Can you usually see a connection between your daytime activities and your dreams?
4 Would you ever change a course of action because of a dream you have had?
5 Dreaming of spiders, irrespective of any fear you may have of them, is supposed to be a token of good luck or good news, particularly in matters of money. Do you know any other interpretations of dreams?

b In this extract from a book about dreams there are some mistakes in the use of articles – *a/an*, *the* and zero article. Write the corrections above the mistakes, inserting the article if it is missing. If the use of the article is correct, put a tick above it. The first sentence has been done for you.

PROBLEM SOLVING DREAMS

In Western world we tend to rely heavily on a value of reasoning. [*the* above Western; ✓ above; *the* above value]
The scientific research is based on the power of the deductive thinking. But it is by no means the only way of reaching conclusion. How often have we heard a phrase 'Let's sleep on it',
5 which shows clearly that, amid all rational logic, part of us acknowledges an intuitive power of unconscious to deal with a problem overnight.

There are many examples of solutions to problems arriving in a dream. In 1869, a Russian chemist Dmitri Mendeleev, having
10 attempted in vain to find the solution, went to the bed one night and dreamed that he saw a table of the elements, in which 'they fell into the place as required'. When he woke up he carefully made a note of the dream and subsequently found that only one change was necessary to what later
15 became known as periodic table of the elements, the major development in science.

There are many such reported cases in the 19th century, and similar dreams are still being experienced. The American golfer Jack Nicklaus, for example, found that his play had slipped
20 until 79 was his best round-the-course average. He didn't know why. He just wasn't doing his best any more. Then one night he had a dream about his golf swing. In a dream he was playing much better than the usual, and he realized he was holding the club in the different way.

In the Western world we tend to rely heavily on a value of reasoning. [*the* above Western; *the* above value; ✓]

4 VOCABULARY Expressions with *make* and *do*

In the text in 3 we read *he **made** a note of* and *he just wasn't **doing** his best*. Certain phrases take *make* and others *do*.

a Put the correct form of *make* or *do* into these sentences.

1 She's .... arrangements to take some time off in the autumn.
2 If we .... more exercise, I'm sure we would feel better.
3 Even .... the housework can be a way to get fit!
4 I'm losing concentration; I .... the same mistake twice.
5 He .... 80 miles per hour all the way; no wonder he's stressed out.
6 They .... research into sleep patterns over the past 20 years.
7 A lot of perfume companies .... a lot of money out of .... people feel good.
8 I think I'll .... an exception and leave work on time today instead of late.
9 Could you .... me a favour and take this over to Sara's office, please?
10 The coffee machine .... such a noise, I thought it was going to explode.

b Work in pairs and discuss the meaning of these expressions with *make*. Identify which expressions are particularly informal.

1 He's got it made.
2 It made my day.
3 He made such a meal of it!
4 I think we've made a hash of this.
5 We'll have to make do with this.
6 It's difficult to make ends meet.
7 I can't make head nor tail of this.
8 It's make or break this year.
9 Make yourself scarce.
10 You're making a mountain out of a molehill.

14 Style file

1 INTRODUCTION

a Work in pairs. Look at the pictures and discuss these questions.

1 Describe the styles in the pictures. How do you react to the way these people look? Which styles do you like the most and the least?
2 Why do you think they have chosen to wear these clothes and look like this?
3 How would you describe your own style?

b Work in pairs and match these words to the pictures in **a**.

baggy trousers   sloppy T-shirt
suit and tie   ankle bracelet
muted colours   slinky dress
bare-footed   belt   frayed
faded jeans   high-heels   scarf
straw hat   trainers

2 READING AND SPEAKING

a You are going to read a magazine article about English men and their lack of dress sense. Do you think women are more fashion-conscious than men in your country? If you are a man, do you like shopping for clothes? If you are a woman, do you know any men who like shopping for clothes?

b Read the article on page 51. Then, working in pairs, choose the best heading, A–H, for each paragraph, 1–6. There are two extra headings which do not fit.

A It's in his genes
B Don't let him out on his own
C Evenly matched
D He's mine
E Act on impulse
F Drastic measures
G A war of attrition
H Style means suffering

c Work in pairs and expand the headings in **b** or write a few sentences in your own words to summarise the paragraphs of the article. Do not worry too much about the meaning of individual words – just summarise the general meaning of each paragraph.

d Find words in paragraphs 1–3 of the article which mean:

1 extremely ugly
2 the most impressive item
3 importance
4 walking without lifting your feet properly off the ground
5 ragged from extensive use
6 speak in a soft quiet voice
7 become creased
8 be strongly affected by feelings when we admire something
9 trouble or fighting
10 concerning tailoring
11 even though it is
12 kind or gentle
13 try to persuade by saying nice things
14 persuade by speaking in a gentle way
15 careful attention
16 in case

e Go through paragraphs 4–6 and underline any words you do not know.

f Work in pairs. Ask your partner if he/she knows any of the words you have underlined in **e**. Then use English–English dictionaries to find out the meanings of the words you do not know.

Style wars

1 A

Men are genetically programmed to choose the most hideous shirt, pair it with a nasty pair of trousers and, the pièce de résistance, some 'fun' socks.
5 Men buy slip-on shoes, polyester blousons, navy blazers with gold buttons and ties adorned with naff motifs. They think a T-shirt they get free by collecting lager-can ring-pulls
10 is a bargain. They think coloured underpants prove they are an interesting person. They have no taste.

2

Part of the problem is the premium men put on comfort. A bloke is never
15 happier than when shuffling around in a ten-year-old sweatshirt and jeans so tattered some might consider them a tad risqué. But if style were about comfort, then the shell suit would be
20 on every designer catwalk. The sex who squeeze their toes into stilettos know this. So we coo over beige linen trousers suits – 'Yes they will crumple, you'll just have to avoid sitting down
25 too often, darling' – and we swoon over cashmere sweaters – 'If you're worried about dog hair, we'll get rid of the dog, honey' – while they look at us as though we've just been released
30 from the nearest mental institution.

3

Faced with this kind of attitude, it is little wonder that women will accept nothing less than total surrender in the wardrobe wars. And this is where the
35 strife comes in. For while a chap may be willing to compromise over many things – his mother, his friends, his football practice every Sunday morning – it takes years to wear down sartorial
40 independence. For him to accept sartorial dictatorship, albeit a benign one, requires a variety of assaults. You wheedle, you coax, you threaten. Every bit of ground won must be defended
45 and constant vigilance maintained lest he mount a surreptitious coup d'état.

4

I have an ex-boyfriend who had a collection of truly appalling shoes. You know the type, with little fiddly bits of
50 gold tacked to the side. After several months he was finally persuaded that a new pair might be a good idea. 'I'll come with you,' I said with the merest touch of menace. He wasn't keen.
55 When we arrived at the shop, he adjourned as far as possible from me and began fingering the shoes with gold bits. Here was a man in the grip of a desire to show his independence. In
60 this situation, manners go out of the window. Only a resolute 'They're disgusting' prevented him from purchasing yet more ugly shoes.

5

Dealing with a man who is adamant
65 that he has superlative fashion taste, as opposed to one who merely takes a fancy to something dodgy occasionally, is the most difficult of all. A friend of mine once waited until her partner had
70 gone to work and then filled three bin-bags with all the clothes she hated. She then dispatched them to the nearest charity shop. Yes, he was miffed. Yes, he did force her to tell him which shop
75 they had gone to. And yes, he did march down there the next day to buy back what she had thrown out. Sadly for him, every garment had already been sold.

6

Why do we bother? It is not simply a
80 matter of wanting him to look better. In the same way that a cowboy brands his steer, so a girl feels the need to place her stamp on her man. And why do women do this? If you have a new
85 boyfriend you immediately want to remove any trace of forerunners. This means not only a new haircut and new aftershave but a whole new wardrobe as well.

3 WRITING

You totally disagree with the article in 2. If you are male, perhaps you find it insulting; if you are female, perhaps it does not in any way reflect the attitude of your boyfriend, husband, brother or father.

a Work in pairs and prepare to write an article for the same magazine giving the opposite point of view. Choose which points in the article you want to oppose, plan your ideas, find some good words and expressions and then produce a first draft of your article.

b Exchange first drafts with another pair and comment on these points.

1 the layout and organisation of ideas
2 grammatical queries and range of grammar
3 vocabulary – appropriateness and range
4 the use of linkers
5 the tone of the article
6 the effect the article will have on the readers

c Write the final version.

4 STUDY SKILLS Writing

a How did you feel about doing the writing activity in 3? How do you usually feel when you have to write something in English or your own language?

b Make a list of the things you might have to write in English now and in the future. Give each type of writing you have listed one, two or three stars to indicate how easy or difficult you think it is (* = easy).

c What do you usually do about the mistakes you have made in your writing?

d extra You will find one writer's response to the article in 2 on page 62. Work in pairs and discuss what is good about this learner's work. Correct any mistakes you can find.

PART B

1 SPEAKING

a What sort of style do you associate with different countries? Some people say that France stands for elegant fashion and good food. What would you say about these countries? If you prefer, choose four countries of your own to talk about.

1 Italy
2 USA
3 Japan
4 Switzerland
5 Argentina
6 Britain

b How would you describe the style of your country if it is not listed in **a**?

c When you talked about Britain did you talk about historical or contemporary things? Why?

2 READING AND SPEAKING

a Very rich families in Britain used to have butlers and some still do. The butler, in novels, plays and jokes, has come to represent the 'English gentleman'. What is your opinion about employing servants to work in your home? Is it common in your country?

b Read this extract from an article called 'The English butler', then close your books and, in pairs, summarise in your own words how the world of a butler has changed.

Butlering has inevitably adapted to modern ways – a dark suit is more common now than tails and a stiff collar – but the demand for ⁵servants of all sorts has actually been increasing. It was estimated recently that the middle classes now spend £4 billion a year on nannies, cooks, cleaners and ¹⁰gardeners, four times as much as ten years ago. Historically the number of live-in servants is in decline – 200,000 in the UK, compared with 1.4 million just ¹⁵before the second world war – but the nature of employers is changing too.

The nouveaux riches find it more difficult to strike the balance ²⁰between formality and intimacy that characterises the archetypal butler-employer relationship. First-name terms are clearly not on, but Americans find that difficult to ²⁵handle. The politically correct lifestyle also limits a butler's range. A British butler to an American singer once quit through boredom, because the health-conscious ³⁰singer was on a diet of carrots.

The butler of the future will need all the discretion of his predecessors but some new skills as well. British butlers being trained for the American market ³⁵are now instructed in how to deflect passes from their employers' wives. The approved response is, 'Madam, I am trusted by your husband. Never would I ⁴⁰defile anything that is so sacred to him. Because I am trusted by you, what has just occurred will be forever locked in my memory.'

3 GRAMMAR Inversion

In the extract in 2 there is an example of an inversion in *Never **would I** defile anything that is so sacred to him*.

a Look at these other examples of inversion. Underline the phrase or word which determines the use of inversion and highlight, in a different colour, the inversion structure.

e.g. *No sooner had we arrived than the butler brought us cocktails.*

1 Hardly had lunch finished when we were brought a sumptuous tea.
2 On no account was the butler permitted to smile.
3 Should we require your services later in the evening, we will ring for you.
4 So badly did my boss treat me that I had no option but to resign.
5 Lord Barchester has estates in Scotland, as do many of the aristocracy.
6 Not only was the butler expected to iron the newspapers but he was also expected to warm the toilet seat!
7 Here are your letters.
8 Above the mantlepiece hung a portrait of Lady Barchester.
9 'I'm so glad I'm not a butler.' 'So am I.'
10 Neither in France nor in Italy have I seen so many fine clothes as here.

b When do we use inversion and how do we construct it?

c What is wrong with these sentences?

1 In the garden did stand a statue of Venus.
2 Here is coming Mr Franklin.
3 Across the road dashed she.

d Complete these sentences.

1 As soon as she had gone to sleep, the phone rang.
   No sooner ....
2 'I'd better be going now.'
   'So .... I'm late too.'
3 Mick is a talented singer and he also plays the piano very well.
   Not only ....
4 The butler was not allowed to enter a room without knocking under any circumstances.
   Under no circumstances ....
5 I didn't expect for one moment to see you here.
   Not for one moment ....

e Rewrite these sentences, starting with the words in italics.

1 We had *hardly* taken in the news when the police knocked on the door.
2 If I *had* known who he was, I would have introduced myself immediately.
3 She was *so* embarrassed that she ran out of the room.
4 We met them *only* yesterday.
5 The most beautiful woman I had ever seen was *opposite* me at dinner.

f You will hear 10 statements on the cassette. Listen and agree with what you hear using *So … I* or *Neither … I*. Remember to change the verb according to what you hear.

e.g. I like big dogs.
So do I.
I've never had a pet.
Neither have I.

g Listen again and this time disagree with the statements.

e.g. I like big dogs.
Do you? I don't.
I've never had a pet.
Haven't you? I have.

4 SPEAKING AND READING

A popular image of British lifestyle is that families like pets, and to a large extent it's true – cats, dogs, guinea pigs and fish being some of the most popular.

a Work in pairs and discuss these questions.

1 What do you think about keeping pets? What are the advantages and disadvantages?
2 Have you heard of 'electronic pets' called Tamagotchis, the very small computer games which you have to 'feed' and 'look after', otherwise they begin to 'fade away'? Why do you think such a thing became popular?

b Read these extracts from a review of dog breeds and match the descriptions (A–D) to the pictures (1–4).

Puppy love – *the fashion that can vanish at the flick of a tail*

A An elegant, glamorous dog that can look wonderful if a lot of time is spent grooming its coat. Aloof, even stand-offish with strangers, but bred to chase at high speed, so even at 30kg can cover 100 yards in ten seconds.

B Devoted pet (average weight 7kg), which doesn't need much exercise and is happiest pottering round the house and garden. Inclined to snort and snore in old age and, like all smaller breeds, lives a long time, into its late teens.

C Smallest breed in the world, weighing around 2kg. Easy to pick up, but not a dog for children – dropping from a child's arms is the equivalent of our falling from a first-floor window. Good house dog that will bark to tell you when anyone's about. Short-haired ones need no more than a polish with a duster, but the long-haired variety takes more time.

D Average weight 12kg. The Pembroke variety lives in palaces; the Cardigan has a long tail. Small dogs, easily carried. The dense undercoat keeps water out but can collect mud – and worse. With hearty appetites and short legs, weight-watching is essential to avoid owning a walking barrel.

c Ask a partner about his/her family and lifestyle (it can be true or made up). Then advise him/her which dog would be suitable as a pet.

5 VOCABULARY Compound words

a *Weight-watching* is an example of a compound word from paragraph D in 4. What does it mean and what part of speech is it in the text?

b Underline the other compound words in the extracts in 4 and discuss with a partner what they mean and what part of speech they are.

c Match a word from the left with a word from the right to make 10 compound words. Decide if the words are adjectives or nouns. There is a hyphen for the words which are hyphenated.

1	back	a	splitting
2	butter	b	activated
3	camera-	c	handed
4	day-	d	shy
5	get-	e	biting
6	high-	f	boggling
7	late	g	fingers
8	mind-	h	together
9	side-	i	comer
10	voice-	j	tripper

d Listen to the compound words from **c** and mark the stress on each one, e.g. '*weight-watching*.

e What is the general rule for the stress in compound words and which of the compound words in **c** is an exception to the rule?

f Write a short paragraph describing your 'style' in clothes, music or decor using some compound words.

15 Basic instinct

1 INTRODUCTION

Work in pairs and discuss these questions.

1 What do we mean when we say *basic instinct*?
2 How many basic instincts do we have and what are they?
3 Does education teach us to refine our instincts?
4 To what extent should we follow our instincts and to what extent should we conform to society's 'rules'?

2 READING

a You are going to read an article about a woman who got a job studying primates in a remote area of Zaïre. The man who chose her for the job relied on his instinct to some degree. Before you read the article, discuss these questions in pairs.

1 Would you be able to give up your life as you know it to do research in a remote place?
2 Which subjects might you be interested in researching and why?
3 Do you think there is a natural difference between the subjects men are good at and the subjects women are good at?
4 To what extent do mothers bring up boys to be boys and girls to be girls?

b Read the article and answer the questions on page 55.

BASIC instinct

SIX WEEKS AFTER leaving hospital minus her appendix, Dian Fossey received a letter from the famous palaeontologist, the late Louis Leakey.
5 'Actually,' he wrote, 'there is really no dire need to have your appendix removed. That's only my way of testing applicants' determination.'
To sacrifice your appendix for the
10 chance to live alone in a small hut on damp and misty slopes in Zaïre to get to know a group of mountain gorillas shows real commitment, which is precisely what Leakey needed for the
15 project. Fossey passed his careful scrutiny. She also fulfilled another criterion: she was a woman, and

Leakey felt strongly that women were more suited to the job of studying
20 primate behaviour.
Fossey was one of three women who were to transform our knowledge of primate society and become famous for their studies of primates under
25 Leakey's auspices. His choice of the three women was governed more by a reckoning of character than by formal credentials. Two of the three did not have a degree, which Leakey felt was
30 a positive recommendation. He believed it was better to have an observer who was not a scientist, whose data-collection methods were not already embedded in a paradigm

35 of scientific theory, an observer with an unfettered mind. It was also no accident that he selected women. As Mary Smith, a senior editor at *National Geographic* magazine, who
40 worked closely with Leakey, said: 'He trusted women for their patience, persistence and perception – traits which he thought would make them better students of primate behaviour.'
45 Perhaps women are more patient and persistent, better able to sit for hours in solitude. Men appear to want results faster, needing a 'breakthrough' to keep them
50 motivated. But there may be more to it than that – qualities of empathy and intuition may be more significant in making women good observers of animal behaviour. It has been
55 suggested that women have these qualities because until recently they spent much of their time raising babies. To be a good mother you not only have to be patient but you also
60 have to understand the needs of an infant who cannot speak. Women might therefore have built-in advantages in studying animals whose communication is non-verbal.
65 The intriguing question is, while women may possess many qualities which make them suited to studying animals in the wild, what motivates them to give up the trappings of their
70 lives in the West, leave behind lovers, family and friends for a simple, solitary and often dangerous life in the bush?

1 Explain in your own words why Louis Leakey had suggested Dian Fossey should have her appendix taken out.
2 What sort of life would the successful applicant have in Zaïre?
3 Explain in your own words the phrase *more by a reckoning of character than by formal credentials*.
4 Why did Leakey think it may be an advantage to have researchers who did not have a degree?
5 Which qualities in researchers did Leakey think an advantage in the study of primates?
6 In which ways may male researchers be different to female ones?
7 Which two less tangible characteristics may make women better researchers in this field?
8 Explain in your own words why non-verbal communication may come more naturally to women.
9 What, according to the author, is the big unanswered question?
10 In a paragraph of 70–90 words summarise the possible advantages of having unqualified female researchers.

3 VOCABULARY Prepositions

In the article in 2 you read that Leakey believed women *were more suited to the job* of working with primates. *To be suited* is followed by the preposition *to*.

Complete these sentences with the correct prepositions.

1 Dian was committed .... her work from the outset.
2 She has become famous .... her work with primates.
3 Certain male/female attitudes are embedded .... our society.
4 Not everyone would be good .... carrying out meticulous research.
5 Dian accepted that for much of the time she would live her life .... solitude.
6 There were several occasions when her life was .... danger
7 She was determined to complete her research .... all costs.
8 She gathered behavioural information .... means of almost constant surveillance.
9 .... the main, she achieved her life's dream.
10 Giving up before completing the project was .... the question.
11 She was left to her own devices; few people interfered .... her work.
12 She took great pleasure .... observing female primates with their young.
13 Dian was able officially to take credit .... all her work once the research was published.
14 She took pity .... young primates who had lost their mothers through poaching.
15 Dian's family were not opposed .... her leaving for Zaïre as they knew it was her life's ambition.

4 PRONUNCIATION Chunking

By 'chunking' we mean the way words are grouped together when we speak in 'chunks' of meaning.

a Go through this extract of spoken English and decide where the speaker will pause, where the 'chunks' of speech divide, by putting // for the divisions.

The day a friend of mine disclosed her plan to withdraw her six-year-old son from our local primary school to educate him at home with his two younger brothers, I thought it was mad, bad and dangerous: mad to have three boys under your feet all day long, bad to risk them becoming isolated and withdrawn, and dangerous to attempt teaching them things that most mums have never even heard of. I had this nightmare vision of her sons becoming maladjusted child prodigies constantly chaperoned by pushy over-protective parents.

b Now listen and check where the pauses are.

c Listen again and read in time with the cassette.

d A limerick is a humorous poem which has five lines, a special rhythm and its own way of rhyming. Listen to these limericks and answer the questions.

1 Which lines rhyme with each other?

A skeleton once in Khartoum
Invited a ghost to its room.
They spent the whole night
In the eeriest fight
As to who should be frightened of whom.

2 How many beats are there in each line?

There was an old man of Blackheath,
Who sat on his set of false teeth.
Said he, with a start,
'Oh Lor' bless my heart!
I have bitten myself underneath!'

3 Which words, and which syllables in them, are stressed in each line?

There was a young man of Devizes,
Whose ears were of different sizes.
The one that was small
Was of no use at all,
But the other won several prizes.

e Listen to the third limerick again, one line at a time. Repeat each line to yourself, then listen again and say it aloud. Finally, listen again and say the limerick in time with the cassette.

PART B

1 LISTENING

a You are going to hear three mothers talking about their attitudes to their children watching TV. They all have a different point of view. What different points of view do you think you will hear?

b 📼 Listen to Mrs Rampton, Mrs Hollett and Mrs Tanner. As you listen, complete the table.

	The Ramptons	The Holletts	The Tanners
Parents' job(s)	—	5	10
Number and age of children	1	6	11
Mother's attitude to TV	2	7	12
Mother's policy on children's viewing	3	8	13
Mother's view of children's character	4	9	14

c Work in small groups and discuss what you think of these three families and their attitudes to TV.

d Do you think TV is a 'waste of time' or the world's greatest educator?

2 GRAMMAR Indirect speech

We quite often want to report what someone has said, e.g. you might want to tell someone what the three mothers in 1 said about their children watching TV.

a Read through these sentences and, working in pairs, change the indirect speech back into direct speech. Then talk about which 'rule' of indirect speech the underlined section of each sentence illustrates.

1 She said she thought that programme <u>was</u> facile.
2 She said we had to turn it off <u>right away</u>.
3 They said they had lived <u>there</u> all their lives.
4 He said we <u>should</u> only watch documentaries.
5 He asked her <u>if</u> she approved of daytime TV.
6 We wondered <u>who</u> the main actor was.
7 They say watching TV <u>is</u> bad for our eyes.
8 He's promised that he <u>will buy</u> a TV in the New Year.
9 Can you believe it? She said she <u>was</u> 15.
10 He told us <u>to turn</u> the TV off at 9pm.

b Change the direct speech in these sentences into indirect speech.

1 'We have decided to raise our daughter in a TV-free environment.'
2 'I can't turn my back on TV completely.'
3 'Do you think TV makes a good babysitter?'
4 'We've lived here since last year.'
5 'My daughters are nine and 10.'
6 'Don't forget to switch the TV off.'
7 'It's difficult to say when the family's TV viewing begins and ends.'
8 'I don't want to fight with my children when I come home from work.'
9 'I think we'd better let our children watch certain programmes so that they can keep up with their friends.'
10 'When Eleanor turned seven she began to feel painfully different.'

c It is usually better style, especially in writing, to use a variety of verbs to introduce indirect speech instead of just *say* or *tell*. This means that a greater range of structures are used, e.g. *-ing* forms and infinitives. Match the reporting verbs (a–o) to the statements (1–15). Then write the direct speech in reported speech.

e.g. 'I think you shouldn't let your children watch so much TV.'
*She **advised** me not to let my children watch so much TV.*

1 'That's only my way of testing applicants' determination.'
2 'I wish I hadn't had my appendix out.'
3 'I'm grateful you gave me this opportunity.'
4 'It will take you about six years to complete the research.'
5 'I'm convinced women make better observers of primates.'
6 'I'm sorry the results have taken so long.'
7 'Yes, some of my researchers don't have a degree.'
8 'You should teach children through activities.'
9 'Don't let adult male primates get too close.'
10 'You shouldn't have tried to educate your children yourself at home.'
11 'I don't think Andrei should be in charge of the project.'
12 'You will have to work late to get these reports finished.'
13 'OK, you can employ another two assistants.'
14 'Don't worry, you'll get used to it.'
15 'Well done! You've completed the research in 10 months.'

a agree
b apologise
c assure
d blame
e confirm
f congratulate
g estimate
h explain
i insist
j object
k order
l regret
m suggest
n thank
o warn

3 SPEAKING

In conversation we often need to use phrases for giving our opinion, agreeing and disagreeing, expressing uncertainty and making suggestions.

a Work in pairs and try to add two or three words or phrases to each section of the table. You are going to need some of these phrases for a mini-debate.

Giving your opinion	Expressing uncertainty
Well, what I think is …	*That's a difficult question.*
Agreeing/Disagreeing	Making a suggestion
That's interesting, but …	*Mmm. Let's think. Shall we …*

b Work in small groups and have a mini-debate on some of these topics. One person from each group can start the discussion with one of the statements or questions. Try to use phrases from a when appropriate.

1 Aggression is a basic instinct so we'll never be able to get rid of violence and wars.
2 Do you think it's true that women make better researchers because they are more patient?
3 Controlling our instincts is the process of civilisation.
4 How do you think parents should 'control' what their children watch on TV?
5 Once children are at school the influence of their peers is greater than that of their parents.
6 I think people who go off into the wilds to live with and study wild animals are social misfits. That's why they do it.

4 STUDY SKILLS Progress review

Complete this self-assessment questionnaire on the progress you have made through *Advance Your English*.

1 Which areas of the language do you feel you have improved the most?
   a speaking   c reading   e grammar
   b listening   d writing   f vocabulary

2 Which areas would you like to work on more in the future?

3 How are you going to do that?

4 How well do you think you have done in these areas?   ☺ ☹
   a taking part in pairwork activities in class   ☐ ☐
   b taking part in class discussion   ☐ ☐
   c trying to improve pronunciation   ☐ ☐
   d listening to the teacher   ☐ ☐
   e listening to other class members   ☐ ☐
   f listening to the cassette   ☐ ☐
   g doing homework   ☐ ☐
   h trying to correct written mistakes   ☐ ☐
   i trying to use new vocabulary   ☐ ☐
   j reviewing new language regularly   ☐ ☐
   k spending your own time learning or practising English ☐ ☐
   l keeping all your notes in your file in good order   ☐ ☐

16 Review of Units 11–15

1 MODAL VERBS AND INDIRECT SPEECH

a You are going to play *What's the problem?* Your teacher will stick a note on your back outlining a problem, but you will not know what it says. Mingle with the class and *silently* read other people's problems. You then have to go to someone and give them advice about their 'problem' without mentioning what the problem is. The person with the 'problem' has to guess what the problem is.

When you give advice use as many of these forms as possible:

> *You can …*
> *You could …*
> *You should …*
> *You ought to …*
> *You will have to …*
> *You might as well …*

b Tell the class what advice you were given using indirect speech.

2 THREE-PART PHRASAL VERBS

a Write the words in these sentences in the correct order. They all contain three-part phrasal verbs.

1 with idea come Fiona brilliant up has a.
2 that know you up I noise can don't with how put.
3 I'll I'm Maria round so get know to when busy visiting don't I.
4 your on you neighbours with get do?
5 from to at away forward are it we looking Christmas all getting.

b Work in pairs and look back to Unit 11 to find three more three-part phrasal verbs. Write a sentence for each and ask your teacher to check that it is correct. Now write your sentence out again in large letters and cut it up into individual words. When you are ready, exchange words with another pair to put in the correct order.

c How many different three-part phrasal verbs can you make from these words?

face	along	at
grow	out	with
go	up	to
cut	on	on
keep	down	for
miss	in	of
come		
settle		

d Choose five of your phrasal verbs from **c** and write a sentence for each which shows the meaning and use of the verb.

3 COUNTABLE AND UNCOUNTABLE NOUNS

Work in pairs and label the pictures using a countable phrase for each.

e.g. *a bar of soap*

4 THE PASSIVE

extra Divide into two groups. Group A prepares answers to Questionnaire B on page 62. Group B prepares answers to Questionnaire A on page 62. When you are ready, choose a person from the other group and ask him/her your questions.

5 ARTICLES

In this extract from a book called *Human Jungle*, there are some mistakes in the use of articles – *a/an*, *the* and zero article. Read through the text and correct the mistakes. Put a tick where the use of the article is correct. The first sentence has been done for you.

Primary territory: our homes

~~The~~ ^A animals mark out their personal territory by means of ✓ variety of ^a signals and scents which indicate they will defend it aggressively if necessary. When outside their own territory, the domestic animals such as dogs engage in the temporary marking but are less likely to defend
5 this territory. Often when they meet some other dog in the more public terrain which has been marked by many dogs, they move into an series of sniffing rituals to decide on the response.

Primary territory of humans is their home or land. Ownership is documented by means of a contract and other formal records, but is also
10 usually signalled by the physical boundaries such as the fences and doors. The defence of this space is enshrined in law and anybody crossing boundaries without permission faces potential sanctions. Underlying territorial possession is an idea of control. Owners are seen to have absolute control over their primary space. Clear markers of a
15 ownership such as signs and boundaries serve to prevent any invasion.

Animals exhibit less conflict when the ownership of space is clearly demarcated. There is some suggestion that a similar situation may prevail for the humans. Where the ownership of primary areas is distinguished unambiguously, the relationships may be more harmonious. However,
20 the unambiguous marking of territory (and the resulting harmonious relationships) can only occur when those involved accept the boundaries. The possession of broader based territories can be seen with the urban gangs who mark the boundaries of their territory with a graffiti. The acceptance by other gangs of these boundaries reduces the conflict,
25 and gang conflict arises where territory is disputed, and when the boundaries are less clear or not marked.

6 EXPRESSIONS WITH *MAKE* AND *DO*

a Which of these words form an expression with *make* and which with *do*?

arrangements
a deal
an exception
a favour
homework
a good/bad impression
money
research
time
someone credit
an effort
exercise
harm
housework
inquiries
a mistake
a noise
sense
way

b Can you add any more expressions to the list?

c Write three sentences using an expression with *make* and three with *do*. Erase the verb *make* or *do* in each sentence and then give it to a partner to complete.

7 COMPOUND WORDS

Complete the crossword using the clues to help you find the missing compound words. A = across, D = down.

1A	where you stick pictures, articles, etc., to make a collection (plural)
2D	saying unpleasant things about someone who is not present
6D	temporary and probably poor quality
17D/16A	an informal meeting or party
8A	so shocked you cannot speak
9D/1D	extremely frightened
11A	a person who drops or cannot catch something
12D/3D	verbal rebuke from someone for something you have done wrong
13A/5A	very competitive, not caring if you harm another person to get what you want
13D/4D	nervous or uncomfortable about being filmed or having a photo taken
14A	someone who arrives after the time they should have done
15A/18A	so complicated or amazing it is very hard to imagine
7D/10A	using authority in an unnecessarily forceful way

59

UNIT 2, PART A, 4 READING AND WRITING, a, PAGE 7

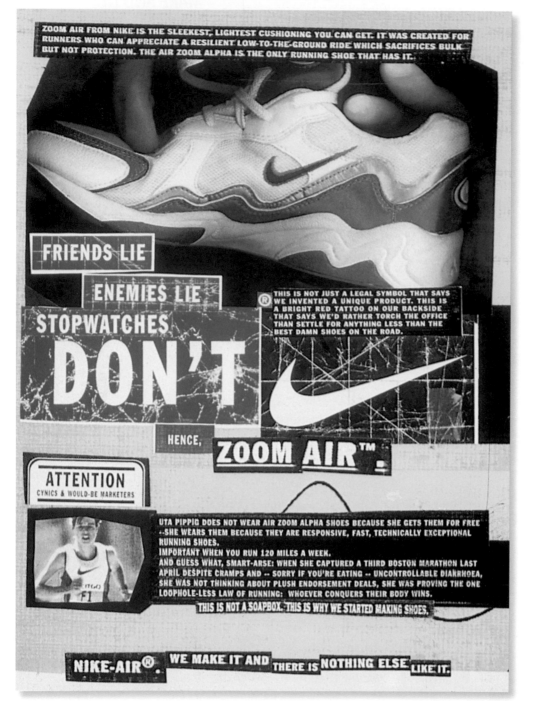

UNIT 4, PART A, 3 GRAMMAR, d, PAGE 15

Future chairs

Put four chairs at the front of the class and label them *will/shall*, **present continuous**, **present simple** and *to be going to*. Your teacher will give you a piece of paper with a use of the future written on it, e.g. *to make a promise*. You write a sentence to illustrate that use on a piece of paper. You can make it funny if you like. When everyone has written one sentence, the teacher will collect the pieces of paper, shuffle them and leave them on the desk face down. You then take turns to pick up a piece of paper, sit on the chair which represents the future form used in the sentence, e.g. *will/shall* for *making a promise*, and say the sentence, e.g. *I'll make dinner tonight*. The others must guess who wrote the sentence.

UNIT 8, PART A, 2 SPEAKING AND READING, c, PAGE 28

Colour choice	You see yourself as
red	ambitious, energetic, extroverted
pink	affectionate, compassionate, sympathetic
maroon	sensuous, emotional, gregarious
orange	competent, action-oriented, impatient
peach	gentle, charitable, dexterous
yellow	expressive, social, people-oriented
mint green	modest, insightful, composed
apple green	innovative, self-motivated, changeable
green	benevolent, service-oriented, scientific
blue green	faithful, sentimental, inventive
light blue	creative, perceptive, analytical
dark blue	intelligent, responsible, self-reliant
mauve	reserved, sensitive, encouraging
purple	intuitive, regal, spiritual
brown	honest, down-to-earth, supportive
black	disciplined, strong-willed, independent
white	individualistic, lonely, having low self-esteem
grey	passive, non-committal, overburdened
silver	chivalrous, trustworthy, romantic
gold	idealistic, successful, having high values

UNIT 8, PART A, 2 SPEAKING AND READING, g, PAGE 28

Colour	Message
red	'Look at me, I'm physical and emotional.'
pink	'I like to love, be loved and care for others.'
peach	'I'm charitable, kind and like to be involved.'
yellow	'Let's communicate, I like to share.'
light blue	'Let me show you how creative yet analytical I am.'
dark blue	'I love to be the boss and the decision-maker.'
purple	'I like to express my feelings and have others recognise how great I am.'
black	'Don't tell me what to do, for I know best.'
white	'I like to be by myself, even in a crowd, for I need my own space.'
grey	'I hear what you say, but I don't want to be involved.'

UNIT 8, PART B, 3 STUDY SKILLS, PAGE 30

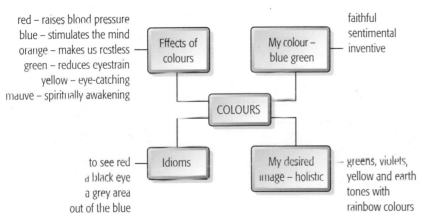

red – raises blood pressure
blue – stimulates the mind
orange – makes us restless
green – reduces eyestrain
yellow – eye-catching
mauve – spiritually awakening

Effects of colours

My colour – blue green

faithful
sentimental
inventive

COLOURS

to see red
a black eye
a grey area
out of the blue

Idioms

My desired image – holistic

greens, violets, yellow and earth tones with rainbow colours

UNIT 9, PART A, 6 VOCABULARY, a, PAGE 33

Snap

Work in groups. As a group, make one set of these word cards. Shuffle the cards and place them face down in the centre of the group where everyone can reach them.

Within your groups, divide into two or more teams of roughly equal numbers. As a team, make one set of these suffix cards. Shuffle the cards and deal them out among yourselves.

water	resource	trouble	elect	neighbour	scanda
employ	tall	arson	renew	fail	bed
short	bound	tend	trust	callous	architec

ural	ness	worthy	ency	less	age
ridden	ure	al	ist	ish	ee
monger	hood	ion	some	ful	proof

You are now read to play. Roll a dice; the player with the lowest number starts the game by turning up a word card to reveal the word. The first player with the matching suffix who shouts *Snap* and puts the correct card down for the word (e.g. *proof* + *water* = *waterproof*) wins a point for his/her team and turns up the next card. Continue until all the cards are gone. The team with the most points at the end wins the game.

UNIT 14, PART A, 4 STUDY SKILLS, d, PAGE 51

I'm very sorry to hear that women are in the war against men to get the superiority in choosing the proper clothes While men are struggling to get the money for women.

In general men are not good in choosing a proper cloth and matching the clothes. But I think that's not because they have no taste for the clothes but because they have no time for choose the clothes. Men has
5 to go out to work everyday while women are just turning over the leaves of some fashion magazines.

In my oppinion, all this difference between men and women don't come from thier gender but from social education. Men are educated to be men. Imagine a boy who don't like to play football for he doesn't want to dirty his clothes. Grown-ups will say what a shame you're not a girl.

Society do this becuase she wants to allot some different kind of work to different genders, whether it's
10 fair or not.

Here comes the point. If we think the difference are from genes, we can't stop the war. But if we think it comes from the social structure, we can understand each other more easily and work together against some absurd tradition.

UNIT 16, 4 THE PASSIVE, PAGE 58

Questionnaire A

1 Have you ever been given a very special present? Who gave it to you and when?
2 Which goods are made in your country?
3 Is money thought to be an important asset in your culture?
4 When are you expected to return to your country/your home?
5 Have you ever been deafened by loud music? Where and when?
6 Are you being given enough homework?
7 Have you ever been accused of something you didn't do, even something minor?
8 Have you ever been mistaken for someone else?
9 When will you be allowed to go home?
10 What would you have done if you had been locked out of your house?

Questionnaire B

1 Have you ever been invited to something really special? Who invited you and when?
2 Which famous people were born in your country?
3 Is a couple living together before they are married thought to be improper in your culture?
4 Is there to be an election in your country quite soon?
5 Have you ever been paralysed by fear? When and what happened?
6 Are you being helped by your classmates?
7 Do you know of anyone who is thought to have acted unprofessionally, like a politician?
8 Have you ever been phoned up in the middle of the night? Who phoned you and why?
9 When will you be made to do a test?
10 What would you have done if you had been locked out of your car?

UNIT 12, PART B, 5 STUDY SKILLS, b, PAGE 45

An uncalculated risk

A PIONEERING operation promises to save thousands of lives now and many more in the future. But it is feared it could unleash a new and deadly plague. The benefits from the treatment are obvious and immediate, the risks unknown and so far impossible to estimate.

What do you do? Press on optimistically on the grounds that there would be no progress if everyone worried about every possible risk? Or take the pessimistic view that too many of the world's problems have been caused because people saw the immediate gains but not the long-term problems? Usually, the optimists win the day. And despite a few hitches, the nightmare scenarios envisaged by the pessimists do not come to pass.

Xenotransplantation – the transplantation of body parts from one species into another – is hurtling along the optimists' route. But there are good reasons for thinking the brakes should be applied, not to bring progress to a complete halt as some pessimists are demanding, but in order to proceed with more caution.

Tremendous pressure is being applied to hurry xenotransplantation along. The demand for human organs has vastly outgrown the supply. Already, around half of all people who need a transplant die while still on the waiting list. And there is not much prospect of increasing the supply. Organs need to come from healthy bodies, but fewer young people are dying in accidents.

Animal organs seem to be the only solution and pigs the best bet. They are roughly the same size as humans and we already breed them in large numbers. And there has been rapid progress in genetically engineering pigs so that their organs are less likely to be rejected by a human body.

So far, so good. Unfortunately, there is also a risk. All animals harbour viruses and placing an organ from another species inside you is the perfect way for those viruses to jump the species barrier. The AIDS epidemic probably began when HIV crossed from monkeys to humans. HTLV, which causes leukaemia, is another virus that crossed the species barrier, as did those causing Marburg disease and Lassa fever. It's a pretty nasty list to which you can add various strains of influenza.

The big question is whether xenotransplants will be followed by epidemics of viruses new to humans. Researchers have been hoping to get around this risk by breeding pigs completely free of the viruses that could grow in humans. But the latest evidence suggests that this will not be possible. All pig cells appear to contain multiple copies of retroviruses that can infect human cells. And as the viruses are integrated into the pig's DNA, breeding them out is likely to be impossible.

This is not to say that xenotransplantation should be banned. The risks are unknown and there is little chance of a blanket ban anyway – experiments using pig livers are already beginning in the US. But we can ask that the use of xenotransplantation be delayed while better ways are found of assessing and monitoring the risk.

Regulations in the US and Britain already demand that xenotransplantation patients are subject to lifetime surveillance. The problem is that no one has worked out how that surveillance should be carried out or what to make of any data gathered. We lack inventories of pig viruses and knowledge of how infectious the viruses are likely to be. Even if we followed a patient with a pig's liver and found pig retroviruses in blood tests we would not know for sure whether an infection was spreading or pig cells had simply escaped into the bloodstream.

Before taking the next step, we need to be certain that our surveillance methods are likely to be successful. The methods can be tested in pig-to-primate transplants. Some experiments have already begun and the results must be examined before we rush headlong into xenotransplant operations.

With reliable follow-up, we could at least feel that we had a chance of catching problems early on. Should something go seriously wrong the alternatives are too horrible to contemplate: at worst a new epidemic or, at best, state control of those carrying a new communicable disease. Imagine if pigs' livers saved lives but condemned those receiving them to life in a remote sanatorium. It is a scenario far too reminiscent of an old horror movie.

1 Achievers

1 LISTENING

b and c

INTERVIEWER Now, Dot Evans is to be presented with a 'Women in film and television' award for craft. Her craft involves jumping off office blocks and turning over cars. She's been dragged behind a speed boat and had a fight on a cable car 3,000 feet above Rio de Janeiro, with no safety wire. She is a stunt woman. Some people would say 'You're mad, Dot'. How did you do that, on the cable car, with no wire?

DOT EVANS At first when we got up there, it was a bit hair-raising because you looked down into the harbour and all you could see were the boats, which looked like little matchboxes. But after a while ... At first the man didn't even want to move the cable car because he was frightened of us falling off, but he got used to it and, once you're up there, it's just like you're sitting in a room. And I used to sunbathe up there between shots. I had a black suit on and I used to unzip it and have a bikini underneath.

INTERVIEWER And you can actually look down and not be completely frozen with vertigo?

DOT EVANS Well, I wouldn't be any good if that was the case!

INTERVIEWER I really don't envy you that. How did you become a stunt woman?

DOT EVANS My parents used to supply horses and carriages for films and I used to go as a child groom, looking after the horses, and I used to hold the horses for actors and make sure they were comfortable. And then I would teach them little things. And then they asked me to ride, then side-saddle, then can you fall off? And it started like that. Then they set up a stunt guild which I joined and I took up judo, trampolining, karate, sort of a bit of everything really, and that's how I came in.

INTERVIEWER What's the most important thing you need to know to stay safe?

DOT EVANS You have to assess every stunt and try and work it out to be the safest you can. That's why it's a stunt. That's why they're paying you to do it and not letting the actresses do it and get hurt. Sometimes you can pad up, sometimes you can't. Most of the girls can't put pads on because they're usually in dresses; men can because they wear suits and they can put loads of body pads on.

INTERVIEWER So you're at even more risk than the men. Now your injury list is, I think, spectacular.

DOT EVANS No, not if you consider all the years I've been doing it. But I fell through a roof with no pads and cracked vertebrae, the sternum and a rib there, but I was back working within eight weeks.

INTERVIEWER And you were knocked over once rather badly, weren't you?

DOT EVANS I did a car knock-down, and because I hadn't got a wig because my hair was the same as the actress's, I agreed to do it without padding my head. Usually I do that under a wig. I got knocked out when I hit the windscreen, and then I went up onto the roof, back onto the bonnet, and then I just fell off the car, but I was already unconscious. I broke my wrist, my hand, my cheekbone, my jaw and knocked a tooth out. Other than that ...

INTERVIEWER My goodness ... What kind of relationship do you develop with the person that you're doubling for?

DOT EVANS Most of them, especially if you're on location, you get very friendly with and you go out for dinner, you know. A lot of them are good friends now who come to my home.

INTERVIEWER How do you double for actresses who are completely different in shape to you?

DOT EVANS If the actress is taller, it really doesn't matter as long as you're working on your own. If you're quite slim, you can double anyone really.

INTERVIEWER You often don't even get a credit at the end of the film. But do you envy the glamorous actresses that you stand in for?

DOT EVANS No, I've always been asked that. Wouldn't you rather be the actress? And I say, 'Well, I can drive into the studio in a nice car and some of them get off the bus and walk in.'

INTERVIEWER So there's plenty of money in it?

DOT EVANS There is if you're one of the top ones. Yes, there is, but some of the girls today are going to find it hard to earn a living out of it because there are so many girls in it now.

INTERVIEWER Computers are taking over as well, aren't they?

DOT EVANS Yes, my husband says I'll be outmoded, obsolete in time, but not in my time. It won't really affect me, so I'm not too worried.

INTERVIEWER Do you think the technology will get so good that they won't need stunt people.

DOT EVANS Well, there'll still be the small little stunts and things but anything big, where you could earn quite a bit of money, they will, yes, they will.

INTERVIEWER How does your family react to you going out risking your life all the time?

DOT EVANS   I never used to tell my mother, really, I just said, 'Oh I'm just riding a horse today mum.' And then she saw the programme *Stunt Challenge* on TV; she's slightly deaf, and she went deaf for a week! She just couldn't believe I was in a car doing one of those stunt car rolls.

INTERVIEWER   And what about your husband?

DOT EVANS   Well, he always just says 'drive carefully' when I'm going to work.

INTERVIEWER   And presumably you do.

3   PRONUNCIATION

a

sit
alley
stop
bench
bus
could

2 Shop till you drop

PART A

2   LISTENING

b and c

ROB   So have you thought, then, what you'll do when you leave university, after your degree?

ANNE   Not really, not so far, because, well, I had thought about journalism, but I've kinda decided that's not what I want to do now. And I've thought about advertising as well. But I can see myself going into that job and then in so many years' time waking up in the morning and not being able to look at myself because, well, I don't think, I don't think it's right to sell people what they don't want and what they don't need.

ROB   But surely that's not what advertising is doing most of the time. It's not selling you something you don't want. It's perhaps influencing your choice of manufacturer.

ANNE   No, not at all, because when you buy an aftershave or a perfume or something like that, what they're selling you mostly is the image, you know there's a perfume and the ultimate image is of true and everlasting love and if you have *this* aftershave, then you're an adventurer, if you have *that* one, then you're elegant and suave.

ROB   But surely the basic factor there is that if you don't buy it, you'll smell bad.

ANNE   I think you're reducing the argument rather than actually looking at the way people do actually advertise.

ROB   Oh, I'm surrounded by advertising every day as we all are, more and more, but I still think that this idea that you're talking someone into buying something he doesn't want, isn't really what advertising is about now. They might like it to be about that, but it's not. The fact is that most people will go out and buy aftershave anyway. You have to influence their choice of aftershave.

ANNE   I think you're crediting people with far too much intelligence because there are people who are intelligent enough to direct their own lives in the way that they want, they know where they're going, things like that. But the great majority of people, they don't know where they're going, what they're doing, and they get influenced by television, well television advertising, magazine advertising, and they're just led along like sheep by the latest fashions, no matter how ridiculous things look or how awful something smells.

ROB   Well, you say how ridiculous things look. Take the catwalk, now I don't think people buy what they see on the catwalk because the fashions are ridiculous. They're there to catch the eye, to make you remember this designer but they're not there to persuade you that this is the garment that you want.

ANNE   Yeah, but advertising relies on creating a need, satisfying a need and then destroying that satisfaction, because whatever you buy, it no longer gives that satisfaction so it creates a need for another thing. Most of our lives are driven towards material gain, to buying this, to getting that, to aspiring to the next car. But it never really offers satisfaction in the end. And these adverts, they're showing something which is much deeper, as in showing qualities that people aspire to, like not so much looking this way or that way, but, well, appearing courageous or adventurous and these various things you could be. And it just isn't like that at all. People buy these things, then they realise they don't come with the same lifestyle that they want to lead.

ROB   I can see what you're saying there and in particular about things like four-wheel drive advertising which invariably shows the car going along mountain tracks, through forests …

ANNE   Yeah, in the Himalayas, and then most people drive round the city centre in their four-wheel drives.

ROB   And people are influenced into buying this particular type of car because they like the idea of being an adventurer, but then all they do is they drive to the shops in it and it never ever leaves the tarmac. I can see that point there. But I don't think they buy that as a second car when they only need one car. I think they buy that sort of car instead of buying an ordinary family saloon car.

ANNE   But how does that change the fundamental issue?

ROB   Oh, it does, it takes us back to the point I was making in the first place that they're not persuading you to part with money which you wouldn't otherwise part with. You want to buy a car, you have the money to buy a car. The advertisers will try to persuade you that you want *their* car and not the other person's.

ANNE   Just because you have the choice between alternatives, it doesn't mean you can't be manipulated.

ROB   Oh, sure, we're being manipulated, yes, I'm not disputing that.

ANNE   In that case you're agreeing with me. And what I'm saying is that manipulation is wrong.

ROB   But your original point was that you couldn't live with yourself if you made someone buy something they didn't want. All I'm saying is you haven't persuaded them to buy *a* car, you've persuaded them to buy *your* car.

PART B

3 PRONUNCIATION

a

1   What do you want to do?
2   I ordered three but I only got two.
3   Of course you can come too.
4   I thought we would lose the match but we drew.
5   I'm afraid you can't go through.
6   I'm sorry, I haven't a clue.
7   I love that kind of shoe.

c

1	comb	9	salmon
2	muscle	10	autumn
3	sandwich	11	pneumatic
4	foreign	12	cupboard
5	neighbour	13	iron
6	whether	14	island
7	honest	15	guide
8	knife	16	wrong

3 Freedom

PART B

5 LISTENING

b and d

It's 8 o'clock on Tuesday June 22. The news with Charlotte Adams.

The police have been accused of corporate failure in investigating a boy's murder. The chief constable is resisting calls for him to resign.

Fears have been voiced as jets fill the skies. Air traffic controllers warn that packing planes closer together is not a solution to crowded skies.

The Health Secretary tells nurses he's sorry he's had to pay their annual salary increase in two stages and hopes he won't have to do it again.

Anti-smoking groups have turned the heat up on film stars.

The government says primary school children should do half an hour's homework each day while secondary school pupils should do an hour and a half.

6 PRONUNCIATION

a and b

Health watchdogs are preparing to name and shame Hollywood superstars whose films have been deemed to encourage young people to smoke.

Doctors are worried that while smoking has been outlawed in most cinemas in Britain, the number of film scenes showing cigarette or cigar smoking has increased fourfold over the last eight years.

This week the Health Education Authority will appeal to film directors to cut back on smoking scenes. It will also point the finger at actors with teen-appeal whose films or lifestyle may appear to make smoking glamorous.

4 2020

PART B

1 LISTENING

b and c

NARRATOR   It is 6.30am on June 1, 2020. A silent image of a seashore on the bedroom wall suddenly springs to life, replaced by a warm friendly face you have named Molly, who cheerily announces …

MOLLY   It's time to wake up.

NARRATOR   As you walk into the kitchen, the appliances sense your presence. The coffeepot turns itself on. Bread is toasted to the setting you prefer. Your favourite music fills the air. The intelligent home is coming to life.

MOLLY I have scanned the Internet and printed out your personalised edition of the newspaper and it's on the breakfast table.

NARRATOR As you leave the kitchen, the refrigerator scans its contents and announces …

REFRIGERATOR You're out of milk and the yoghurt is sour.

NARRATOR Molly adds …

MOLLY We're low on computers. Pick up a dozen more at the supermarket while you're at it.

NARRATOR Molly is your 'intelligent agent', a computer program equipped with reason and common sense. She is your link to the 'Magic Mirror', the worldwide electronic membrane that holds all human knowledge. Before you leave home, you instruct the robot vacuum cleaner to get cracking. It springs to life and, sensing the wire tracks hidden beneath the carpet, begins its job. As you drive out of the city to your greenfield office in your electric/hybrid car, Molly has tapped into the Global Positioning System satellite orbiting overhead.

MOLLY There is a delay due to roadwords on the M4. Here is an alternative route.

NARRATOR A map appears ghostlike on the windscreen. The traffic lights, sensing no other cars on this smart highway, all turn green. You whizz by the toll booths, which register your vehicle PIN number with their laser sensors and electronically charge your account. At your desk at Computer Genetics, a giant firm specialising in personalised DNA sequencing, you scan your video mail. A few bills. You insert your smart wallet card into the computer in the wall. A laser beam checks your iris for identification, and the transaction is done. Then at 10am two staff members meet you via the wall screen.

MOLLY It's 4pm, time for your doctor's appointment.

NARRATOR As Molly's image fades, your virtual doctor appears on the screen. Like Molly he is a computer program with a human face.

DOCTOR We've used the new MRI machine to take a peek inside your arteries. At the present rate of plaque build-up, we calculate that within eight years you will have an 80 per cent increased risk of a heart attack. I'm video-mailing you a strict programme of exercise, relaxation, meditation and yoga.

NARRATOR Molly will just love taking over as your personal trainer. That evening you attend a cocktail party. As you wander among the guests, the video camera in your glasses scans the faces in the crowd and Molly matches the faces with the computer profiles in her memory. She whispers in your ear who each person is from a special miniature transmitter in your glasses. By the end of the party you have drunk a bit too much and Molly whispers …

MOLLY If you drink any more, the breath analyser on the dashboard won't allow you to start the car.

NARRATOR Late that night you tell Molly to find out why your lover, Robin, has not called. Molly scans the Magic Mirror and reports …

MOLLY Robin's inaccessible.

NARRATOR At midnight? Furious, you tell Molly to scan the names of all the eligible single people in the area, matching them to your tastes and interests. A list of faces appears on the screen with a brief description beneath each picture. You ask Molly for her opinion.

MOLLY Well, I think numbers three and five look rather promising. They're an 85 per cent match to your interests.

NARRATOR Molly then scans the facial features of each person and performs some computations on their facial measurements.

MOLLY Plus I think numbers three and six are rather attractive, don't you? And don't forget number 10. Good parents.

NARRATOR Finally, before you go to sleep you ask Molly to run an old film, *Casablanca*, but replacing Ingrid Bergman's and Humphrey Bogart's faces with yours and number three's. Yes, the future's looking good.

2 PRONUNCIATION

b and c

Molly is your 'intelligent agent', a computer program equipped with reason and common sense. She is your link to the 'Magic Mirror', the worldwide electronic membrane that holds all human knowledge. Before you leave home, you instruct the robot vacuum cleaner to get cracking. It springs to life and, sensing the wire tracks hidden beneath the carpet, begins its job. As you drive out of the city to your greenfield office in your electric/hybrid car, Molly has tapped into the Global Positioning System satellite orbiting overhead.

7 P's and Q's

PART A

5 PRONUNCIATION

a

1 berry 2 vanish 3 bigger 4 boat 5 vow

c

1 bat vat	3 bolt volt	5 buy vie
2 bend vend	4 beer veer	

PART B

2 VOCABULARY

b

1 I'm sorry?
2 Wait a minute, I'm not sure I see what you mean.
3 Do you think you could possibly go through that again for me?
4 I'm not quite sure what that means. Is it that … ?
5 Are you telling me that … ?
6 I wonder if you could explain what that means exactly.
7 Would you mind explaining that part? I don't think I've really understood.
8 I'm totally lost now. Can you go over it again?
9 I can't make head nor tail of this.
10 I didn't get that at all.

8 The language of colour

PART B

1 LISTENING

b

COLOUR ANALYST   The effects of colour on our minds and bodies is a subject of increasing interest. Scientific studies show that red raises the blood pressure, quickens the pulse, and increases the rate of breathing. Blue, by contrast, slows down body activity and stimulates the mind. These facts, along with other scientific and empirical evidence, are already widely used by the fashion and advertising industries for profit. Have you ever noticed that the popular fast-food chains have high-energy colours such as orange in their interiors? Orange is not only a strong appetite stimulant, but it can also make the viewer impatient and restless, encouraging customers to 'eat and run'. Men always remember the 'woman in red' because that hue is the strongest and longest ray in the visible spectrum, making a greater impression on the retina, not to mention speeding up the emotions! Green, in the middle of the spectrum, has a calming, balancing effect. It can even reduce eyestrain, especially in a minty shade such as the one chosen by hospitals in their operating and recovery rooms. Have you ever noticed a yellow flyer in your advertising papers and junk mail? This stimulating colour was used on purpose to make eye contact – yours – to promote upcoming sales. In many modern office and professional decors there's a popular surge of mauves and violets. Is it a fad, or a revolution – a reaction to the increasing number of sensitive women in the work force? Violets and purples bring out the intuitive in people which is why they were identified with a spiritual-awakening movement in the sixties.

e

COLOUR ANALYST   What is colour and why is it important? This fascinating question continues to intrigue us. Colour is reflected light. We feel it and see it through our eyes, our sensory makeup, and our minds. Humans can see 40 per cent of the rays of light energy as the visible spectrum, the rainbow of colour. These vibrations of electromagnetic energy travel from the sun to reach us. Upon contact, they penetrate our bodies through our eyes and skin, sending instant signals to the brain. When we lie out-of-doors in the sun, our bodies absorb light energy. That same energy in a lesser intensity is colour. Colours stimulate an emotional and mental response to what our eyes and bodies record. Strong energy is present in all bright, warm colours, as they are the longest rays of the visible spectrum of light. Not so with the cooler blues and violets or pastel colours, whose intensities are lesser in length and strength. Our brains, the masters of our bodies, respond to each vibratory electron of colour, accepting or rejecting each sensation. Colour, then, is a sensation of light. Colour is a resource of passive solar energy!

4 PRONUNCIATION

a

1 see she	3 sake shake	5 sour shower
2 saw shore	4 socks shocks	

c

1 share chair	3 sheer cheer	5 washing watching
2 sheep cheap	4 shoes choose	6 wish which

9 Time out

PART A

5 PRONUNCIATION

a

1 plant	5 grated	9 swallow
2 break	6 quickly	10 shrimp
3 dreadful	7 frequent	
4 clash	8 thrill	

c

1	splash	6	sixth	11	thanked
2	spread	7	mixed	12	tourists
3	strength	8	months	13	tasks
4	scratch	9	announced	14	fifths
5	squeaks	10	revenged		

PART B

1 LISTENING

b

REPORTER   I went to meet Leila Josefowicz at her parents' Los Angeles home. The granddaughter of Polish immigrant textile workers and the daughter of a Polish-English-Canadian marital amalgam of huge intellectual achievement, Leila is 150 per cent Californian girl. I asked her how she felt about playing at the Albert Hall.

LEILA JOSEFOWICZ   I'm *very* excited about playing at the Albert Hall in August. It's my first time to play there. I've played at the Royal Festival Hall a couple of times. First time I was about 11. But I'm really looking forward to doing this. I just love London too.

REPORTER   Leila runs through her other summer appearances as though they were no more than school tennis-tournament fixtures – Paris, Helsinki, Seoul, Tokyo, Budapest. Then she rattles off the list of works she's recording on her next CD and her recent appearances as an orchestra soloist. Like all the world's truly exceptional violinists, Leila started young – at the age of three. By five she was practising four hours a day and was already a favourite with Californian audiences who ooh-ed and aah-ed at her tiny physical presence and her astounding talent. But Leila's home life and family are infused with as much normality as possible in her abnormal situation. The house is not the display case crammed with medals, trophies and news clippings in which so many child stars live.

LEILA JOSEFOWICZ   I've attended normal school as well as studying music; I'm glad I didn't miss out on that. My parents have kept my feet on the ground, but in the end it has been me in charge from an early age and I've just carried on learning, picking up new repertoires at my own pace.

REPORTER   But didn't she sacrifice some things while she was growing up?

LEILA JOSEFOWICZ   No, I've done everything the way *I* wanted. I'm a serious musician and I'm going to stay that way. I don't go round doing things just because other people tell me to. I mean, *I'm* the one who has to go out on to that stage to face that audience. I'm in charge of myself. Everything I've done was necessary to get this far. I don't regret anything.

REPORTER   It is rather disconcerting talking to a girlish sugar-spun teenager wrapped in a skimpy DKNY T-shirt and shorts, her toenails painted pink, her toes ringed in silver, only to find she's pure steel inside.

LEILA JOSEFOWICZ   Musically I may seem grown-up beyond my years and it's true I've always mixed with adults, but I can be just as silly as anyone else when I want to.

REPORTER   Despite all the praise which has been heaped on her, Leila has so far avoided the affliction known as 'stardust poisoning' because there is something inside her that remains untouched by all the glitter. She's survived all the praise and flattery. Her force of personality has resisted the demands of the industry too. By all the ordinary laws of the classical-recording business, Leila should have begun to clamber into transparent dresses, paint a seductive pout on her face and boost sales with sexual imagery. But she's having none of that.

LEILA JOSEFOWICZ   I'm not going to try and sell myself on anything but my music.

REPORTER   Leila's life has never been anything less. It began at three when her parents enrolled her on a Suzuki violin programme. By the age of four she was going to grand concerts to hear America's most famous fiddlers. By the age of five she was having formal tuition, at eight she was a pupil of California's top violin teacher. Her professional career started at nine and by 13 she had outgrown her Californian teacher and moved to Philadelphia to attend a special music academy for America's top young musicians. But even though Leila had already played most of the capitals of the world, an invitation to play at Carnegie Hall at 16 still excited her.

LEILA JOSEFOWICZ   You just feel so many incredible people have been on the stage. But I wasn't nervous; I was well prepared. I was ready to play and ready for people to hear me. I'm an extrovert, a performer. This is entertainment. You're on stage to entertain and I have no problem with dedicating my life to this for as long as I possibly can.

REPORTER   Things have changed since she graduated from high school and moved to her own apartment in New York.

LEILA JOSEFOWICZ   I'm nearly 20 and people don't talk about me as a cute little prodigy any more. They listen differently now, to an adult performer, and I like that. I'm not totally alone either, as my boyfriend's coming over there. He's a pianist and travels too – not as much as me, but I hope we'll get to see something of each other.

REPORTER   Then I ask her to play and suddenly she is transformed. She straightens up and begins.

11 Doing time

5 LISTENING

b

NEWSREADER   A local hotelier has been fined for polluting her Cornish crab soup with foreign bodies – Norwegian crabs. Hotel owner, Mrs Sandy Watson, was ordered to pay £220 in court yesterday after admitting displaying a label which was likely to mislead. Her husband, Anthony, an accountant, has described the whole affair as a genuine mistake. Our reporter Susan Bushell has been following the story.

SUSAN BUSHELL   Yes, and to shed some light on this strange story is Trading Standards Officer, David Grant. Mr Grant, could you tell us how this 'deception' was discovered?

DAVID GRANT   Yes, we had a tip-off from a holiday-maker who'd been staying at the hotel. She had the Cornish crab soup and thought it tasted a bit 'commercial'. Then she actually saw neatly stacked rows of tins labelled 'Lusty Crab Bisque' as she walked past a cupboard.

SUSAN BUSHELL   And she complained to you. What did you do about it?

DAVID GRANT   We went to the hotel and took away a sample to send to the Public Analyst. When the results came back, it turned out that the crab wasn't Cornish at all, but was from Norway and this sort of misrepresentation is a very serious matter.

SUSAN BUSHELL   Thank you, Mr Grant. Well, on the phone now we've got Mrs Brooks who works in the kitchen at the hotel. What's been going on here, Mrs Brooks, you must know?

MRS BROOKS   Well, what's happened, you see, is the company that supplies the soup has changed hands. I mean, we thought we were still getting Cornish crab.

SUSAN BUSHELL   I see, but hadn't anyone noticed a difference?

MRS BROOKS   Well, no. And we've served gallons of the soup and we've had compliments about it from guests. Several have even asked for the recipe. If anything, the new soup tastes better. I think the whole thing is ridiculous.

NEWSREADER   A local pensioner has been warned she could go to prison if she continues to attract hundreds of birds to her garden in defiance of an injunction. Judge Michael Nicholls yesterday told Mrs Robin Samson to stop feeding birds from her lawn and pavement or face a possible jail sentence. Mrs Samson and her retired postman husband, Arthur, have been living in their bungalow in Harston for 30 years. Our reporter, Mark Weston, takes up the story.

MARK WESTON   Well, here with me now is Councillor Harry Pierson. Councillor Pierson, I understand Harston Council asked the court to jail Mrs Samson because she's been breaking an injunction forbidding her from feeding birds from her garden. Is that right?

HARRY PIERSON   Yes, it is. Quite frankly, the council's become so exasperated with Mrs Samson's behaviour, we felt we had no alternative. Mrs Samson literally attracts hundreds of birds to her garden – pigeons, rooks, starlings – it's awful. All day long birds perch on neighbours' houses waiting for her to come out and feed them. They're an incredible nuisance. Neighbours are always complaining about the noise and the smell and now they've got a problem with rats in the area too, which is hardly surprising – Environmental Health Officers found bird food 15 cm deep in some places.

MARK WESTON   I see. But the judge has decided not to grant your request to imprison Mrs Samson and in fact he's not only let her off with a warning, he's allowing her to feed birds from a bird table in her garden.

HARRY PIERSON   Yes, that's right, and of course we have no desire to see Mrs Samson go to jail. We just want her to stop putting out all this bird food and creating such a nuisance in the neighbourhood.

MARK WESTON   Thank you, Councillor Pierson. Well, with me now is Mrs Samson's daughter, Jean Anderson. How did all this start?

JEAN ANDERSON   Mum began feeding the birds about, well, it must have been 15 years ago when a sick baby sparrow landed on her doorstep. Since then she's been feeding them, you know, with nuts and a few scraps, on her front lawn.

MARK WESTON   And what do you think of the council's demand for her to be sent to jail?

JEAN ANDERSON   I think it's totally unreasonable. These birds, they're like children to her now. And she'd be prepared to go to prison if they stopped her feeding them altogether. Honestly, I can't see what all the fuss is about. She's only taking care of birds. How can somebody be sent to prison for that?

12 Moral maze

PART A

3 LISTENING

a and b

Victor Bridges   Well, frankly, I'm surprised you've chosen to go into this field of work, helping people to choose the sex of their child. Surely you've come in for a lot of criticism and most of it well-founded?

Janet Rainer   Well, I can't agree that it's well-founded. It's not as though I'm doing it to hit the headlines or become some sort of trailblazer. I've been deeply hurt by a lot of the criticisms which have been levelled at me and in particular the ones that suggest I'm doing it for the power.

Victor Bridges   How do you justify to yourself the need for such treatment?

Janet Rainer   It's not difficult when you understand the tremendous pressure some people are under to have a child of a particular sex. Women can be driven by a very strong maternal urge and I believe they have the right to choose whether they have a boy or a girl. Some couples already have three or four boys or girls and they really want a child of the opposite sex to complete their family.

Victor Bridges   But, in fact, the success rate of the treatment is very low, isn't it?

Janet Rainer   Well, we calculate the success rate is about 30–35 per cent for each treatment cycle. Couples whose first attempt to have a baby fails will often have two or three treatment cycles and we charge a sliding scale of fees for that. Over three cycles, the success rate goes up as high as 80 per cent. We're not in this to make money, although we believe there will be an enormous demand for this treatment and, if there is, we plan to open clinics in several other countries. In my view, sex selection is a natural development of infertility treatment and, if you look back 20 years, some sectors of British society were up in arms about starting life in a test tube, but today we can find thousands of healthy children who were born as a result of IVF. Now I'm convinced that in another 20 years people will wonder what all the fuss about sex selection was about. It just so happens that our clinic is the first to grasp the nettle.

Victor Bridges   Well I happen to believe that it is totally unethical to manipulate nature like this. Just because we have highly advanced technology, it doesn't mean that we should be involved in something which could have serious repercussions. If people are lucky enough to have a healthy baby, that's marvellous. But with this method, if a couple wants a boy, for example, it means throwing away five little girl embryos to do it.

Janet Rainer   You haven't understood the depth of human suffering caused by not being able to have a child of a particular sex. You know yourself that in some cultures if a family doesn't have a son, they have a baby girl instead, it can mean that the baby girl may suffer neglect and even die. In fact, we don't need to look abroad. Here in Britain we can see a higher-than-average suicide rate among certain communities. A woman can be driven to such lengths by her inability to have a son.

Victor Bridges   Yes, but surely the very couples you're talking about often don't have access to this treatment for perhaps financial or cultural reasons.

Janet Rainer   But only by introducing this treatment will it eventually become widespread and freely available worldwide. We are trying to help people plan for their future, not condone what's happening at the moment, which in some instances is nothing short of infanticide.

Victor Bridges   But in many cultures you must admit there is a preference for boys. The consequences of a resulting imbalance in the sexes are unthinkable.

Janet Rainer   That isn't born out by the facts. At our clinic, out of more than 100 enquiries only about 55 per cent wanted a boy. That means 45 per cent actually want a girl. And most of the couples want a child of a particular sex because they already have at least two children of the same sex.

Victor Bridges   Yes, but you're looking at it from a European perspective only. It's true that recent studies have shown that in European couples 63 per cent wanted a girl but look further afield, the studies also showed that Indian, Chinese and Middle Eastern couples almost all wanted a boy. If this treatment were to be freely available, the resulting distortion in the sex ratio would be a serious problem.

PART B

2 PRONUNCIATION

b

1   You might have reached the age where it's perhaps better not to drive so much.
2   Well, you could always try to cut down on the number of cigarettes you smoke.
3   I think you really ought to use one of your own ideas.
4   Have you thought about the fact that this could have serious consequences for your father?

d

1   I thought she'd put her career first.
2   He was talking to the Spanish teacher.
3   Anne wasn't laughing because of what he said.
4   Tony told me he was going away for the weekend.
5   I might have known Simon would turn up.
6   That's all I need.

13 Feel-good factors

2 LISTENING

c

AROMATHERAPIST Aromatic oils are used in three classes of consumer goods: foods, toiletries and medicines. In food they're used as natural flavourings, such as oils of lemon, orange and lime in marmalades. In cosmetics they're incorporated both in perfumes and, less often, as natural active ingredients; they're also widely used in toothpaste flavourings. In medicine they're used not only as flavouring agents but as therapeutic ingredients in their own right. The use of clove oil for toothache, peppermint oil for indigestion and eucalyptus for inhalations is very well known.

Essential oils are scented and highly volatile, which means they readily evaporate in the air. They're quite different from fatty oils and have a consistency more like water than oil. Their chemistry is complex. The oils are present in tiny droplets in a large number of plants, especially those most commonly used for their culinary and medicinal properties. They can occur in roots, leaves, flowers, barks, resins and the rind of some fruits. The presence of essential oil in oranges, for example, can be demonstrated by squeezing a section of the peel next to a lighted match. The oil droplets will spray out and briefly ignite as they pass through the flame. The scent of flowers and herbs is due to their essential oil content, as is the spiciness of spices.

While they are in the plant, the essences are constantly changing their chemical composition and move from one part of the plant to another according to the time of day and the seasons. This is why plants destined for oil extraction must be picked at a certain time of the year, in certain weather conditions and usually at a certain time of day. The odour and chemical constituents of essences change with different soil conditions too, variations in climate and methods of cultivation. This is why oils from certain countries, like Bulgarian Rose, for example, and Sri Lankan cinnamon, are considered to be of a higher quality than those from other countries.

Now the effects of heat, light, air and moisture generally have a damaging effect on essential oils. They should therefore always be kept in dark, airtight bottles and in cool, dry conditions.

There are hundreds of aromatic plants, only some of which are used to produce essences commercially. About a third of the plants traditionally used in herbal medicine are aromatic. No two of them smell exactly alike and the properties of each are unique. The essence of a plant is like its personality. All animals, including humans, have their own characteristic smell, quite apart from what we call body odour. We are not commonly aware of our own scent, nor usually of other people's. We may, however, perceive it on a subconscious level and it may influence our feelings towards each other more than we realise.

There's little doubt that scent has some practical use in the plant kingdom. Animals and probably humans are sexually attracted by aromatic substances called pheromones. It's been suggested that essences in plants have a similar role, flowers emitting a strong fragrance until they die or are fertilised. This idea places plants in a more sexual or animal light than has so far been generally accepted. Nevertheless, there are plants which exhibit other animal traits, such as carnivorous plants, which eat insects. A more commonly accepted idea is that the scent of a plant attracts certain insects which, by moving from plant to plant, cause fertilisation to take place. Essential oils are in fact used commercially to attract or repel certain insects. The essences of many plants are a natural defence mechanism, repelling insects which would otherwise harm the plant.

1 STUDY SKILLS

b and c

1 Yes, I know I only moved out of London last November. I thought the South West was going to be an idyllic haven where I could avoid the stress of living in London. It was a disaster; the shops had nothing in them, everybody had to know everybody else's business, the local newspaper couldn't keep me awake for longer than two minutes, the cinema only showed last year's films so I'd seen them all and I think I own more books than the library does. OK, London's crowded, it's dirty, but it's alive. It's got an energy you can taste.

2 I know, don't say anything, it's awful, isn't it? What do you think? Top's too short and back's too long? I told her I just wanted a trim, but you know what they're like. You might as well not say anything, they just do what they want. You're supposed to feel good, pampered, on top of the world after a haircut. I feel like walking around with a paper bag over my head until it grows back!

3 What about including more fresh fruit in your diet? Pineapples are plentiful and quite cheap at this time of the year. One very good reason for buying pineapples is that they are a very good source of vitamin C. However, selecting a good pineapple is essential. First, smell the pineapple. If it smells sweet, it means it's ripe. Pineapples stop ripening once they are picked so you must buy a ripe one. Then, tug on one of the inner leaves. This will come away easily if it is ready to eat. What's more, pineapples contain an enzyme called bromeline, that's spelt b-r-o-m-e-l-i-n-e, which breaks down protein, so they are very good served at the end of a very rich meal.

4 When you're feeling low, your thoughts may well turn to cakes and chocolate. But you're much more likely to get a mental boost from foods high in carbohydrate rather than fat, and that means eating plenty of healthy potatoes, pasta, rice and cereals. High-fat foods can make you feel dreamy or sluggish whereas a high-carbohydrate meal stimulates the brain's production of serotonin, which improves your mood.

5 Well, I, um, I think that, er, yeah well, er, it's the way we, er, I mean, um, we sit, like, er, slouched over desks and, um, and keyboards and stuff and, er, we carry heavy bags, like, um, yeah, like, er, shopping bags or school bags, right? And, um, I think that's … well, it's obvious, sitting like that, it's um … What we should do, well we shouldn't, um, sit in large squashy sofas, you know like, er, watching TV, cos, well, you know, it's not so good, well, really bad, in fact for your, um, er … back.

6 A Mmm, look at him.
   B What, the one with the blond hair?
   A No, silly, the other one, the tall dark handsome one.
   B Mmm, I see what you mean … bit old though, isn't he?
   A Old? You mean mature, distinctive … yes, I'm just going to get a closer look …

f

1 Please stop that. If you carry on fighting over that car
2 Could I have your ticket, please? Window or aisle? The flight …
3 If you'd been looking where you were going …
4 Excuse me, could you … ?

2 PRONUNCIATION

b

1	chocolate	6	literature
2	cholesterol	7	preferable
3	comfortable	8	medicine
4	difference	9	temperature
5	interesting	10	vegetable

c and d

1 What d'you want?
2 He shouldn't've had it.
3 D'you wanna giv'em to me?
4 How much longer're you gonna be?
5 I'll have fish 'n' chips 'n' a sausage.

14 Style file

PART B

3 GRAMMAR

f and g

1 I'm so glad we've met.
2 He didn't get back till late last night.
3 We always enjoy staying here.
4 She's had a nose job.
5 I wish I hadn't brought a coat.
6 I hadn't forgotten his face.
7 He'd never go there again.
8 We won't go by train again.
9 I'd better phone home.
10 I can see her now.

5 VOCABULARY

d

1	backbiting	6	high-handed
2	butterfingers	7	latecomer
3	camera-shy	8	mind-boggling
4	day-tripper	9	side-splitting
5	get-together	10	voice-activated

15 Basic instinct

PART A

4 PRONUNCIATION

b and c

The day a friend of mine disclosed her plan to withdraw her six-year-old son from our local primary school to educate him at home with his two younger brothers, I thought it was mad, bad and dangerous: mad to have three boys under your feet all day long, bad to risk them becoming isolated and withdrawn, and dangerous to attempt teaching them things that most mums have never even heard of. I had this nightmare vision of her sons becoming maladjusted child prodigies constantly chaperoned by pushy over-protective parents.

d and e

1 A skeleton once in Khartoum
   Invited a ghost to its room.
      They spent the whole night
      In the eeriest fight
   As to who should be frightened of whom.

2 There was an old man of Blackheath,
   Who sat on his set of false teeth.
      Said he, with a start,
      'Oh Lor' bless my heart!
   I have bitten myself underneath!'

3 There was a young man of Devizes,
   Whose ears were of different sizes.
      The one that was small
      Was of no use at all,
   But the other won several prizes.

PART B

1 LISTENING

b

MRS RAMPTON Although I'm convinced that most programmes on TV are a waste of time and, what's worse, they don't even make a good babysitter, I have to admit that TV is part of what you might call common currency. People seem to use discussions of TV programmes as a way of connecting so I can't reject it outright. So I sit on the fence while my daughters grumble about not having seen the programme that all their mates at school watched the night before. It seems as though what I do makes them feel deprived. You see, my system is every Thursday evening I flop down with my two daughters, one's nine and the other's 10, and we watch the latest instalment of *Animal Hospital* – a good wholesome programme presented by a clean jolly presenter. I let them watch this programme because I know it's safe. I know the presenter will never be mean, aggressive or promote any kind of anti-social behaviour. My children are sweet and good-natured and I'd like them to stay like that as long as possible. But I suppose, if I'm honest, I also make it a ritual because I want to show my children that although we've only got a grotty old telly and the sofa we sit on has seen better days, we too are part of the in-crowd, the television-watching population.

MRS HOLLETT We're both in business, we live in a modern house and we've got two children, Tom nine and Georgina six, five television sets and a satellite dish. In our house at least one television always seems to be on. We tend to watch TV in bed, fall asleep with it on and then wake up to the breakfast show. The children are inseparable from the TV – they have TV breakfasts and TV dinners. The moment they come in from school they switch it on for the cartoons and it entertains them through the evening. I know you'll think we should be reading them bedtime stories but we're both shattered by the time we get back from work. We need a rest too. We don't even think about trying to impose limits on how many hours they watch TV. I don't want to be squabbling with the children over that. Their TV watching is a real blessing for us. It gives us a quiet life. As far as we're concerned the children can do what they like with their free time. Well, I don't mean they can watch filthy programmes at any hour of the night. But honestly, at the end of a hard day the last thing I want to be doing is baking cakes with them or making models. Anyway, it doesn't seem to be having any adverse effect on them; they're sociable and popular.

MRS TANNER My husband is a retired doctor and we live in a nice suburb of London. We have one daughter Eleanor who is 10. We took an important decision early on and that was to bring Eleanor up in a television-free environment. It seemed the right thing to do at first. I don't want to sound philosophical about it but I believe it's our duty to teach children how to use their time productively and watching TV is exactly the opposite, it's a waste of time. But we were overtaken by events when Eleanor turned seven. She began to feel very excluded at school where all the other children talked about TV programmes, especially soaps. So what we decided to do was buy a TV, remove the receiver and use the hollow monitor to screen suitable programmes like nature documentaries at appropriate times. Eleanor sometimes still has a go at us about not letting her watch soaps but generally speaking the compromise seems to be working. As a result our daughter is more creative, more discriminating and she can draw on her own resources more than other children of her age. During the time she's not watching TV she reads, does ballet, plays the piano. We also insist that she eats at the table with us; social conversation is very important. Mind you, no home is hermetically sealed and Eleanor has no restrictions when it comes to the radio and I'm afraid she listens to rubbish, pop music mostly.